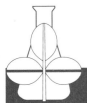

The Local Environment

FAST 1, Foundational Approaches in Science Teaching

Second Edition

Francis M. Pottenger III
Donald B. Young

A Publication of the University of Hawai'i's
Curriculum Research & Development Group
Honolulu, Hawai'i

Curriculum Research & Development Group Staff
Arthur R. King, Jr., Director
Francis M. Pottenger III, Director, Science Projects
Francis M. Pottenger III and Donald B. Young, Directors, *FAST* Project
Edith K. Kleinjans, Managing Editor
Gayle Y. Hamasaki, Publications Coordinator

ISBN 0–937049–67–0

Layout and production by Belknap Publishing & Design, Honolulu
Cover design by Wayne M. Shishido

Distributed by the *FAST* Project
Curriculum Research & Development Group
University of Hawai'i
1776 University Avenue
Honolulu, Hawai'i 96822

ACKNOWLEDGMENTS

Contributors

Abraham Blum, Terry Boomer, L. Reed Brantley, Michael Dabney, Ronald M. Flegal, John Hall, Keven Keller, E. Barbara Klemm, Frank E. Lutz, Harold J. Morowitz, Edwin A. Phillips, Larma Pottenger, Patricia O'Sullivan Robins, Martin W. Schein, Sanford M. Siegel, Caren V. Walsh, and Karen N. Yamamoto

FAST Steering Committees 1967–1980

Physical Science Strand

Frank O. Orrall, Professor of Physics and Astronomy, University of Hawai'i

J. Arthur Campbell, Chair, Chemistry Department, Harvey Mudd College

John W. Gilge, Assistant Professor of Chemistry, University of Hawai'i

Burton L. Henke, Professor of Physics, University of Hawai'i

Richard G. Inskeep, Professor of Chemistry, University of Hawai'i

J. Adin Mann, Associate Professor of Chemistry, University of Hawai'i

Chester T. O'Konski, Coordinator, School Science Group, University of California at Berkeley

Robert L. Pecsok, Chair, Department of Chemistry, University of Hawai'i

Laurence E. Strong, Chair, Department of Chemistry, Earlham College

Ecology Strand

David E. Contois, Dean, College of Arts and Sciences, University of Hawai'i

Doak C. Cox, Director, Water Resources Research Center, University of Hawai'i

John R. Hendrickson, Professor of Biological Sciences, University of Arizona

E. Allison Kay, Professor of Zoology, University of Hawai'i

Harold J. Morowitz, Professor of Molecular Biophysics and Biochemistry, Yale University

Edwin A. Phillips, Professor of Ecology and Plant Physiology, Pomona College

Saul Price, Staff Meteorologist, National Oceanic and Atmospheric Administration, Honolulu, Hawai'i

Martin W. Schein, Centennial Professor of Biology, West Virginia University

Barbara Siegel, Associate Professor of Microbiology, University of Hawai'i

Sanford M. Siegel, Professor of Botany, University of Hawai'i

Jimmie B. Smith, Vice President of Research and Engineering, Dole Company, San Francisco

Relational Study Strand

Sanford M. Siegel, Professor of Botany, University of Hawai'i

Clair E. Folsome, Professor of Microbiology, University of Hawai'i

Joseph J. Schwab, Professor of Education, University of Chicago

John A. Winnie, Assistant Professor of Philosophy, University of Hawai'i

CONTENTS

UNIT 2. CHANGES OF STATE IN MATTER

SECTION A. BOILING AND MELTING

SECTION B. GASES AND LIQUIDS

SECTION C. CONDITIONS FOR CONDENSATION

UNIT 3. TEMPERATURE AND HEAT

SECTION A. TEMPERATURE AND THE MEASUREMENT OF HEAT

SECTION B. CONSERVATION OF HEAT

ECOLOGY

UNIT 1. PLANT GROWTH

SECTION A. SEED GERMINATION

SECTION B. PLANT PROPAGATION

SECTION C. SCIENTIFIC REPORTING

UNIT 2. THE PHYSICAL ENVIRONMENT

SECTION A. SOIL

SECTION B. SOIL AND WATER

SECTION C. WATER IN THE AIR

SECTION D. THE AIR AROUND US

SECTION E. WATER ALL AROUND US

SECTION F. WATER OUT OF PLANTS

UNIT 3. ANIMAL CARE

UNIT 4. FIELD ECOLOGY

SECTION A. FIELD SURVEY

RELATIONAL STUDY

UNIT 1. AIR POLLUTION

UNIT 2. WATER RESOURCE MANAGEMENT

SECTION A. WATER IN MY COMMUNITY

SECTION B. MONITORING WATER QUALITY

SECTION C. MAKING DECISIONS

APPENDIXES

The *Foundational Approaches in Science Teaching* (*FAST*) program is one of several curriculum development projects of the Curriculum Research & Development Group (CRDG) of the University of Hawai'i. CRDG is a branch of the College of Education. The CRDG staff of about a hundred members conducts curriculum research and design, develops and evaluates educational materials, disseminates them, and offers training and follow-up services. CRDG programs serve children and youth at elementary-school, middle-school, and high-school levels. Its programs are tested and used in the University Laboratory School, in the schools of Hawai'i, in selected schools in the Pacific Basin, and in the mainland United States.

Members of the *FAST* staff have developed a series of interdisciplinary science courses that emphasize the foundational concepts and methods of the physical, biological, and earth sciences. By directly engaging students in investigating events in their everyday environment and carrying out experiments to answer questions about those events, *FAST* courses give students a sense of how the modern scientific community operates. This process of inquiry and subsequent research is used throughout each course.

FAST activities are organized into three strands. The Physical Science strand includes study of physics and chemistry. The Ecology strand includes study of earth science and biology. In addition, *FAST* includes study of the interrelationships among science, technology, and society in a third strand called the Relational Study. Thus, through an inquiry approach, these courses give students an understanding of both the concepts of science and their applications to the everyday environment.

Titles of the courses developed thus far are *The Local Environment, Matter and Energy in the Biosphere*, and *Change over Time.*

The *Foundational Approaches in Science Teaching (FAST)* program is designed to engage you in the activities of science. As a *FAST* student you will learn the foundational skills, concepts, and methods of the physical, biological, and earth sciences. You will perform investigations, design experiments, make instruments, record data, and interpret your findings. You will write your own textbook from your experiences at the lab bench and in the field.

As the year progresses, you will take different roles that will help you understand what science means to our modern society. In your chief role you will be a scientist seeking to understand our physical and biological environment and trying to predict what will happen in it. But you will also take the roles of engineer, technician, politician, economist, and citizen—all to get insight into how our society uses the knowledge that scientists discover.

ORGANIZATION
This book is arranged in three strands:

1. The Physical Science strand contains investigations in chemistry and physics—the sciences that investigate the composition and interactions of matter.
2. The Ecology strand contains investigations in the biological and earth sciences—the sciences that investigate relations between organisms and environments.
3. The Relational Study strand focuses on understanding the relations of sciences to each other, to technology, and to society.

Strands are divided into units, each of which is a collection of investigations on a common topic.

An appendix in the back of this book tells you how to measure things and make graphs. Other important information comes in reference booklets that go with the units. They tell you how to build and use instruments and give you suggestions for designing experiments.

STUDY AIDS

This book is organized to help you understand explanations, follow directions, and review major ideas.

1. New science words are printed in *italics.*
2. Points of special importance in experiments are printed in **boldface.**
3. Cautions and safety notes are also printed in **boldface.**
4. In the summaries of investigations, the key questions are marked with a key (⚷).
5. At the end of each section is a list of words you should learn because they are part of the scientist's vocabulary.
6. Each investigation is marked with a symbol to show which strand it belongs to:

 stands for Physical Science. 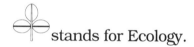stands for Ecology.

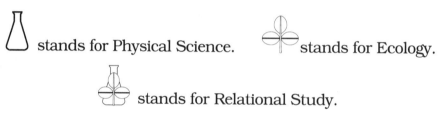 stands for Relational Study.

INVESTIGATIONS

Each investigation has six parts:

Background introduces the investigation and reviews earlier related investigations.

Problem or **Activity** tells what you are to investigate.

Materials lists the things you will need to use in an investigation.

Procedure gives you instructions for doing an investigation.

Summary lists a set of steps or questions to help you summarize and interpret your findings.

Challenge provides a set of additional investigations or questions that can expand your understanding of work you've already done.

LABORATORY SAFETY

Follow these safety rules in all laboratory classes:

1. Always wear a lab apron to protect your clothing and your skin.
2. Always wear goggles when you work with chemicals, hot liquids, or other things that could harm your eyes.
3. Always stand up to avoid spilling chemicals in your lap.
4. Always wear closed shoes to protect your feet from spills.
5. Wash at once with plenty of water to dilute and remove chemicals if you spill them on your clothing or skin.
6. Never taste any chemical unless your teacher tells you to.
7. Tie or pin long hair back to keep it away from flames and chemicals.
8. Know where the fire blanket and fire extinguisher are and how to use them.
9. Report any injury immediately to your teacher.

UNIT 1. INTRODUCTION TO THE PROPERTIES OF MATTER

Section A. Introduction to Buoyancy

1. LIQUIDS AND VIALS

Background
When something happens that we do not understand, we are often curious enough to try to find an explanation. Scientists have made many exciting and valuable discoveries while trying to find out how and why something happens.

In this investigation you will experiment with three vials and two liquids. Make as many observations as you can of what happens in this liquids-and-vials system.

Problem
In the liquids-and-vials system, which observations can you explain? Which ones can't you explain?

Materials
- set of liquids and vials
- chopsticks
- empty vials
- corks to fit vials
- apron and goggles

Procedure
1. Your teacher will demonstrate the liquids-and-vials system first. Then you will get a liquids-and-vials system to work with.

CAUTION: Do not open any of the vials. Do not taste any of the liquids. Be sure to stand when you do your investigations.

2. In your notebook, record your observations or draw pictures of what happens. Use a table like Table 1–1.

Table 1–1 Investigation of the liquids-and-vials system

Observations	My Explanations (My Hypotheses)	Phenomena I Cannot Explain

3. Try to explain your observations. Record your explanations in your notebook.

4. Test your explanations. Ask your teacher for any equipment you need for your test. Record what you do and what happens.

5. When you finish, put the materials away where your teacher asks you to.

Summary

In science, an event or a "happening" is often called a *phenomenon* (plural *phenomena*). Scientists often try to find explanations for phenomena to help them make better predictions about future events.

In scientific work, the first explanation is usually a guess. A guess or an explanation that can be tested is called a *hypothesis* (plural *hypotheses*). A good hypothesis should lead to successful predictions about planned experiments.

If something happens in the experiment that does not fit our hypothesis, we have an *anomaly*. An anomaly shows us that a hypothesis may be wrong or incomplete. When we discover an anomaly, we often have to revise or change our hypothesis.

1. Review your notes or drawings of your observations of the liquids-and-vials system. A *system* is a set of things related to each other in some way.

   a. List the phenomena you **can** explain. Write your hypotheses or draw pictures to explain each of these phenomena.

   b. List the phenomena you **cannot** explain. Put a question mark next to each phenomenon that seems to be an anomaly.

2. If you tested a hypothesis, record what the hypothesis was.

   a. What were the results of the tests?

   b. Did the results of your tests support your hypothesis? Explain.

3. If you did not test a hypothesis, how might you have tested one or more of your hypotheses?

Challenge
Think of a way to sink a can or a jar in a bucket of water so that only half of it is submerged. Test your method. Explain what you did and how you did it.

2. SINKING A STRAW

Background

Too many events happened in the liquids-and-vials system to explain at one time. Instead, let's look at just the floating events.

To understand floating events, we need to understand *buoyancy*. Floating is a buoyancy phenomenon. We will study buoyancy by experimenting with objects that float in water. In this investigation we will share our data and explanations. In science, sharing helps us to further check our data and test our hypotheses.

Problem

How can you predict the quantity of BBs necessary to sink a straw to any chosen depth in water?

Materials

- sinking straws
- BBs (#9 lead shot)
- metric ruler
- beaker or jar
- water
- apron and goggles

Procedure

1. Move the rubber band around the straw so that it is 4 centimeters (cm) from the plugged end as shown in Figure 2–1. Measure the distance with a metric ruler. Refer to the appendix Metric Linear Measurement for instructions on using a metric ruler.

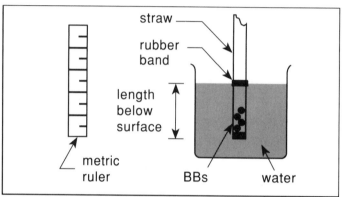

Figure 2–1 Measuring the length of a straw below the surface of water

2. Find the quantity of BBs it takes to sink the straw to the 4-cm mark. Record in your notebook the quantity of BBs you used to sink it to the 4-cm mark. Use Table 2–2 as a guide in making a chart for recording data.

Table 2–2 Data on sinking a straw

Length of Straw below the Surface (cm)	Predicted Quantity of BBs	Actual Quantity of BBs	Observations
4			
5			
6			
7			

3. Move the rubber band so it is 5 cm from the plugged end of the straw. Sink the straw to the 5-cm mark. Record in your notebook the length below the surface of water and the quantity of BBs you used to sink the straw that deep.

4. Predict the quantity of BBs it will take to sink the straw to the 6-cm mark. Record your prediction. Test your prediction by finding what quantity of BBs it actually takes. Record your results.

5. Predict the quantity of BBs it will take to sink the straw to the 7-cm mark. Record your prediction. Test your prediction by finding what quantity of BBs it actually takes. Record your results.

6. If you can predict the quantity of BBs needed to sink the straw to any depth, ask your teacher for a "challenge depth." Record your prediction. Test your prediction and record your result.

Summary

1. If you were able to predict the quantity of BBs necessary to sink the straw to any desired depth, explain how you made your prediction.

2. If you were unable to make a prediction, follow these steps:

    a. Compare your data on the length of straw below the surface of the water with the quantity of BBs necessary to sink the straw.

    b. Are there any *relationships* or connections between the length of straw below the surface and the quantity of BBs? That is, does the quantity of BBs seem to have any effect on the length of straw below the surface of the water? If so, what is the relationship?

3. Predict the quantity of BBs needed to sink 8 cm and 9 cm of the straw. Test your prediction.

Challenge

Using your metric ruler, make the following measurements in millimeters (mm), in centimeters (cm), and in meters (m). Refer to the appendix Metric Linear Measurement for information on how to make these measurements.

1. The width (↔) of this sheet of paper   = ___ mm = ___ cm = ___ m.

2. The length (↕) of this sheet of paper   = ___ mm = ___ cm = ___ m.

3. The diagonal (↗) of this sheet of paper = ___ mm = ___ cm = ___ m.

3. GRAPHING THE SINKING-STRAW DATA

Background

No measurement is exact. Every measurement contains some *uncertainty*. Uncertainty in measurement is due partly to (1) *instrument error* because no instrument is perfect, partly to (2) *human error* because each person measures a little differently.

We assume that some measurements will be greater and some smaller than a "true" measurement. By making many careful measurements and *averaging* them, we are more likely to be close to the "true" value than we are by making just one measurement.

One of the best ways to show all the measurements is to make a *graph*.

Problem

How can the data on the sinking of a straw be put in the form of a graph?

Materials

• graph paper

Procedure

1. Graph a single set of data on the sinking of a straw. Refer to the appendix Introduction to Graphing for information on how to prepare a graph. Use the *horizontal axis* (÷) of the graph for the length of the straw below the surface of the water. Use the *vertical axis* (◊) for the quantity of BBs.

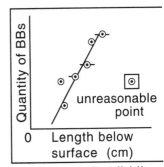

Figure 3–1 A solid line drawn through a pattern of points and an unreasonable point that does not fit the pattern

2. Look at the points you plotted on your graph. Put a box (❏) around any that seem unreasonable or far from the rest of the points as shown in Figure 3–1.

3. Draw a line through or between the pattern of points. See the example in Figure 3–1. Now look at your graph.

| single | 2 repeats |
| 1 repeat | 3 repeats |

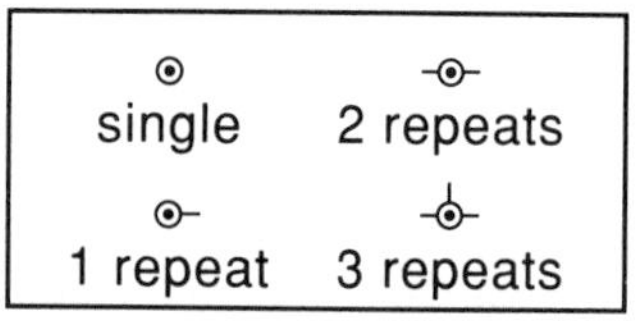

Figure 3–2 A method for showing duplicate points on a graph

4. Graph the data of the whole class the same way you graphed the single set of data. Show any duplicated points on the graph by adding a line that radiates from the point each time it is repeated. See Figure 3–2.

5. Draw a line through or between the pattern of points that shows the average of the class data.

Summary

1. Refer to the measurements you just made in Investigation 2, Sinking a Straw.

   a.   What kinds of **instrument error** could have affected your data?

   b.   What kinds of **human error** could have affected your data?

2. Compare the graph of the single set of data with the graph of the class data.

   a.   How are the graphs similar?

   b.   How do the graphs differ?

   c.   Why, do you think, are the graphs similar or different?

3. Refer to the graph of the class data.

   a.   What quantity of BBs would sink the straw to 12 cm?

   b.   What quantity of BBs would sink the straw to .5 cm?

❡4. What properties of the BBs do you think cause the straw to sink? *Properties* of objects are qualities we can see, feel, or taste, such as color, roughness, and flavor.

Challenge
Explain *buoyancy*.

4. MASS AND THE SINKING STRAW

Background

Graphs of data sometimes show regularities and patterns. From these patterns we can predict events. For example, we can use the graph of the class data on the sinking of straws to predict the quantity of BBs needed to sink a straw to different depths.

The straw sinks a little with no BBs in it, so the BBs and the straw may have some similar property or properties.

Both the straw and the BBs have the property of mass, which under the pull of gravity gives them weight. *Mass* is the measure of the amount of "stuff" in objects such as a straw or BBs.

Problem

What is the mass necessary to sink a straw to any chosen depth in water?

Materials

- sinking straw
- BBs (#9 lead shot)
- balance
- graph paper
- apron and goggles

Procedure

1. Use the class graph from Investigation 3, Graphing the Sinking-Straw Data, to find the average quantities of BBs needed to sink the straw to the 4-cm, 5-cm, 6-cm, and 7-cm marks. Record the quantity of BBs for each depth in a table like Table 4–1.

Table 4–1 Data on the mass of a straw and BBs

Length of Straw below Surface (cm)	Quantity of BBs (Average)	Total Mass of Straw and BBs (g)
4		
5		
6		
7		

2. Put into the straw the quantity of BBs needed to sink it to the 4-cm mark. Using a balance, measure the total mass of the straw and the BBs. Refer to the appendix Metric Mass Measurement for information on how to use the balance.

3. Find the total mass of the straw and the BBs necessary to sink the straw to the 5-cm mark. Record the total mass in the data table.

4. Predict the total mass of straw and BBs necessary to sink the straw to the 6-cm mark. Record your prediction. Test your prediction by finding what mass it actually takes. Record your results.

5. Predict the total mass of straw and BBs necessary to sink the straw to the 7-cm mark. Record your prediction. Test your prediction by finding what mass it actually takes. Record your results.

Summary

¶1. Graph the class data on the total mass of the straw and the BBs.

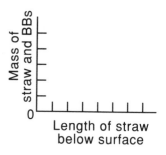

Mass of straw and BBs

0

Length of straw below surface

   a.   Draw a line that shows the average of the data.

   b.   What are the relationships between the mass and the depth of sinking?

¶2. Compare your graph of the total mass of straw and BBs with the class graph of the quantity of BBs and the depth of sinking.

   a.   How are the graphs similar?

   b.   How do the graphs differ?

   c.   Why, do you think, are the graphs similar or different?

Challenge

1. Use your class graphs of Investigation 3, Graphing the Sinking-Straw Data, and Investigation 4, Mass and the Sinking Straw, to predict the mass of a straw. Test your prediction.

2. Suppose that the diameter of one straw is twice the diameter of another. If both straws contain the same quantity of BBs, would they both sink to the same depth in a container of water? If so, why? If not, why not?

New Vocabulary for Section A

anomaly
average
balance
buoyancy
centimeter
consensus
data
diagonal
experiment
explanation
extrapolate
gram
graphing

horizontal axis
human error
hypothesis
instrument error
interface
interpolate
interpretation
investigation
linear measurement
mass
metric measurement
negative axis
observe

origin
pattern
phenomenon
prediction
properties
quantity
regularity
relationship
system
uncertainty
vertical axis
weight

Section B. Volume

5. SINKING CARTONS

Background
Mass is the property of an object that seems to cause it to sink in water. In the sinking-straw experiment, the straw and the BBs had mass. The greater the mass of an object, the deeper it sinks. Are there any other properties that might help us determine the depth of sinking?

Problem
If the same amount of water is put into cartons of different sizes, how can you predict the depth to which each carton will sink?

Materials
- half-gallon carton
- half-pint carton
- rubber bands
- metric ruler
- bucket
- water
- apron and goggles

Procedure
1. Cut the tops off a half-gallon carton and a half-pint carton so you can pour water in and out easily. See Figure 5–1, a. Put a rubber band around each carton.

2. Fill the small carton about half-full with water as shown in Figure 5–1, b. The water is used as *ballast*. Any material added to a floating object to make it sink is called ballast.

3. Predict how deep the carton will sink in a bucket of water. Record your prediction in a table like Table 5–2.

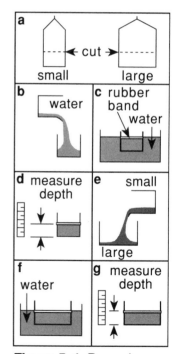

Figure 5–1 Procedure for investigating the sinking of cartons

20

4. Put the carton into a bucket of water. Move the rubber band to mark the depth to which the carton sinks when it is carefully held upright as shown in Figure 5–1, c. **Do not** push it down.

5. Measure the actual depth of sinking from the bottom of the carton to the rubber band. See Figure 5–1, d. Record the depth.

6. Pour all the water from the small carton into the large carton. See Figure 5–1, e. Predict how deep the large carton will sink in a bucket of water. Record your prediction.

7. Move the rubber band to mark the depth you predicted. Put the large carton into the bucket of water. Holding the carton lightly, move the rubber band to mark the depth of sinking. See Figure 5–1, f.

8. Measure and record the actual depth the large carton sank. Pour the water out of the carton. See Figure 5–1, g.

9. Fill the small carton three-quarters full with water. Try to predict how deep the carton will sink in a bucket of water. Record your prediction. Follow procedures 3 through 8 and record your results.

Table 5–2 Data on sinking cartons

Amount of Ballast (water)	Size of Carton	Depth of Sinking (cm)		Other Observations
		Predicted	Actual	
Equal to 1/2 filled small carton	small			
	large			
Equal to 3/4 filled small carton	small			
	large			

10. Predict how much water it will take to sink the large carton completely. Record your prediction on a table like Table 5–3. Test your prediction. Record your result and your observations.

Table 5–3 Data on sinking a large carton completely

Amount of Water to Sink Large Carton Completely		Other Observations
Predicted	Actual	

Summary

1. How are the cartons similar? How do they differ?

2. Refer to your data on sinking cartons, Table 5–2. Compare your predictions with your results. Were your predictions for each carton accurate?

   a. If so, how did you make your predictions?

   b. If not, how might you make better predictions?

3. Refer to your data on sinking a large carton completely, Table 5–3. Compare your predictions with the actual amount of water it took to sink the carton completely. Were your predictions accurate? Explain why or why not.

4. Compare your data on the sinking of cartons, Tables 5–2 and 5–3. What are the relationships, if any, between the amount of ballast, the size of the carton, and the depth of sinking in water?

5. What kinds of things seem to affect the depth to which the cartons sink?

Challenge

What would you have to know to predict how deep a ship would sink in water after it is loaded?

6. VOLUME AND THE SINKING CARTONS

Background
When a carton is put into water, it pushes some of the water out of the way as it sinks. The water pushed away is *displaced*, so it is called *displaced water.*

Do you think there are any relationships between the size of an object put into water and the amount of water it displaces?

Problem
1. How much water is displaced by cartons of different sizes sinking to different depths in water?

2. Can the volume or amount of displaced water be predicted if the volume of the part of a carton that is below the surface of the water is known?

Materials
- plastic box
- rubber band
- metric ruler
- metric area grid
- sand
- graduated cylinder
- overflow container
- water
- graph paper
- apron and goggles

Procedure
1. Determine the submerged volume of the cartons. *Submerged volume* is the amount of space occupied by the part of the carton below the surface of the water.

a. Measure and record the base area of the carton as shown in Figure 6–1 or Figure 6–2. Refer to the appendix Metric Area Measurement for further information on measuring area.

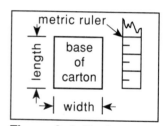

Figure 6–1 Finding base area by using a metric ruler

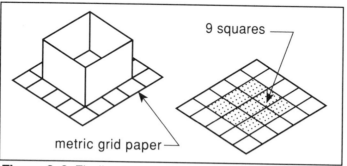

Figure 6–2 Finding base area by using a metric grid

b. Put a rubber band around the carton to mark any depth you choose for sinking. Measure and record the depth as shown in Figure 6–3.

c. Calculate the submerged volume of the carton by multiplying the area of the base by the depth of sinking as shown below:

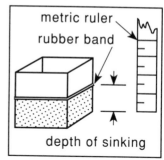

Figure 6–3 Measuring the depth of sinking

$$\text{Area of base} \quad \times \quad \text{Depth of sinking} \quad = \quad \text{Submerged volume}$$

Example:

$$9 \text{ cm}^2 \quad \times \quad 1 \text{ cm} \quad = \quad 9 \text{ cm}^3$$

Refer to the appendix Metric Volume Measurement for further information on how to measure volume.

d. Record the submerged volume of the carton on a table like Table 6–5.

2. Put the carton into a container of water. Add sand to the carton until it sinks to the depth marked by the rubber band.

3. Determine the amount of water displaced by the carton and sand.

a. Use an overflow container as shown in Figure 6–4.

b. Measure the volume of water displaced and record it in your table. Record any other observations.

---

1. Fill the overflow container with water and let the excess water drip into a beaker.

2. Put the carton into the water in the overflow container. Use a graduated cylinder to catch the water displaced by the carton.

3. Note the volume of water displaced in the graduated cylinder.

4. Repeat steps 1, 2, and 3 for each measurement of water displaced. Be sure to refill the overflow container each time.

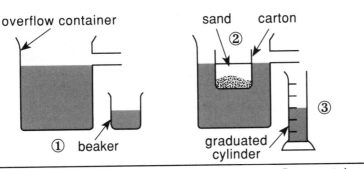

Figure 6–4 Finding displaced volume by using an overflow container

4. Predict the volume of water that will be displaced when the same carton sinks to a different depth. Record and test your prediction. Record your result.

5. Predict the volume of water that will be displaced by cartons of different sizes sinking to different depths. Record your predictions. Record the volumes of displaced water and any other observations.

Table 6–5 Data on the submerged volumes of cartons and displaced water

Base Area (cm²)	Depth of Sinking (cm)	Submerged Volume of Carton (cm³)	Volume of Water Displaced (mL)		Other Observations
			Predicted	Actual	

Summary

1. Graph the class data on the **submerged volume** of the cartons and the **volume of water displaced**.

2. What are the relationships, if any, between the submerged volume of a carton and the volume of water displaced?

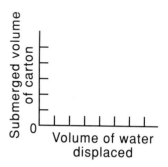

3. Compare your predictions with the actual amount of water displaced. Were your predictions accurate?

   a. If so, how did you make your predictions?

   b. If not, how might you make more accurate predictions?

Challenge

1. How might you predict the amount of water an object will displace before you actually float the object in water?

2. What are the relationships, if any, between the total volume of a carton and the volume of water displaced?

7. FLOATING AND SINKING OBJECTS

Background
A hypothesis that explains only a few situations is not very useful. In science, we try to find a *universal explanation*—that is, an explanation that is useful in all related situations. We are now searching for a universal explanation of buoyancy.

Problem
1. Can the volume of displaced water be predicted if the mass of a **floating** object is known?

2. Can the volume of displaced water be predicted if the mass of a **sinking** object is known?

Materials
- plastic box
- floating objects
- sinking objects
- balance
- graduated cylinder
- water
- graph paper
- apron and goggles

Procedure
1. Use the balance to determine the mass of a floating object. Record the mass of the object in a table like Table 7–1.

Table 7–1 Data on the volume of water displaced by objects

| Mass of Object (g) | Volume of Water Displaced (mL) | |
	Predicted	Actual
Floating objects		
Sinking objects		

2. Measure and record the volume of water displaced by the object. Refer to the appendix Metric Volume Measurement for information on measuring volume.

3. Predict the volume of water that will be displaced by other floating objects with different masses. Record your predictions. Repeat procedures 1 and 2. Record the actual volume of water displaced in Table 7–1.

4. Repeat procedures 1–3 for sinking objects. Record your data in Table 7–1.

Summary

1. Graph the class data of the mass of objects and the volume of water displaced by the objects. Plot the points for floating objects and sinking objects on the same graph.

a. Mark the points for floating objects ⚠f.

b. Mark the points for sinking objects ⬜b.

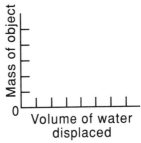

2. What relationships, if any, are there between the mass of an object and the volume of water displaced?

3. Refer to your table. Compare your predictions with the actual volume of water displaced. Were your predictions accurate?

   a. If so, how did you make your predictions?

   b. If not, how might you make more accurate predictions?

Challenge

1. What are the relationships, if any, between the **mass** of water displaced by objects and the **volume** of water displaced by objects?

2. Can you predict whether an object will float or sink before you put it in water? If so, how? If not, why not?

3. Can you predict the depth to which an object will sink before you put it in water? If so, how? If not, why not?

New Vocabulary for Section B

area
ballast
buoyancy
cubic centimeter
cm²
cm³
displaced
displaced volume

explanation
graduated cylinder
milliliter
mL
submerge
submerged volume
universal explanation
volume

Section C. Density and Buoyancy

8. INTRODUCTION TO THE CARTESIAN DIVER

Background
We have looked at the effects of mass and size on the depth an object sinks.
We have also measured the volume of water an object displaces.

Now we will use a Cartesian diver to investigate the conditions under which
objects float and the conditions under which they sink.

Problem
How does a Cartesian diver operate?

Procedure
The Cartesian diver is the object in the water-
filled plastic container. Before starting, be sure
the diver is floating.

1. Squeeze the bottle as shown in Figure 8–1
   and observe what happens.

2. Experiment with the diver and record your
   observations. Try to explain how the diver
   works. If possible, test your explanation.
   Ask your teacher for any equipment you
   need for your test.

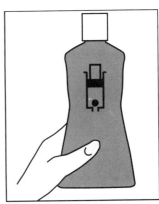

Figure 8–1 Operating a
Cartesian diver by
squeezing the bottle

Summary
1. What is your hypothesis to explain how the diver operates? Include
   diagrams in your explanation.

2. If you tested a hypothesis, what were the results of the test?

3. If you did not test a hypothesis, how might you have tested your
   hypothesis?

Challenge

Design and build your own Cartesian diver. Test it.

9. DENSITY AND THE CARTESIAN DIVER

Background
We have observed the Cartesian diver floating at the surface, subsurface floating, and resting on the bottom of the container.

We now look more closely at the volume of water the diver displaces in these three positions. We will also investigate the relationship between the mass and the volume of the diver at these positions.

One relationship between an object's mass and its volume is called *density*. Density is expressed as the number of grams in 1 cubic centimeter (cm³) of the object.

Problem
1. Can the mass of the diver be predicted if the volume of water it displaces is known?

2. What is the density of the diver as it floats at different positions in a container of water?

Materials
- Cartesian diver
- graduated cylinder
- balance
- graph paper

Procedure
1. Determine the volume of water displaced by the diver at different positions in the container. Your teacher will explain how to measure volume. Record the volume of water displaced by the diver for each position listed in Table 9–1.

Table 9–1 Data on the Cartesian diver

Position of Diver	Volume of Water Displaced (mL)	Mass of Diver		Total Volume of Diver (cm³)
		Predicted	Actual	
Surface				
Subsurface				
Bottom				

2. Predict the mass of the diver at each position listed in Table 9–1. Test your predictions. Measure and record the actual mass of the diver. Record any other observations.

3. Determine and record the volume of the diver at each position listed in Table 9–1.

Summary

1. Graph the class data of the mass of the diver and the volume of water it displaced. Mark the points as follows:

△f floating at the surface
Ⓢ floating submerged
☐b resting on the bottom

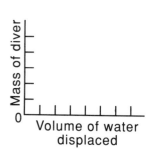

a. Draw a line through the patterns of points marked △f and Ⓢ .

b. What are the relationships, if any, between the mass of the diver and the volume of water it displaces?

2. Graph the class data of the mass of the diver and the total volume of the diver. Mark the points as follows:

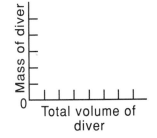

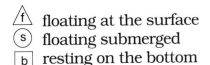 floating at the surface
(s) floating submerged
[b] resting on the bottom

a. Draw a line through the pattern of points marked (s).

b. What are the relationships, if any, between the mass and the volume of the diver?

3. Compare the two graphs of the class data of the Cartesian diver. What are the relationships, if any, between the volume of water displaced by the diver, the mass of the diver, and the volume of the diver?

4. Density can be read directly from a graph of the mass and volume of an object as shown in Figure 9–2. It is expressed as the amount of mass in 1 cubic centimeter (cm³) of the object. Refer to the appendix Introduction to Density for further information on density. Look at your graph of mass and volume of the diver.

a. What is the density of the diver as it floats? As it subsurface floats? As it rests on the bottom?

b. Is the density of the diver greatest when it floats, when it subsurface floats, or when it rests on the bottom?

1. Find the point on the density line that intersects the 1 cm³ line.

2. Read the corresponding number of grams on the vertical axis. Example: 2 g.

3. Density can be expressed in g/cm³ or g/mL (1 cm³ = 1 mL). Example: Density = 2 g/cm³.

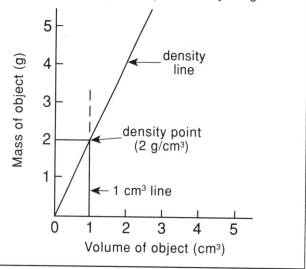

Figure 9-2 Reading a graph of the density of an object

5. Refer to Table 9–1. Compare your predictions with your measurements of the mass of the diver at each position in the container. Were your predictions accurate?

   a. If so, how did you make your predictions?

   b. If not, how might you make more accurate predictions?

6. Does the shape of the Cartesian diver affect the volume of water it displaces? If so, how? If not, why not?

Challenge

Can you predict the mass of water displaced by the diver when it is floating at the surface, subsurface floating, and resting on the bottom? If so, how? If not, why not?

10. DENSITY OF OBJECTS

Background
We investigated the Cartesian diver to test our universal explanation of buoyancy.

The depth the diver sinks seems to be related to its density. We will further investigate density by determining the densities of several other floating and sinking objects.

Problem
What are the densities of objects that float? Of objects that sink?

Materials
- floating objects
- sinking objects
- graduated cylinder
- overflow container
- balance
- graph paper
- apron

Procedure
1. Select several objects that float in water. List them on a table like Table 10–1.

Table 10–1 Data on the densities of objects

Kind of Object	Mass of Object (g)	Volume of Object (cm³)

2. Select several objects that sink completely in water. List them on your table.

3. Determine the mass of each object and record it on your table.

4. Determine the volume of each object and record it on your table.

Summary

1. Graph the data of the mass and volume of the objects.

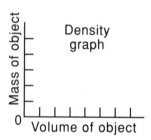

a. Draw a straight line from the origin to each plotted point. You may extend the line beyond the point.

b. Determine and record the mass in 1 cubic centimeter (cm³) of each object.

2. What is the density of each object?

3. How do the densities of sinking objects compare with the densities of floating objects?

Challenge

If an object is to be put in a container of a liquid other than water, can you predict whether it will float at the surface, subsurface float, or sink to the bottom? If so, how? If not, why not?

11. DENSITY OF LIQUIDS

Background
We have compared the density of the Cartesian diver at different positions in a container of water and measured the densities of other objects. But we have not investigated the densities of liquids.

Problem
What are the densities of liquids?

Materials
• liquids supplied by your teacher
• graduated cylinder
• balance
• graph paper
• apron and goggles

Procedure

CAUTION: Liquids used in this investigation may be hazardous. Do not taste any liquids. Do not allow any flame in the classroom.

1. Select at least two liquids other than water to use in this investigation. List the liquids in a table like Table 11–1.

Table 11–1 Data on the densities of liquids

Name of Liquid	Mass of Liquid (g)	Volume of Liquid (mL)

2. Determine the mass of 10 to 25 milliliters
   (mL) of each liquid. Record the mass and the
   volume in your table.

Summary

?1. Graph the data on the mass and volume of the liquids.

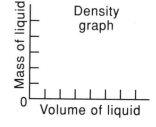

    a.   Use a different symbol to identify the
          data for each liquid.

    b.   Draw a separate straight line from the
          origin through the data points for each
          liquid. You may extend the lines beyond
          the data points.

    c.   Determine and record the mass of 1
          milliliter (mL) of each liquid.

?2. What is the density of each liquid?

12. BUOYANCY OF LIQUIDS

Background

We have been searching for a universal explanation of buoyancy phenomena. Thus far we have explained buoyancy by the relationships between the mass of an object, the volume of water it displaces, and the mass of water it displaces. We have found buoyancy to be the mass of material that can be supported by 1 milliliter (mL) of liquid. If our explanation is universal, it should apply to all liquids.

Problem

1. Can the mass of any displaced liquid be predicted if the mass of a floating object is known?

2. What are the relationships, if any, between buoyancy and density?

Materials

- liquids from Investigation 11, Density of Liquids
- graduated cylinder
- overflow container
- balance
- floating objects
- graph paper
- apron and goggles

Procedure

1. Determine the mass of an object that floats about half-submerged in water. Record the mass of the object in a table like Table 12–1.

Table 12–1 Data on liquids displaced by floating objects

Name of Liquid	Mass of Object (g)	Volume of Liquid Displaced (mL)		Mass of Liquid Displaced (g)	
		Predicted	Actual	Predicted	Actual

2. Predict the volume of liquid that will be displaced by the object as it floats in water.

    a. Record your prediction in your table.

    b. Test your prediction.

    c. Record the actual volume of water displaced.

3. Predict the mass of liquid that will be displaced by the object as it floats in water.

    a. Record your prediction in your table.

    b. Test your prediction.

    c. Record the actual mass of water displaced.

4. Using the same object, repeat procedures 1, 2, and 3 with each of the liquids you used in Investigation 11, Density of Liquids. Record your data.

5. Predict the mass and volume of each liquid that will be displaced by other floating objects having different masses. Test your predictions. Record your data.

Summary

1. On one graph, plot the class data of the masses of the objects and the volumes of liquids displaced for all the liquids tested.

    a. Identify the data for each liquid with a different symbol.

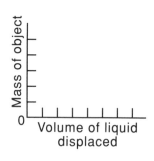

b. For each liquid, draw a line through the points for that liquid.

c. Compare the masses of the objects with the volumes of liquids displaced. Do all liquids buoy the same mass for each milliliter of liquid displaced?

͡2. Compare the graph in Summary 1 with your density graph from Investigation 11, Density of Liquids.

a. How are the graphs similar? How do they differ?

b. What are the relationships, if any, between buoyancy and density?

͡3. On a second graph, plot the class data on the masses of the objects and the masses of liquids displaced for all the liquids tested.

a. Identify the plotted points of each liquid with a different symbol.

b. Compare the mass of the object with the mass of liquid displaced.

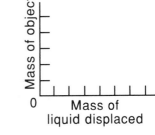

c. Do all liquids buoy the same mass for each gram of liquid displaced?

4. Compare the graph of the masses of objects and the volumes of liquids displaced with the graph of masses of objects and the masses of liquids displaced. What are the relationships, if any, between the buoyancy of water and the buoyancy of other liquids?

5. Refer to your data table. Compare your predictions with the actual results of your test. Were your predictions of the mass of liquids displaced accurate?

a. If so, how did you make your predictions?

b. If not, how might you make more accurate predictions?

6. When the mass of an object is known, can you predict whether it will sink completely or float in any liquid? If so, how? If not, why not?

₹7. Refer to your observations from Investigation 1, Liquids and Vials.

    a.   What is your hypothesis to explain the floating of one liquid on another?

    b.   What is your hypothesis to explain the floating of a vial at the *interface*—the place where the two liquids meet?

    c.   What is your hypothesis to explain the sinking of a vial to the bottom of the two liquids?

₹8. What is your universal explanation of buoyancy?

Challenge

1. An object has a volume of 6 cm³ and a mass of 3 g. It is put into a liquid with a density of 1.5 g/mL.

    a.   What is the density of the object?

    b.   Will the object float, sink completely, or subsurface float in the liquid?

    c.   How much liquid will the object displace?

2. An object is supported by a balance in each of the three positions shown in Figure 12–2. Note that this kind of balance has no weighing pan. The object has a volume of 10 cm³ and a mass of 25 g. The liquid has a density of 1 g/mL.

    a.   What is the mass reading on the balance for the object in position 1?

    b.   Suppose that only 5 cm³ of the object is submerged in the liquid. What is the mass reading on the balance for the object in position 2?

c.	What is the mass reading on the balance for the object in position 3?

d.	What effect, if any, does buoyancy have on your answers to questions b and c?

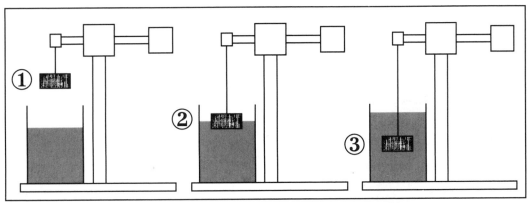

Figure 12–2 Determining the mass of an object in different positions

3. Find a way to determine the mass of any solid or any liquid without using a balance.

New Vocabulary for Section C
buoyancy
density
determine
explanation
subsurface float
universal explanation

13. BALLOONS IN WATER

Background
To expand our understanding of buoyancy, we now investigate the events in a balloon-and-water system and try to explain them.

Problem
How can the events of the balloon-and-water system be explained?

Materials
- balloons
- string
- large jar or beaker
- tap water
- hot water
- ice
- apron and goggles

Procedure
1. Duplicate your teacher's demonstration of a balloon in water as shown in Figure 13–1.

   a. Fill a balloon with tap water. Make sure there are no large air bubbles inside. Tie the end of the balloon and put it in a large container half-filled with tap water. Observe and record what happens.

   b. Add hot water to the container. Record your observations.

   c. Add ice or cold water to the container. Record your observations.

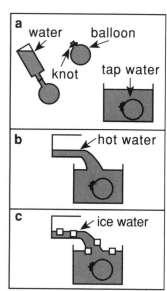

Figure 13–1 Procedure for investigating balloons in water

2. Develop a hypothesis to explain your observations of the balloon in water. Record your hypothesis.

3. Test your hypothesis. Record your results and observations.

Summary

1. What is your hypothesis to explain the events of the balloon-and-water system?

2. What evidence supports your hypothesis?

Challenge

1. What is matter?

2. What is energy?

14. SUBMARINE PROJECT

Background
Imagine that we need to use a submarine to investigate the oceans surrounding the Hawaiian Islands. Can you design a submarine that we could use?

Activity
Design a submarine.

Procedure
1. Design at least **two** different submarines.

2. Write a brief explanation of how each submarine would work. Include drawings of your submarine designs.

3. Using materials you have at home or in the laboratory, build a submarine according to one of your designs.

Summary
ʃ1. Which design is best? Why?

2. What factors did you use to decide which design is best?

New Vocabulary for Section D
Celsius

°C

economics

engineering

feasibility

maneuver

technology

thermometer

thermal effects

15. BUBBLES IN GASES

Background
We now investigate events in a bubbles-and-gases system.

Problem
How can the events of the bubbles-and-gases system be explained?

Materials
• gases supplied by your teacher
• bubble solution
• straws
• large jar or bucket
• apron and goggles

Procedure

**CAUTION: Some of the gases you will use are
hazardous. Read the directions and safety
precautions at each station. Follow your
teacher's instructions. Wear an apron and
goggles.**

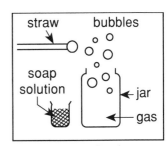

Figure 15–1 Equipment used in investigating floating bubbles

1. Duplicate your teacher's demonstration of
    the bubbles-and-gases system as shown in
    Figure 15–1.

    a. Fill the jar with a gas.

    b. Dip your straw into the soap solution.
        Then blow bubbles **over the top** of the
        container so that some bubbles fall into
        the jar. Do not blow into the jar because
        the gas will spill out.

    c. Record your observations.

2. Use other gases to make bubbles.

   a. Before you blow any bubbles over the jar, predict what will happen when the bubbles fall into the jar of gas. Record your predictions.

   b. Test your predictions and record your observations.

3. Suggest a hypothesis that allows you to predict what will happen when different gases are used in the bubbles-and-gases system.

   a. Devise experiments to test your hypothesis.

   b. Have your teacher approve your plans before you start your test.

   c. Record your hypothesis, predictions, test results, and other observations.

Summary

ℑ1. What is your hypothesis to explain the events of the bubbles-and-gases system?

2. What evidence supports your hypothesis?

Challenge

What properties do all kinds of matter have in common?

16. DENSITY OF GASES

Background
The *relative density* of a substance refers to whether it is more dense or less dense than other substances. In this investigation we will try to determine the relative densities of some gases.

Problem
1. What is the relative density of each of the gases you used in Investigation 15, Bubbles in Gases?

2. What are the densities of these gases?

Materials
- 250-mL Erlenmeyer flask
- #6 two-hole stopper
- 2 pinch clamps
- 6-cm length of glass tubing
- 15-cm length of glass tubing
- two 6-cm lengths of rubber tubing
- balance
- bucket
- water
- graduated cylinder
- gases from Investigation 15, Bubbles in Gases
- graph paper
- apron and goggles

Procedure

CAUTION: Some of the gases you will use are hazardous. Read the directions and safety precautions at each station. Follow your teacher's instructions. Wear an apron and

goggles. Handle the flask with cloth to protect your hands in case the flask breaks.

1. Predict the relative density of each gas you used in the previous activity, Bubbles in Gases. Record your predictions in your notebook. List the most dense gas first and the least dense gas last.

2. Set up the equipment as shown in Figure 16–1.

   a. Fill a dry flask with gas. Record the name of the gas in a table like Table 16–7.

   b. Measure the mass of the flask with the clamp, stopper, tubing, and gas contents as shown in Figure 16–2.

   c. Record the total mass of the flask, attachments, and gas.

3. Remove the gas from the flask as shown in Figure 16–3.

   a. Open the clamp. Pull the syringe plunger so that some gas moves into the syringe.

   b. Close the clamp. Remove the syringe from the tube. Push the plunger forward to empty the gas out of the syringe.

   c. Reconnect the syringe to the tube. Repeat procedures 3.a. and 3.b. until you can't remove any more gas from the flask.

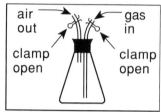

Figure 16–1 Filling the flask with gas

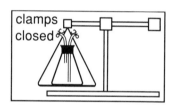

Figure 16–2 Determining the mass of gas and flask

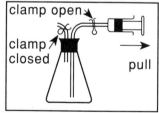

Figure 16–3 Removing gas from the flask

d. Measure the mass of the flask, attachments, and remaining gas as shown in Figure 16–4. Record the mass of the flask and remaining gas in your Table 16–7.

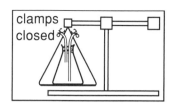

Figure 16–4 Measuring the mass of flask and remaining gas

4. Determine the mass of gas removed from the flask. Subtract the mass of the flask and the remaining gas from the mass of the flask and gas at the start. Record the mass of gas removed.

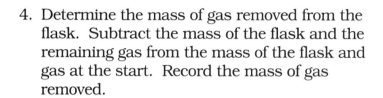

Total mass of gas and flask − Mass of flask and remaining gas = Mass of gas removed

5. Determine the volume of gas removed from the flask.

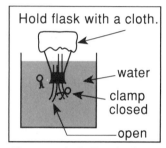

Figure 16–5 Replacing volume of gas removed with water

a. Put the flask under water as shown in Figure 16–5. Make sure both tubes and clamps are under water.

b. Open one of the clamps while the tubes are under water. Keep the levels of water inside and outside the flask the same.

c. Using a graduated cylinder, measure the volume of water in the flask as shown in Figure 16–6. The volume of water is equal to the volume of gas removed from the flask. Record the volume of gas removed.

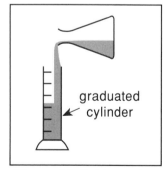

6. Repeat procedures 2 through 5 for each gas you used in Investigation 15, Bubbles in Gases. Record all your data in your table.

Figure 16–6 Measuring the volume of gas removed by determining the volume of replaced water

Table 16-7 Data on the densities of some gases

Name of Gas			
Mass of flask and gas at the start (g)			
Mass of flask and remaining gas (g)			
Mass of gas removed (g)			
Volume of gas removed (cm³)			
Density of gas (g/cm³)			

Summary

¶1. Graph the class data on mass of gas and volume of gas. Include the data on all the gases on the same graph. Identify the plotted points of each gas with a different symbol.

    a.   For each gas draw a line or curve through the points for that gas.

    b.   What is the relative density of each gas?

    c.   What is the actual density of each gas?

2. Look at your predictions and your measurements of the relative density of each gas. Were your predictions successful? Explain.

¶3. Compare your observations of the bubbles-and-gases system with your observations of the liquids-and-vials system and the balloon-and-water system.

    a.   How are these three systems related?

    b.   What is your hypothesis to explain your observations of the three systems?

¶4. What properties do all kinds of matter have in common?

Challenge

1. How might you determine the density of moist air? What effect, if any, does moisture have on the density of air?

2. Do all kinds of matter have the properties of buoyancy and density? Explain.

17. WEATHER BALLOON PROJECT

Background

We have seen that gases, like liquids, have the property called buoyancy. Some objects float in gases just as other objects float in liquids. This knowledge can help us design devices for carrying things such as weather instruments up into the air.

Activity

Design a weather balloon that can carry instruments into the upper atmosphere.

Procedure

1. Design a weather balloon.

   a. The device should be able to carry instruments, objects, or people to take measurements.

   b. The device should be able to operate at any chosen altitude.

2. Write a brief explanation of how your device operates. Include drawings of your design.

3. Try to build an operating model of your device.

Summary

1. Share your design with the class.

2. Which design in the class is best? Why?

3. What factors did you consider in deciding which design is best?

New Vocabulary for Section E
buoyancy
density
relative density
technology

UNIT 2. CHANGES OF STATE IN MATTER

18. BOILING WATER

Background
In this unit we investigate the effects of heat on matter. Heat seems to change the properties of water. We have already seen that the buoyancy of liquids changes when they are heated or cooled.

We begin investigating the effects of heat on matter by studying boiling water.

Problem
What is boiling?

Materials
- test tube
- 250-mL beaker
- thermometer
- ring stand and ring
- wire gauze
- clamp
- heat source
- water
- apron and goggles

Procedure
1. Set up the equipment as shown in Figure 18–1.

   a. Fill a beaker about half-full with tap water.

   b. Fill a test tube with **tap water**. Rest the open end of the test tube on the bottom of the beaker as shown. Be sure that the test tube is **completely filled** with water.

c. Suspend the thermometer in the water as shown in Figure 18–1. Make sure the tip of the thermometer is under water but is **not** touching the beaker.

CAUTION: Wear an apron and goggles. Use only heat-resistant glass. Use care in handling hot glass and metal.

2. Put the heat source under the beaker. Heat the water until it boils. Record the temperature of the water and any other observations of the water as it heats. Continue heating until the test tube is about half-full of gas.

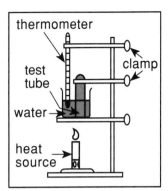

Figure 18–1 Boiling water in a beaker

3. Remove the heat source from under the beaker. Let the equipment cool. Record your observations of cooling and any changes in the volume of gas in the test tube.

4. Completely fill the test tube with previously **boiled water** that has been cooled. Rest the open end of the test tube on the bottom of the beaker as shown in Figure 18–1. Repeat procedures 2 and 3. Record any observations as the water heats.

Summary

1. Compare your observations of the boiling of tap water and the boiling of previously boiled water.

   a. How are the observations similar?

   b. How are the observations different?

   c. How can you explain any similarities or differences?

12. Review your observations of boiling water.

    a. How can you tell when the water is boiling?

    b. At what temperature does water begin to boil?

Challenge

1. When a thermometer is put in water, does it **immediately** give a reading of the water temperature? Explain your answer. Test your explanation.

2. What is evaporation?

    a. How are boiling and evaporation similar?

    b. How are boiling and evaporation different?

3. What is condensation?

19. HEATING ICE IN A BALLOON

Background

We observed what happened when we heated tap water to boiling and when we heated previously boiled water to boiling. Now let's see what happens when we heat a balloon filled with ice.

Problem

What happens to ice heated in a balloon?

Materials

- ice balloon
- 2 thermometers
- ring stand and ring
- wire gauze
- clamp
- heat source
- 250-mL beaker
- saltwater bath
- ice
- stirring rod
- watch or clock
- graph paper
- apron and goggles

Procedure

1. Before starting the experiment, decide which team member will do each of these jobs:

    a. Note the time and stir the liquid bath.

    b. Read the temperature of the ice in the balloon, read the temperature of the saltwater bath, and make observations.

    c. Record the data and other observations.

2. Make a data table like Table 19–2 with a column for each kind of data:

   a. Time in 30-second intervals, starting with zero seconds

   b. Temperature of the saltwater bath

   c. Temperature of the ice in the balloon

   d. Other observations

CAUTION: Wear an apron and goggles. Use only heat-resistant glass. Use care in handling hot glass and metal.

3. Set up the equipment as shown in Figure 19–1. **Do not** get the ice-filled balloon until you are ready to begin the experiment. If you get it earlier, it will get warm before you are ready to measure temperatures.

   a. Get about 100 mL of saltwater bath.

   b. Measure the temperature of the bath. Add ice or salt as needed to cool the bath to about –10°C.

   c. Remove all pieces of ice. Then get your ice balloon.

4. Suspend the two thermometers in the liquid as shown in Figure 19–1. Make sure the balloon is in the liquid but is **not** touching the bottom of the beaker.

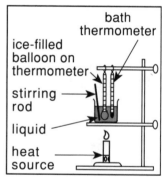

Figure 19–1 Heating ice in a balloon

5. Read the starting temperatures of the ice-filled balloon and the saltwater bath **immediately**. Record these temperatures at zero seconds in your data table.

6. Put the heat source under the beaker and begin timing. Record data in 30-second intervals. Stir the saltwater bath with a stirring rod. **Do not use the thermometer for stirring.**

  a. Read and record the temperature of the liquid bath and the ice in the balloon every 30 seconds. Record your observations.

  b. Continue heating until the water in the balloon boils. Record your observations of boiling and the volume of the balloon.

7. Remove the heat source from under the beaker. Let the equipment cool.

Table 19–2 Data on heating ice in a balloon

Time (sec)	Temperature (°C)		Other Observations
	Liquid Bath	Ice in Balloon	

Summary

↑1. Graph your data. Plot your data on the heating of the ice in the balloon and the heating of the saltwater bath on the same graph. Draw a line or curve through the pattern of points you plotted for the balloon. Draw another line or curve through the pattern of points you plotted for the saltwater bath.

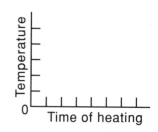

  a. What are the relationships, if any, between the temperature of the water in the balloon and the length of time of heating?

  b. What are the relationships, if any, between the temperature of the liquid in a bath and the length of time of heating?

  c. Are these relationships similar or different? Explain.

↑2. Review your observations of heating ice in a balloon.

  a. What happens to the volume of ice as it is heated?

  b. At what temperature does ice seem to melt?

↑3. Review your observations of heating water in a balloon.

  a. What happens to the volume of water in the balloon as it is heated and as it boils?

  b. At what temperature does water seem to boil?

Challenge

  1. At what temperature does water freeze? How could you test your prediction?

  2. At what temperature does steam condense? How could you test your prediction?

20. FREEZING, MELTING, BOILING, AND CONDENSING OF PURE SUBSTANCES

Background
The graphs of the temperature changes of the ice in the balloon and the liquid in the bath looked very much alike. The graphs may show differences during melting and boiling.

Matter exists in three states: as a solid, as a liquid, and as a gas. Matter may be either a pure substance or a mixture of substances. *Pure substances* contain only one kind of substance; *mixtures* contain more than one kind of substance.

By using water, a pure substance that exists in all three states, we can study the effects of temperature changes on matter.

Problem
At what temperatures do pure substances freeze? Melt? Boil? Condense?

Materials
- syringe barrel or small test tube
- water
- ice
- saltwater bath
- 2 thermometers
- ring stand and ring
- wire gauze
- two 250-mL Erlenmeyer flasks
- 6-cm length of glass tubing
- 15-cm length of glass tubing
- two 400-mL beakers
- two #6 two-hole stoppers
- heat source
- pure substances supplied by your teacher
- watch or clock
- graph paper
- apron and goggles

Procedure

1. Review your observations and your graph of Investigation 19, Heating Ice in a Balloon.

    a. Predict the shape of the line or curve for graphs of heating and cooling a sample of water. Draw your predicted line or curve on graphs like the ones in Figure 20–1.

    b. On the graphs mark the points where you think the pure substance will melt, freeze, boil, and condense. Predict the temperature at which each change will happen.

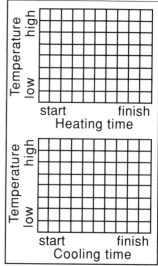

Figure 20–1 Predicted graphs of the heating and cooling of a pure substance (water)

2. Test your predictions. Follow procedures 3 through 8. Test water first, then other pure substances.

CAUTION: Wear an apron and goggles. Use only heat-resistant glass. Use care in handling hot glass and metal. Follow your teacher's instructions for handling the substances in this experiment.

3. Before you start the experiment, decide which team member will do each of these jobs:

    a. Note the time.

    b. Read the temperature and make observations.

    c. Record the data and other observations.

4. Make data tables like Tables 20–2, 20–3, 20–4, and 20–5.

Table 20–2 Data on FREEZING a pure substance

Time (sec)	Temperature (°C)	Observations
0		
30		
60		
90		

Table 20–3 Data on MELTING a pure substance

Time (sec)	Temperature (°C)	Observations
0		
30		
60		
90		

Table 20–4 Data on BOILING a pure substance

Time (sec)	Temperature (°C)	Observations
0		
30		
60		
90		

Table 20–5 Data on CONDENSING a pure substance

Time (sec)	Temperature (°C)	Observations
0		
30		
60		
90		

5. Determine the **freezing** temperature of a pure substance.

   a. Set up the equipment as shown in Figure 20–6. Put about 2 mL of the pure substance to be tested into the syringe barrel. **Do not** put the syringe barrel in the cooling bath yet.

   b. Record the starting temperature of the substance in the syringe barrel at zero seconds. Use another thermometer to check the temperature of the bath.

   c. Put the thermometer and the syringe barrel with the pure substance into the cooling bath. Start timing immediately. Make sure the level of substance in the syringe barrel is below the level of the cooling bath.

   d. Holding the barrel, gently stir with the thermometer as shown in Figure 20–7. Record the temperature of the substance every 30 seconds. Record any other observations on freezing.

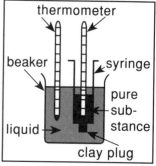

Figure 20–6 Equipment for determining freezing and melting temperatures

NOTE: You may use the thermometer for stirring in this experiment only. Because the syringe barrel is soft plastic, it won't damage the thermometer. If you use a glass test tube, stir with a piece of insulated wire.

   e. Continue recording temperatures until both are about the same.

6. Determine the **melting** temperature of a pure substance.

   a. Set up the equipment as shown in Figure 20–6.

   b. Record the starting temperature of the ice or other frozen pure substance.

   c. Gently heat the liquid bath. Start timing immediately.

   d. Holding the barrel, stir the liquid gently as shown in Figure 20–7. Record the temperature every 30 seconds.

   e. Continue until the temperature of the water or other pure substance is about room temperature.

   f. Record any other observations on melting.

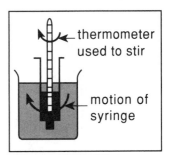

Figure 20–7 Stirring liquids

7. Determine the **boiling** temperature of a pure substance.

   a. Set up the equipment as shown in Figure 20–8. Make sure the collection flask is above and away from the boiling flask. Keep the bulb of the thermometer below the surface of the water. When heating substances other than water, use a liquid bath to control heating and prevent flammable substances from catching fire. Always use an ice bath around the collection flask to ensure condensation of vapors. Heat slowly.

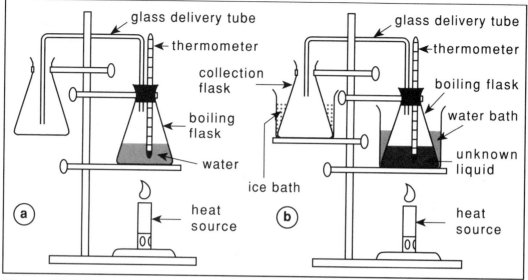

Figure 20–8 Determining the boiling point of water (a) and of other liquids (b)

CAUTION: Keep your equipment at least a meter away from your neighbor's equipment. Make sure the gas delivery tube is open so that gas flows freely through it.

    b. Record the starting temperature of the water or other pure substance at zero seconds.

    c. Gently heat the liquid bath. Record the temperature of the water or other pure substance every 30 seconds. Record any other observations on boiling.

    d. Continue heating until the pure substance has boiled for a few minutes.

8. Determine the **condensing** temperature of a pure substance.

    a. Set up the equipment as shown in Figure 20–8. This time make sure the bulb of the thermometer is about 1 cm **above** the pure substance as shown in Figure 20–9.

b. Heat the water or other pure substance to boiling. Remove the heat source.

c. Record the temperature of the steam or gas every 30 seconds for about 3 minutes. Record any other observations on condensing.

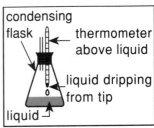

Figure 20–9 Change in placement of thermometer for determining the condensing temperature

9. Determine the freezing, melting, boiling, and condensing temperatures of other pure substances. Follow procedures 3 through 8. Follow the precautions for flammable substances.

Summary

¶1. Graph your data. Plot your data on freezing and melting of water and any other pure substance on one graph. Plot your data of boiling and condensing on another graph.

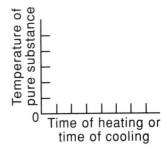

a. Draw a line or curve through the pattern of points you plotted for each pure substance.

b. On the graphs mark the points where each substance froze, melted, boiled, and condensed.

c. What are the relationships, if any, between melting and freezing?

d. What are the relationships, if any, between boiling and condensing?

2. Compare the graphs of your predictions with your graphs of the data on heating and cooling water. Also compare your predictions of freezing, melting, boiling, and condensing temperatures of water with the results of your experiment. Were your predictions successful?

⁑3. What are the conditions under which any pure substance will freeze? Melt? Boil? Condense?

Challenge

1. Collect and identify the condensed liquid of each pure substance. Determine whether the liquid is the same as or different from the original pure substance.

2. What is freezing? Melting? Boiling? Condensing?

21. FREEZING, MELTING, BOILING, AND CONDENSING OF MIXTURES

Background
Heating a pure substance changes it from a solid to a liquid to a gas. Cooling reverses the changes.

We next investigate what happens when two pure substances are mixed. Then we will observe what happens when we heat and cool these mixtures.

Problem
1. What happens when pure liquid substances are mixed?

2. How do observations of the freezing, melting, boiling, and condensing of mixtures compare with the observations of changes in state of pure substances?

Materials
- small test tube or syringe barrel
- water
- ice
- saltwater bath
- 2 thermometers
- ring stand and ring
- wire gauze
- two 250-mL Erlenmeyer flasks
- 6-cm length of glass tubing
- 15-cm length of glass tubing
- two 400-mL beakers
- two #6 two-hole stoppers
- heat source
- mixtures supplied by your teacher
- watch or clock
- graph paper
- apron and goggles

Procedure

1. Mix the pure substances listed in Table 21–1.

CAUTION: Wear an apron and goggles.

   a. Pour about 2 mL each of the two pure substances into a test tube and shake the contents.

   b. Let the mixture stand for about 2 minutes. Record your observations in a table like Table 21–1.

   c. Ask your teacher for instructions on disposing of the chemicals. **Do not return chemicals to their original containers.**

Table 21–1 Observations of some mixtures

Mixture	Observations
Ethyl alcohol + water	
Butyl stearate + water	
Butyl stearate + ethyl alcohol	

2. Prepare data tables like Tables 21–2, 21–3, 21–4, and 21–5.

Table 21–2 Data on FREEZING a mixture

Time (sec)	Temperature (°C)	Observations
0		
30		
60		
90		

Table 21–3 Data on MELTING a mixture

Time (sec)	Temperature (°C)	Observations
0		
30		
60		
90		

Table 21–4 Data on BOILING a mixture

Time (sec)	Temperature (°C)	Observations
0		
30		
60		
90		

Table 21–5 Data on CONDENSING a mixture

Time (sec)	Temperature (°C)	Observations
0		
30		
60		
90		

CAUTION: The mixture is flammable. Be careful. You must use a water bath for boiling and condensing. Use only heat-resistant glass. Use care in handling hot glass and metal. Keep your equipment at least a meter away from your neighbor's equipment. Make sure the gas delivery tube is open so that gas flows freely through it.

3. Determine the freezing and melting temperatures of ethyl alcohol and water. See procedures 5 and 6 in Investigation 20, Freezing, Melting, Boiling, and Condensing of

Pure Substances. Record the time, temperature, and any other observations of boiling and condensing of the mixture.

4. Determine the boiling and condensing temperatures of ethyl alcohol and water. See procedures 7 and 8 in Investigation 20, Freezing, Melting, Boiling, and Condensing of Pure Substances. Record the time, temperature, and any other observations of boiling and condensing of the mixture.

Summary

¶1. Graph your data. Plot your data on freezing and melting on one graph. Plot your data on boiling and condensing on another graph.

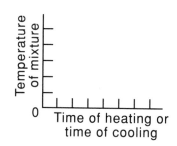

a. Draw a line or curve through the pattern of points on each graph.

b. Indicate the starting and ending temperatures of freezing, melting, boiling, and condensing of the mixture.

c. What are the relationships, if any, between melting and freezing of a mixture?

d. What are the relationships, if any, between boiling and condensing of a mixture?

¶2. Compare the changes in state of mixtures with the changes in state of the pure substances you tested in Investigation 20.

a. How are the changes in state similar? How are they different?

b. Why, do you think, are the changes in state similar or different?

3. Compare your observations of the mixtures you prepared.

   a. How are the mixtures similar?

   b. How are the mixtures different?

4. How might you determine whether a liquid is a mixture or a pure substance?

Challenge

Collect and identify the condensed liquid of a mixture. Determine whether the collected liquid is the same as or different from the original mixture.

22. IDENTIFYING UNKNOWN SUBSTANCES

Background

The freezing and melting temperatures and the boiling and condensing temperatures seem to be the same for pure substances. But these temperatures seem to differ for mixtures.

Substances can be identified by their *physical properties*. Physical properties are the characteristics used to describe substances. We looked at the property of solubility of pure substances. Substances that were *soluble* in each other formed liquid mixtures called *solutions*. These solutions did not separate after standing. But mixtures of *insoluble* substances separated into layers after standing. Other physical properties of substances are color, density, melting temperature, and boiling temperature.

Activity

Identify unknown substances by their physical properties.

Materials

- small test tube or syringe barrel
- water
- ice
- saltwater bath
- 2 thermometers
- ring stand and ring
- wire gauze
- two 250-mL Erlenmeyer flasks
- 6-cm length of glass tubing
- 15-cm length of glass tubing
- two 400-mL beakers
- two #6 two-hole stoppers
- graduated cylinder
- balance
- heat source

- unknown substances supplied by your teacher
- apron and goggles

Procedure

CAUTION: **Wear an apron and goggles.**

1. Determine whether each of your unknown substances is a pure substance or a mixture. Record all your procedures and observations.

2. Identify the pure substance(s) in your unknown. See Table 22–1 for help in identifying pure substances from their physical properties.

Table 22–1 Physical properties of some pure substances

Name	Color	Density (g/mL)	Melting Point (°C)	Boiling Point (°C)	Solubility
Butyl Stearate	White	1	17–21	343	Insoluble in water
Ethyl alcohol	Colorless	0.79	–177	79	Soluble in water
Magnesium sulfate (Epsom salts)	White	1.6	Decomposes at 150	– –	Soluble in water
Glycerin	Colorless	1.26	17.9*	290	Soluble in water and in ethyl alcohol
Methanol	Colorless	0.80	–97	64	Soluble in water and in ethyl alcohol
Naphthalene	White	1.15	80	217	Insoluble in water
Paradicholorobenzene	White	1.46	53	173	Insoluble in water
Water	Colorless	1.0	0	100	Soluble in alcohol

*Solidifies at a much lower temperature

Challenge
How might you identify unknown gases?

New Vocabulary for Section A

boiling

condensing

freezing

insoluble

melting

mixture

physical property

pure substance

soluble

solution

Section B. Gases and Liquids

23. A TORRICELLI TUBE AND A FOUNTAIN

Background

In the last section we investigated the changes of state of both pure substances and mixtures. Next we investigate other properties of liquids and gases.

Substances that flow, such as liquids and gases, are called *fluids*. We will use a Torricelli tube and a fountain to investigate the properties of some fluids.

Problem

1. How are liquids supported in a Torricelli tube?

2. How are liquids moved in a fountain?

Materials

- Torricelli tube
- fountain
- 20-cc syringe
- pinch clamp
- apron

Procedure

1. Your teacher will demonstrate the operation of a Torricelli tube and a fountain as shown in Figures 23–1 and 23–2.

   a. Before each demonstration, record in your notebook a description of the operation and your prediction of the results.

   b. After each demonstration, record the actual results and any other observations.

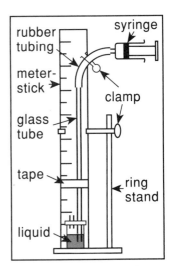

Figure 23–1 Operation of a Torricelli tube

2. Predict what will happen if other liquids are used in a Torricelli tube and a fountain. Record your predictions.

3. Test your predictions. Use water to duplicate the demonstrations. Record the results and any other observations.

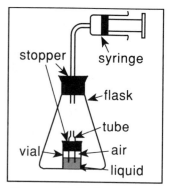

Figure 23–2 Operation of a fountain

Summary

1. Review your observations of the operations of a Torricelli tube. What is your hypothesis to explain how liquids are supported in a Torricelli tube?

2. Review your observations of the operations of a fountain. What is your hypothesis to explain how liquids are moved in a fountain?

24. SYRINGE-AND-FLUID SYSTEMS

Background
We now use syringes to investigate further the properties of fluids.

Problem
What happens to fluids in syringes when the plungers are pushed or pulled?

Materials
- two 20-cc syringes
- tubing connector
- water
- apron and goggles

Procedure
1. Fill the equipment with water or air or both as directed in the notes in Tables 24–1, 24–2, and 24–3.

2. Look at the drawings of the equipment and the operations in each table. The arrows show the direction to push or pull the plungers. **Before** each operation, predict what will happen. Record your predictions.

3. Test your predictions. Record the results and any other observations.

Table 24–1 Data on both syringes filled with air

Note: Set up the equipment as shown. Syringes (A) and (B) are both filled 1/4 full with AIR at the start of each operation.		
Operation	**Final Amount of AIR in Each Syringe after the Plungers are Pushed or Pulled as Directed**	
	Predicted	Actual
1		
2		
3		
4		

Table 24–2 Data on both syringes filled with water

Note: Set up the equipment as shown. Syringes (A) and (B) are both filled 1/4 full with WATER at the start of each operation.		
Operation	**Final Amount of WATER in Each Syringe after the Plungers are Pushed or Pulled as Directed**	
	Predicted	Actual
5		
6		
7		
8		

Table 24–3 Data on syringe (A) filled with water and syringe (B) filled with air

Operation	Final Amount of WATER and AIR in Each Syringe after Plungers are Pushed or Pulled as Directed	
	Predicted	Actual
9		
10		
11		
12		

Note: Set up the equipment as shown. Syringe (A) is filled 1/4 full with WATER and Syringe (B) is filled 1/4 full with AIR at the start of each operation.

Summary

¶1. Compare the results of the syringe-and-fluid systems in Tables 24–1, 24–2, and 24–3.

   a. How are the results similar?

   b. How do the results differ?

¶2. When the volume of a container holding a fluid is decreased, any fluid that squeezes into the smaller space is *compressed.* When the volume of the container is increased, any fluid that fills the larger space is *attenuated.*

   How do gases and liquids compare in their capacity to be compressed and attenuated?

Challenge

1. Does the density of a fluid change when it is compressed? Explain.

2. Does the density of a fluid change when it is attenuated? Explain.

25. FLASK-AND-FLUID SYSTEMS

Background

We have observed what happens to fluids in syringes when the plungers are pushed or pulled. Next we investigate ways to move these fluids from one position to another in flask-and-fluid systems.

Problem

What happens to fluids in flask-and-fluid systems when the syringe plungers are pushed or pulled?

Materials

- two 20-cc syringes
- 250-mL Erlenmeyer flask
- 6-cc length of glass tubing
- 15-cm length of glass tubing
- 2 tubing connectors
- water
- apron and goggles

Procedure

1. Fill the equipment with water or air or both as directed in the notes in Tables 25–1 through 25–5.

2. Look at the drawings of the equipment and operations in Tables 25–1 and 25–2. The arrows show the direction to push or pull the plungers.

   a. Before each operation, predict what will happen. Record your predictions.

   b. Test your predictions. Record the results and any other observations.

Table 25–1 Data on the flask and both syringes filled with air

| Operation | Final Amount of AIR in Each Syringe after the Plungers are Pushed or Pulled as Directed | |
	Predicted	Actual
1		
2		
3		
4		

Table 25–2 Data on the flask and both syringes filled with water

Note: Set up the equipment as shown. The flask is completely filled with WATER. Syringes (A) and (B) are both filled 1/4 full with WATER at the start of each operation.

| Operation | Final Amount of WATER in Each Syringe after the Plungers are Pushed or Pulled as Directed | |
	Predicted	Actual
5		
6		
7		
8		

Table 25–3 Data on the flask-and-fluid system with two syringes

Note: Set up the equipment as shown at the right. Syringe (A) is 1/4 full of AIR while Syringe (B) is 1/4 full of WATER and the tube leading to it is filled with water. a. Predict your solution to each problem. Record your predictions. b. Test your predictions. Record your solutions and other observations.	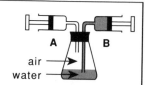

Problem	Solution	
	Predicted	Actual
9. In what ways could more water enter Syringe (B)?		
10. In what ways could water enter Syringe (A)?		
11. What would happen if both Syringes (A) and (B) were pulled?		
12. What would happen if both Syringes (A) and (B) were pushed?		

Table 25–4 Data on the flask-and-fluid system with a syringe and an open tube

Note: Remove Syringe (A) from the system so that one of the tubes is open as shown at the right. a. Predict your solution to each problem. Record your predictions. b. Test your predictions. Record your solutions and other observations.	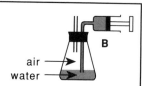

Problem	Solution	
	Predicted	Actual
13. In what ways could more water enter Syringe (B)?		
14. In what ways could air enter Syringe (B)?		
15. In what ways could air leave the open tube so that you could feel the air leaving?		
16. In what ways could air enter the open tube so you could feel the air entering?		

Table 25–5 Data on the flask-and-fluid system with a syringe and a closed tube

Note: Fill Syringe (B) 1/4 full of air and the long tube leading to it with air. Then clamp off the open tube as shown at right.
   a. Predict your solution to each problem. Record your predictions.
   b. Test your predictions. Record your solutions and other observations.
	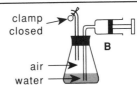	

	Solution	
Problem	Predicted	Actual
17. In what ways could water enter Syringe (B)?		
18. In what ways could air enter the water in the flask?		

Summary

¶1. Compare the results of the flask-and-fluid systems in Tables 25–1, 25–2, and 25–3.

    a. How are the results similar?

    b. How do the results differ?

¶2. Compare the results of the flask-and-fluid systems in Tables 25–1, 25–2, and 25–3 with the results of the syringe-and-fluid systems in Tables 24–1, 24–2, and 24–3.

    a. How are the results similar?

    b. How do the results differ?

  3. Compare your predictions with the actual solutions to the problems in Tables 25–1, 25–2, and 25–3. Were your predictions successful? Explain.

¶4. Review your solutions to the problems in Tables 25–3, 25–4, and 25–5. What is your hypothesis to explain how the water moved in and out of syringe (B) when air was in the flask-and-fluid system?

5. Compare the operations and results of Tables 25–3, 25–4, and 25–5 with the operations and results of a Torricelli tube and a fountain in Investigation 23, A Torricelli Tube and a Fountain.

    a. How are the operations and results similar?

    b. How do the operations and results differ?

    c. Why, do you think, are the results similar or different?

26. FLUIDS AND PARTIAL VACUUMS

Background

A *vacuum* is a space that contains no matter. A *partial vacuum* is a space containing a very small amount of matter.

In this experiment we investigate whether a partial vacuum can be used to move fluids.

Problem

Can a partial vacuum be used to move fluids?

Materials

- two 20-cc syringes
- tubing connector
- pinch clamp
- water
- apron

Procedure

1. Assemble the equipment as shown in Table 26–1.

Table 26–1 Data on vacuum systems

Operation	Results	
	Predicted	Actual
Pull the plunger of Syringe (A) 1/4 of the way out and release.		
Pull both plungers (A) and (B) 1/4 of the way out and release.		

2. Predict what will happen when you push or pull the syringe plungers in the direction shown by the arrows in the diagram. Record your predictions.

3. Test your predictions. Be sure to hold the syringe in the upright position shown in the tables. Record the results and any other observations.

4. Assemble the equipment as shown in Table 26–2. Be sure syringe (B) is below syringe (A) as shown. Follow procedures 2 and 3. If time permits, try other positions of syringes (A) and (B).

Table 26–2 Data on fluid-and-vacuum systems

Operation	Results	
	Predicted	Actual
Fill syringe (B) 1/4 full with AIR. While holding plunger (B) in place, open the clamp and pull plunger (A) out as far as (B). Then close the clamp and release both plungers (A) and (B).		
Fill syringe (B) 1/4 full with WATER. While holding plunger (B) in place, open the clamp and pull plunger (A) out as far as (B). Then close the clamp and release both plungers (A) and (B).		

Summary

¶1. Compare the results of the operations in Tables 26–1 and 26–2.

   a. How are the results similar?

   b. How are the results different?

   c. Why, do you think, are the results similar or different?

¶2. Can a partial vacuum be used to push or pull fluids? If so, how? If not, why not?

3. What evidences, if any, show that a partial vacuum is a space that contains a very small amount of matter?

4. How do different positions of syringes (A) and (B) affect the results of the operations shown in Table 26–2?

27. HEIGHT OF LIQUID COLUMNS IN A TORRICELLI TUBE

Background
In an earlier investigation we removed air from a Torricelli tube containing water. After we closed the clamp, the water remained standing in the Torricelli tube.

Now let's see how high other liquids will rise when air is removed from a Torricelli tube.

Problem
How high do different liquids rise in a Torricelli tube when the same amount of air is removed?

Materials
- Torricelli tube
- 250-mL Erlenmeyer flask
- pinch clamp
- #6 two-hole stopper
- 6-cm length of glass tubing
- 15-cm length of glass tubing
- tubing connector
- 50-cc syringe
- meterstick
- graph paper
- liquid assigned by your teacher
- apron and goggles

Procedure

1. Assemble and adjust the equipment as shown in Figure 27–1.

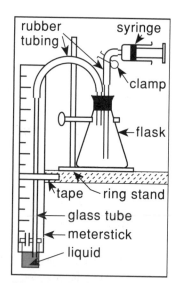

Figure 27–1 Equipment for measuring the height of liquid columns in a Torricelli tube

a. Fill the syringe 1/4-full with air and attach it to the equipment as shown.

b. Check for leaks in the system by opening the clamp and pushing the syringe plunger all the way in. If there are no leaks, air will bubble out of the tube through the liquid in the container.

c. Use the syringe plunger to adjust the level of the liquid in the tube to 0 cm on the meterstick. Close the clamp.

d. Remove the syringe from the tube and empty it of air.

e. Reconnect the empty syringe to the equipment. The apparatus is now ready for use.

NOTE: Do not strain the rubber when you operate the syringe.

2. Determine the height a liquid rises in a
   Torricelli tube when some air is removed
   from the tube. Record the name of the liquid
   in a table like Table 27–2.

Table 27–2 Data on height of liquids in a Torricelli tube

Name of Liquid:		
Height of Liquid (cm)	Volume of Air Removed (cm³)	Total Volume of Air Removed (cm³)*

*Total volume of air removed in each operation is added to the volume of air
removed in previous operations.

   a.   Open the clamp and pull the syringe
plunger back about 5 cm³.

   b.   Clamp the tube and release the plunger.
After you release the plunger, record the
volume of air removed and the height of
the liquid in the tube. The volume of air
removed is the volume of air in the
syringe after the plunger is released.

   c.   Repeat procedures 2.a. and 2.b. until the
liquid reaches the top of the meterstick
or until you have removed about 250 mL
of air, whichever happens first.

3. Using different liquids, repeat procedures 1
   and 2.

Summary

¶1. Graph your data. Plot the data for all the liquids on one graph. Identify the plotted points of each liquid with a different symbol. For each liquid, draw a line or curve through the points for that liquid.

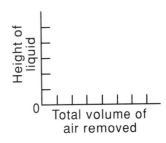

a. For every 10 cm that water rises in the tube, how much does each of the other liquids rise?

b. What properties of liquids might explain these results?

¶2. Compare the operation of the Torricelli tube in Figure 27–1 with the operation of the tube in Investigation 23, A Torricelli Tube and a Fountain.

a. How are the operations similar? How are they different?

b. What is your hypothesis to explain how a Torricelli tube operates?

¶3. Refer to your observations of a fountain in Investigation 23, A Torricelli Tube and a Fountain. What is your hypothesis to explain how fluids are moved in a fountain?

Challenge

1. Suppose that a Torricelli tube is 50 m tall. In the open air, what is the greatest height to which water can be raised in the tube using a vacuum pump?

2. An instrument that measures the pressure of a fluid is called a *manometer*. An instrument that measures air pressure is called a *barometer*. Air pressure is measured in centimeters (cm) or millimeters (mm) of mercury. The average air pressure at sea level is 76 cm (760 mm) of mercury. This means that, on the average, mercury stands 76 cm (760 mm) high in a Torricelli tube or barometer. Design and construct a barometer.

3. What would happen to a barometer carried into Death Valley? Explain.

4. What would happen to a barometer carried to the top of a high mountain? Explain.

28. MOVING FLUIDS PROJECT

Background
The fluids in the ocean and the atmosphere move constantly. Winds and water currents are the results of this constant movement of fluids in the Earth's oceans and its atmosphere.

Activity
1. Devise a method to produce vertical movement in fluids.

2. Devise a method to produce horizontal movement in fluids.

Procedure
1. Design your methods.

2. Have your teacher approve your plans and apparatus before you start working.

3. Demonstrate your method for producing movement in fluids.

Summary
1. What is your hypothesis to explain vertical movement in fluids?

2. What is your hypothesis to explain horizontal movement in fluids?

Challenge
1. What is your hypothesis to explain winds? Ocean currents?

2. What effect, if any, does movement of air have

   a. on weather?

   b. on air pollution?

3. What effect, if any, do mountains have on the movement of air or water currents?

New Vocabulary for Section B

atmospheric (air) pressure
attenuated
barometer
compressed

current
fluids
force
manometer

partial vacuum
pressure
vacuum

Section C. Conditions for Condensation

29. HEATING A LIQUID-GAS SYSTEM

Background
In earlier investigations we observed changes in state of some pure substances and some mixtures. Next we investigate the liquid and gaseous states of substances by heating air and water together in a flask.

Problem
1. How does the volume of gas change as air and water are heated in a flask?

2. What gas is produced when air and water are heated together in a flask?

Materials
- 250-mL Erlenmeyer flask
- thermometer
- #6 two-hole stopper
- 6-cm length of glass tubing
- rubber tubing
- large beaker or jar
- collecting container
- heat source
- ring stand and ring
- clamp
- wire gauze
- water
- watch or clock
- graph paper
- apron and goggles

Procedure

1. Make a table like Table 29–1 for your data on the heating of a liquid-gas system.

Table 29–1 Data on heating a liquid-gas system

Temperature of Gas (°C)	Volume of Gas Collected (cm³)	Observations

2. Set up the equipment as shown in Figure 29–2.

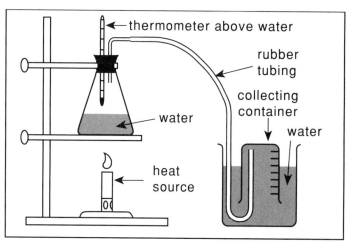

Figure 29–2 Equipment for heating a liquid-gas system and collecting gas

    a.   Clamp a 250-mL flask containing 50 mL of water to a ring stand. Support the flask with a ring and wire gauze.

    b.   Insert the stopper in the flask. Make sure the thermometer is **above** the water.

c. Fill a 250-mL graduated collecting container with water. Invert the collecting container in a large pan or bucket of water.

d. Insert the rubber tubing so that its end is near the top of the collecting container.

CAUTION: Wear an apron and goggles. Use only heat-resistant glass. Use care in handling hot glass and metal. Make sure the rubber tubing is not restricted in any way.

3. Heat the water and air in the flask. Adjust the heat so that the temperature rises about 5°C every 30 seconds.

4. Immediately begin recording the volume of gas in the collecting container at 5°C intervals. Record any other observations.

5. Stop heating when the volume of gas in the collecting container does not seem to change. Remove the rubber tubing from the beaker **before** you turn off the heat. Record the highest temperature. Record any other observations.

6. Identify the gas that collected in the graduated container. Record your observations.

Summary

1. Graph your data on heating the liquid-gas system.

a. What are the relationships, if any, between the temperature of gas in the flask and the volume of gas collected?

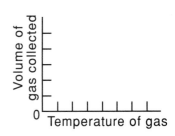

b. What is the total volume of the gas collected?

12. Review your observations and your graph of the heating of a liquid-gas system.

    a. How do the volumes of gas in the flask and in the collecting container before heating compare with the volume in each **after** heating?

    b. What is your hypothesis to explain any change in the volume of gas?

    c. What evidence supports your hypothesis?

    d. How might you test your hypothesis?

13. Look at your data and your observations of the gas that collected in the graduated container.

    a. What gas did you collect?

    b. What evidence supports your identification of the gas?

    c. How might you confirm your identification?

    d. What is the source of the gas?

30. HEATING A GAS SYSTEM

Background
We have seen that when water and air are heated in a flask, the volume of gas increases. Next we compare the heating of air alone with the heating of water and air together in a flask.

Problem
1. How does the volume of gas change as air is heated in a flask?

2. How does the volume of gas collected when heating only air compare with the volume of gas collected when heating air and water together?

Materials
- 250-mL Erlenmeyer flask
- #6 two-hole stopper
- 6-cm length of glass tubing
- rubber tubing
- large beaker or jar
- collecting container
- heat source
- ring stand and ring
- clamp
- wire gauze
- watch or clock
- graph paper
- apron and goggles

Procedure

1. Make a table like Table 30–1 for your data on heating a gas system.

Table 30–1 Data on heating a gas system

Temperature of Gas (°C)	Volume of Gas Collected (cm³)	Observations

CAUTION: Wear an apron and goggles. Use only heat-resistant glass. Use care in handling hot glass and metal. Make sure the rubber tubing is not restricted in any way.

2. Set up the equipment you used in Investigation 29, Heating a Liquid-Gas System. **Do not** put water in the flask. The flask must be completely dry. Make sure the end of the rubber tubing is near the top of the collecting container as shown in Figure 30–2.

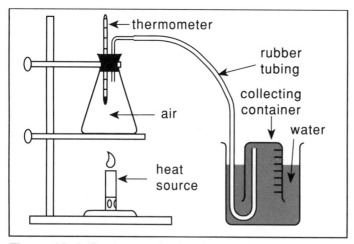

Figure 30–2 Equipment for heating a gas system and collecting gas

3. Heat the air in the flask. Adjust the heat so that the temperature rises about 5°C every 30 seconds.

4. Immediately begin recording the volume of gas in the collecting container at 5°C intervals. Record any other observations.

5. Stop heating when the temperature is about 105°C. Remove the rubber tubing from the beaker **before** you turn off the heat. Record the highest temperature and any other observations.

6. Identify the gas that collected in the graduated container. Record your observations.

Summary

1. Graph your data on heating the gas system.

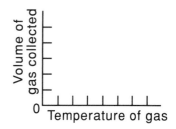

   a. What are the relationships, if any, between the temperature of gas in the flask and the volume of gas collected?

   b. What is the total volume of gas collected?

2. Compare the graph of heating only air with the graph of Investigation 29, Heating a Liquid-Gas System.

   a. How are the graphs similar? How are they different?

   b. Why, do you think, are the graphs similar or different?

3. Compare your observations of heating only air with your observations of heating air and water together.

a. Is the gas that collected when you heated only air the same as or different from the gas collected when you heated air and water together? Explain.

b. What is the source of the gas that collected?

4. What is your hypothesis to explain the change in total volume of gas as the flask is heated?

Challenge

How might you determine the gas pressure when air and water are heated together in a flask?

31. PRESSURE OF GAS IN A LIQUID-GAS SYSTEM: A DEMONSTRATION

Background
When air and water are heated together in a flask, the volume of gas increases. The volume of gas also increases when air alone is heated in a flask, but not as much as when air and water are heated together.

In earlier investigations we used a Torricelli tube to measure the pressure of gases. This time we use a mercury-filled tube, a *manometer*, to measure the pressure of gases when a liquid-gas system is heated.

Problem
What are the relationships between the temperature and pressure of gas when cooling or heating a liquid-gas system?

Materials
- 250-mL Erlenmeyer flask
- #6 two-hole stopper
- thermometer
- 6-cm length of glass tubing
- rubber tubing
- ring stand and ring
- clamp
- wire gauze
- Torricelli tube
- heat source
- graph paper
- apron and goggles

Procedure
1. Make tables like Table 31–1 and Table 31–2 for recording your data on cooling and heating water in a flask. Include columns for the temperature of the gas in the flask at intervals of 5°C, for the height of the mercury

column, for the pressure of the gas, and for other observations.

Table 31–1 Data on cooling a liquid-gas system

Temperature of Gas (°C)	Height of Mercury Column (mm)	Pressure of Gas (mm)	Observations

Table 31–2 Data on heating a liquid-gas system

Temperature of Gas (°C)	Height of Mercury Column (mm)	Pressure of Gas (mm)	Observations

CAUTION: Wear an apron and goggles. Use only heat-resistant glass. Use care in handling hot glass and metal. Make sure the rubber tubing is not restricted in any way.

Because this investigation uses mercury, which is dangerous to handle, your teacher will perform this investigation while you record observations.

2. The equipment for measuring the pressure of gas in a flask is shown in Figure 31–3. Your teacher will follow the steps below.

   a. Pour 50 mL of water into the flask.

   b. Put a source of heat under the **open** flask as shown in Figure 31–3. Heat the water to boiling.

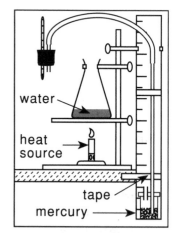

Figure 31–3 Equipment for measuring the pressure of gases in a liquid-gas system

3. Determine the height of the mercury column as water is **cooled** in a flask.

a. Remove the heat source from under the flask. While the water is still boiling, insert the stopper in the flask as shown in Figure 31–4. Be sure the thermometer is **above** the water.

b. Immediately begin to record the temperature of the gas and the height of the mercury column at 5°C intervals. When condensation begins, record the temperature of the gas and any other observations.

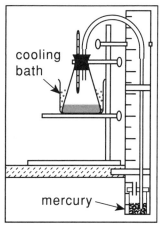

Figure 31–4 Cooling a liquid-gas system

c. When the equipment has cooled enough to be handled, put the flask into a cooling bath as shown in Figure 31–4.

d. Continue to record your observations until the temperature of the gas reaches about 25°C. Then remove the cooling bath, but leave the manometer attached to the flask.

4. The flask will now be heated. Predict the height of the mercury column when the water boils. Record your prediction.

5. Determine the height of the mercury column as water is **heated** in a flask.

a. With the manometer still attached to the flask, put a heat source under the flask as shown in Figure 31–5. Adjust the heat so the gas temperature increases about 5°C every 30 seconds.

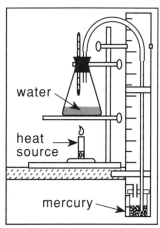

Figure 31–5
Heating a liquid-gas system

b. Immediately begin to record the temperature of the gas and the height of the mercury column at 5°C intervals.

c. Heat the water to boiling. Observe and record the temperature of gas and the height of the mercury column when the water begins to boil.

d. Remove the heat source and detach the manometer from the flask.

6. Calculate the gas pressure in the flask at 5°C intervals for both cooling and heating.

a. Determine the pressure of the atmosphere. If your classroom barometer is not working, assume that the air pressure is about 760 mm of mercury.

b. Subtract the height of the mercury column from the pressure of the atmosphere.

$$\text{Pressure of atmosphere} - \text{Height of mercury column} = \text{Pressure of gas}$$

c. Record the gas pressure in your data tables.

Summary

1. Plot on one graph your data on both cooling and heating a liquid-gas system.

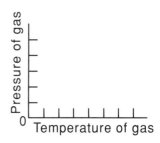

a. Draw a line or curve for cooling, another line or curve for heating. Indicate the starting temperature for boiling and condensing.

b. What are the relationships, if any, between the temperature and the pressure of gas in the flask?

c. What is the temperature and the pressure of the gas in the flask when the water begins to boil?

d. What is the temperature and the pressure of the gas in the flask when the gas begins to condense?

e. At what temperature does the gas pressure inside the flask equal the air pressure outside the flask?

2. Review your observations of the cooling and heating of a liquid-gas system.

a. What gas is in the flask?

b. What evidence supports your identification of the gas?

3. Compare your graph of the pressure of gases in a liquid-gas system with your graph from Investigation 29, Heating a Liquid-Gas System.

a. How are the graphs similar? How do they differ?

b. Why, do you think, are the graphs similar or different?

4. Review your observations of heating air and water in a flask from Investigation 29, Heating a Liquid-Gas System.

a. What is your hypothesis to explain the increase in the volume of gas?

    b. What evidence supports your hypothesis?

15. Review your observations of boiling water in Investigation 20, Freezing, Melting, Boiling, and Condensing of Pure Substances.

    a. What are the conditions under which water boils?

    b. What are the conditions under which steam condenses?

Challenge

1. What are the conditions under which a liquid boils?

2. What are the conditions under which a gas condenses?

3. Under what conditions may clouds form in the atmosphere?

4. Why does it take longer to cook food at higher altitudes than it does at lower altitudes?

5. Why does food cook faster in a pressure cooker than in an open pot?

32. COOLING A LIQUID-GAS SYSTEM

Background
We have investigated a liquid-gas system as it cools from boiling to room temperature. Next we investigate a liquid-gas system as it cools below room temperature.

Problem
Why does liquid appear on the outside of an ice-filled flask?

Materials
- 250-mL Erlenmeyer flask
- #6 solid stopper
- water
- ice
- apron

Procedure
1. Set up the equipment for cooling a liquid-gas system as shown in Figure 32–1.

   a. Pour 50 mL of water and about 25 mL of crushed ice into a flask.

   b. Insert a solid rubber stopper into the flask.

2. Gently swirl the flask. Observe what happens. Record your observations.

3. Develop a hypothesis to explain your observations. Record and test your hypothesis. Record your procedures, results, and other observations.

Figure 32–1 Equipment and procedure for cooling a liquid-gas system

Summary

₹1. What is your hypothesis to explain why liquid appears on the outside of the flask?

₹2. What evidence supports your hypothesis?

Challenge

1. What are the conditions under which water freezes?

2. What are the conditions under which ice melts?

3. What are the conditions under which dew forms?

33. DEW POINT PROJECT

Background

Dew point is the temperature at which water vapor in the air begins to condense.

Saturated air holds the maximum amount of water vapor for its temperature.

If the air is saturated, the dew point is the same as the temperature of the air. But if the air is not saturated, water vapor will not condense unless the air temperature falls.

Activity

Design an instrument to measure dew point.

Procedure

1. Design your instrument to measure dew point.

2. Have your teacher approve your design before you test it.

3. Test your instrument for measuring dew point.

4. Write a brief explanation of how your instrument works.

Summary

1. How is your instrument used to measure dew point?

2. What are the relationships between humidity and dew point? See Ecology Investigation 12, Water Vapor in the Air, for more information on humidity.

Challenge
Under what conditions will water vapor condense and form clouds or fog?

New Vocabulary for Section C
dew point
humidity
saturated air
vapor

UNIT 3. TEMPERATURE AND HEAT

SECTION A. TEMPERATURE AND THE MEASUREMENT OF HEAT

SECTION B. CONSERVATION OF HEAT

34. PREDICTING TEMPERATURE

Background
We have seen that changing the temperature of a fluid can cause a change in its buoyancy. Temperature changes can also change the state of matter.

Now that we have investigated the effects of temperature change on matter, we will attempt to find a method of predicting the amount of temperature change. In this investigation we will try to predict the temperature that will result from mixing hot and cold water.

Problem
1. Can the final temperature of a mixture of hot and cold water be predicted if their starting temperatures are known?

2. If the final temperature is predictable, how is it predicted?

Materials
- two 250-mL beakers
- 2 insulated cups
- cold water
- hot water
- thermometer
- stirring rod
- apron and goggles

Procedure
1. Predict the final temperature of a mixture of 50 mL of water at 80°C with 50 mL of cold (tap) water. Record your prediction in a table similar to Table 34–2.

CAUTION: You will use heat in this investigation. Use heat-resistant glass. Handle everything carefully to avoid burns from hot glass and metal. Wear an apron and goggles.

2. Test your predictions. Add the hot water to the cold water as shown in Figure 34–1. Stir the mixture as you add the hot water. Use a stirring rod, not a thermometer, for stirring. Read and record the highest temperature the mixture reaches as the final temperature.

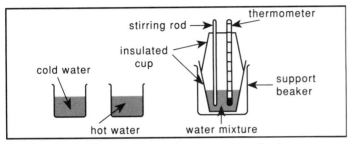

Figure 34–1 Method for determining the final temperature of mixtures

3. Predict the final temperature of several other mixtures of hot and cold water. The samples may have different volumes or different starting temperatures or both. Be sure to record your predictions.

4. Test your predictions. Record the starting and final temperatures of your mixtures and any other observations in your table.

5. Develop a hypothesis that allows you to predict and explain the final temperature of mixtures of hot and cold water. Record and test your hypothesis. Record your results and any other observations.

Table 34-2 Data on the final temperature of water mixtures

HOT Water		COLD Water		Water MIXTURE			Other Observations
Vol. (mL)	Temp. (°C)	Vol. (mL)	Temp. (°C)	Vol. (mL)	Final Temp. (°C)		
					Predicted	Actual	
50	80	50		100			

Summary

¶1. Look at your data on the final temperatures of mixtures of hot and cold water. Compare your predictions with the final temperatures of the mixtures. Were your predictions accurate?

    a. If so, how did you make your predictions?

    b. If not, how might you make more accurate predictions?

¶2. What is your hypothesis that allows you to predict and explain the final temperature of different mixtures of hot and cold water?

35. HEAT PROJECT

Background

In many of our investigations we have heated substances and measured their temperatures. But adding heat does not raise the temperature of a substance when it is melting or boiling. Heating appears to do more than raise temperature, even though heating seems necessary to raise temperature.

We can use two kinds of definitions to explain something. A *descriptive definition* tells what it does. For example, heat melts solids or burns flesh. An *operational definition* explains something by telling how to measure it. For example, the operational definition of *density* is mass divided by volume.

Activity

1. Define heat.

2. Design a device to measure heat.

Procedure

1. Write a description of what heat does.

2. Devise an operational definition of heat.

3. Design a device that can measure the amount of heat gained or lost by hot water in a tin can as shown in Figure 35–1. Your device should be able to measure the amount of heat gained or lost when 50 mL of water at 50°C cools to room temperature (about 25°C).

4. Write a brief explanation of how your device would work. Make a diagram of your device.

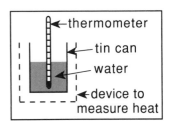

Figure 35–1
Measuring the heat
gained or lost by water

Summary

†1. What is your operational definition of heat?

†2. How is your device used to measure heat?

†3. What are the relationships, if any, between temperature and heat?

Challenge

Suppose that 50 cm³ of steam at 105°C is contained in a tin can. Could your device be used to measure the heat gained or lost by the steam as it cools to room temperature (about 25°C)? If so, how? If not, why not?

36. MEASURING HEAT

Background
You now have an operational definition of heat and have designed a device to measure heat. Use your device to measure the quantity of heat gained or lost by water as it cools.

Problem
How much heat is gained or lost by 50 mL of water as it cools from 50°C to room temperature?

Materials
- small juice can
- thermometer
- hot water
- graph paper
- apron and goggles

Procedure
1. Make a data table similar to Table 36–1 for heat gained or lost by water. Record your measurements at 5°C intervals.

Table 36–1 Data on measurement of heat

Temperature (°C)	Heat Gained or Lost

CAUTION: You will use heat in this investigation. Use heat-resistant glass. Handle everything carefully to avoid burns from hot glass and metal. Wear an apron and goggles.

2. Set up your equipment for measuring the heat gained or lost by water in a tin can. Pour 50 mL of water at 50°C into the can.

3. Measure the heat gained or lost by 50 mL of water as it cools to room temperature (about 25°C). Record your measurements and any other observations.

4. Predict the amount of heat that will be gained or lost by 50 mL of water as it cools from 75°C to room temperature.

5. Test your prediction. Record your measurements at 5°C intervals. Record any other observations.

Summary

1. Graph your data. Include both sets of data (50°C and 75°C) for heat gained or lost by water on the same graph.

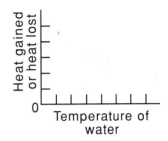

a. Draw one curve or line through the plotted points for water as it cools from 50°C and another curve or line for water as it cools from 75°C to room temperature.

b. What is your unit of heat measurement?

c. How much heat is gained or lost by 50 mL of water cooling from 50°C to room temperature?

d. How much heat is gained or lost by 50 mL of water cooling from 75°C to room temperature?

e. How much heat is gained or lost by cooling 50 mL of water 1°C?

2. Compare your prediction with your measurement of heat gained or lost by 50 mL of water as it cools from 75°C to room temperature. Was your prediction accurate? Explain why or why not.

3. What are the relationships between temperature and heat?

New Vocabulary for Section A
descriptive definition
heat
operational definition

Section B. Conservation of Heat

37. THE CALORIE, A UNIT OF HEAT

Background

Raising the temperature of a large quantity of water by 1°C takes more heat than raising the temperature of a small quantity of water by 1°C. And raising the temperature of an amount of water by 5°C takes more heat than raising it by 1°C. Thus the amount of heat needed to raise the temperature of water depends on the mass of the water and the amount of change in its temperature.

The **change in temperature** (ΔT) of a substance is calculated by subtracting the **starting temperature** (T_s) from the final temperature (T_f). The change in temperature may be either positive or negative.

$$\Delta T = (T_f) - (T_s)$$

For example, if the starting temperature (T_s) is 25°C and the final temperature (T_f) is 30°C, then ΔT is **positive.** The increase in temperature indicates that heat is **gained** by the substance.

$$\Delta T = 30°C - 25°C = +5°C$$
(ΔT is positive.)

However, if the starting temperature (T_s) is 30°C and the final temperature (T_f) is 25°C, then (ΔT) is **negative.** This decrease in temperature indicates that heat is **lost** by the substance.

$$\Delta T = 25°C - 30°C = -5°C$$
(ΔT is negative.)

The unit of heat measurement in the metric system is the *calorie* (cal). One calorie is the amount of heat needed to raise or lower the temperature of 1 gram of water 1°C. This is an operational definition.

Different substances require different amounts of heat to change their temperatures. The *specific heat* (sp ht) of a substance is the number of calories needed to change the temperature of 1 gram of the substance 1°C. For example, the specific heat of water is 1 cal/g°C. That is, it takes 1 calorie to change the temperature of 1 gram of water 1 degree Celsius (°C).

To calculate the calories (cal) of heat gained or lost by a substance, multiply its mass (M) by its change in temperature (ΔT) by its specific heat (sp ht).

For example, it takes 50 cal to raise the temperature of 10 g of water from 25°C to 30°C:

Heat	=	Mass	×	Change in temperature	×	Specific heat
H (cal)	=	M (g)	×	ΔT (°C)	×	sp ht (cal/g°C)
H	=	10 g	×	5°C	×	1 cal/g°C
	=	+ 50 cal				1 cal/g°C

Problem
How many calories are gained or lost by 50 mL of water as it cools from 50°C to room temperature?

Materials
- 2 insulated cups
- small juice can
- 2 thermometers
- hot water
- cold water
- graph paper
- apron and goggles

Procedure
1. Make a data table similar to Table 37–1 for recording calories lost by hot water as it cools. Record your measurements at 5°C intervals.

Table 37–1 Data on loss of heat

Temperature (°C)	Heat Lost (cal)

CAUTION: You will use heat in this investigation. Use heat-resistant glass. Handle everything carefully to avoid burns from hot glass and metal. Wear an apron and goggles.

2. Set up a calorimeter as shown in Figure 37–2 for measuring the heat lost by water cooling in a tin can. A *calorimeter* is a device used to measure heat in calories.

   a. Measure a volume of cold water and pour it into a calorimeter. Record the volume of cold water.

   b. Measure and record the temperature of the cold water.

   c. Pour 50 mL of water at 50°C into the tin can. Set the can in the calorimeter.

3. Predict the number of calories that will be lost by 50 mL of water in a tin can as it cools from 50°C to room temperature (about 25°C). Record and test your prediction. Record your measurements and any other observations.

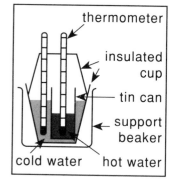

Figure 37–2 Measuring heat with an insulated cup calorimeter

4. Predict the number of calories that will be lost by 50 mL of water as it cools from 75°C to room temperature. Record and test your prediction. Record your measurements and any other observations.

Summary

¶1. Graph your data. Include both sets of data (50°C and 75°C) for the calories lost by hot water on the same graph.

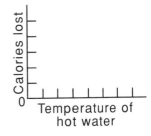

a. Draw a curve or line through the plotted points for water as it cools from 50°C and another for water as it cools from 75°C to room temperature.

b. How many calories are lost by 50 mL of water cooling from 50°C to room temperature?

c. How many calories are lost by 50 mL of water cooling from 75°C to room temperature?

d. How many calories are lost for each 1°C drop in temperature of 50 mL of water as it cools?

2. Compare the graph of calories with the graph of Investigation 36, Measuring Heat.

a. How are the graphs similar? How are they different?

b. How many calories are equal to the unit of measurement you used in Investigation 36, Measuring Heat?

¶3. What are the relationships, if any, between temperature and heat?

Challenge

1. Calculate how many calories would be gained or lost by 10 mL of water at 40°C mixed with 10 mL of water at 30°C.

2. Predict the final temperature of a mixture of 50 mL of water at 80°C mixed with 100 mL of water at 25°C. Test your prediction.

38. EXCHANGE OF HEAT BETWEEN HOT AND COLD WATER

Background

In Investigation 34, Predicting Temperature, we predicted the final temperatures of mixtures of hot and cold water. We also tried to make more successful predictions of temperatures by investigating the quantity of heat lost by different samples of hot water cooling to room temperature.

Next we will predict the quantity of heat that will be gained or lost when hot and cold water are mixed.

Problem

1. How much heat is gained or lost by different masses of hot and cold water mixed in a calorimeter?

2. How can we predict the amount of heat gained or lost by hot and cold water mixed in a calorimeter?

Materials

• calorimeter
• 250-mL beaker
• hot water
• tap water
• balance
• watch or clock
• graph paper
• apron and goggles

Procedure

1. Set up a calorimeter as shown in Figure 38–1. Pour 20 g of tap water into it. Read the temperature of the water. Record the mass and temperature in a table like Table 38–2.

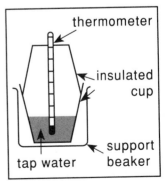

Figure 38–1 Calorimeter

CAUTION: You will use heat in this investigation. Use heat-resistant glass. Handle everything carefully to avoid burns from hot glass and metal. Wear an apron and goggles.

Table 38–2 Data on the exchange of heat between hot and cold water

Set	Mass of Water (g)	Temperature (°C)			Heat (cal)	
		Starting (T_s)	Final (T_f)	ΔT $(T_f - T_s)$	Predicted	Actual
1	Hot: 50	80				
	Cold: 20					
2	Hot:					
	Cold:					
3	Hot:					
	Cold:					
4	Hot:					
	Cold:					

2. Measure out 50 g of water at about 80°C. Record its mass and temperature.

3. Add the hot water to the tap water in the calorimeter. Read the temperature of the mixture at 10-second intervals. Record the highest temperature reached as the temperature of the mixture.

4. Calculate the ΔT and the quantity of heat gained or lost by each sample of hot and cold water mixed in the calorimeter.

5. Predict the quantity of heat that will be

gained or lost by different masses of water at 80°C when mixed with 20 g of tap water in the calorimeter. Record your predictions. Record the mass and starting temperature of the hot water and the tap water.

6. Test your predictions. Record the final temperature of each water mixture. Calculate and record the ΔT and heat gained or lost by each sample.

Summary

¶1. Graph your data of the exchange of heat between hot and cold water.

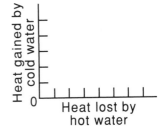

a. What are the relationships, if any, between the heat gained by the cold water and the heat lost by the hot water?

b. What is your hypothesis to explain the heat exchange between hot and cold water?

2. Compare your predictions with the data on heat gained and heat lost when cold water and hot water were mixed.

a. Were your predictions accurate? Explain.

b. How might you predict the temperature of any mixture of hot and cold water?

¶3. If your investigation had been done under *ideal conditions*, no instrument errors or human errors would have affected the measurements of heat gained or lost by each sample.

a. Under ideal conditions, what temperature would you predict for a mixture of 50 g of water at 80°C with 20 g of water at 25°C?

b. What is your hypothesis to explain the heat exchange between hot and cold water mixed in a calorimeter?

Challenge

Develop a hypothesis that will enable you to predict the temperature of a metal at 80°C after it is put into a container of room-temperature water. Assume that the mass of water is equal to the mass of the metal.

39. EXCHANGE OF HEAT BETWEEN METAL AND WATER

Background

Situations in which no human errors or instrument errors occur are called *ideal conditions.* If we think of ideal conditions when we develop a hypothesis, we are often able to make better predictions.

Was your hypothesis for explaining heat exchange between hot and cold water under ideal conditions a universal explanation? We will test the hypothesis by trying to predict the final temperature of equal masses of water and metal at different temperatures when they are put into a calorimeter.

Problem

1. What is the final temperature of equal masses of cold water and hot metal when both are put into a calorimeter?

2. How much heat is gained or lost by equal masses of cold water and hot metal when they are put together in a calorimeter?

Materials

- samples of metals
- tongs
- stirring rod
- balance
- thermometer
- calorimeter
- tap water
- hot water
- watch or clock
- graph paper
- apron and goggles

Procedure

1. Set up the equipment as shown in Figure 39–1 to determine the exchange of heat between metal and water.

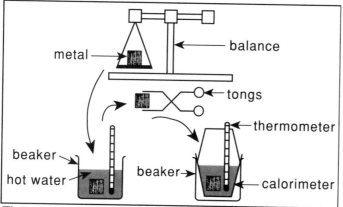

Figure 39–1 Measuring the exchange of heat between metal and water

    a.   Measure the mass of the metal. Record the mass in a table like Table 38–2.

    b.   Put the same mass of tap water into the calorimeter. Record the mass of the water.

CAUTION: You will use heat in this investigation. Use heat-resistant glass. Handle everything carefully to avoid burns from hot glass and metal. Wear an apron and goggles.

2. Predict the final temperature of equal masses of water and metal when a piece of metal at 80°C is put into tap water. Record your prediction.

3. Test your prediction. Determine the quantity of heat exchanged between metal and water.

a. Heat the metal in a hot water bath at 80°C for about 3 minutes. Assume that the metal is the same temperature as the hot water bath. Record the starting temperature of the metal in Table 39–2.

Table 39–2 Data on the exchange of heat between metal and water

Set	Mass of Metal and Water (g)	Temperature (°C)			ΔT $(T_f - T_s)$	Heat (cal)
		Starting (T_s)	Final (T_f)			
			Predicted	Actual		
1	Metal:					
	Water:					
2	Metal:					
	Water:					
3	Metal:					
	Water:					
4	Metal:					
	Water:					

b. Read and record the starting temperature of the tap water. Keep the thermometer in the calorimeter.

c. Using the tongs, quickly move the metal from the hot water bath to the calorimeter. Stir the water with the stirring rod.

d. Read the temperature of the water at 10-second intervals until it begins to cool. Record the highest temperature the water reaches as the final temperature of the water and metal.

e. Calculate the ΔT and the heat gained or lost by the water and the metal. Record the results.

4. Predict the final temperature of equal masses of tap water and metal at different starting temperatures when the metal is put into the tap water. Record your predictions.

5. Test your predictions. Repeat procedure 3.

Summary

⸙1. Graph your data on the changes of temperature (ΔT) of the water and the metal.

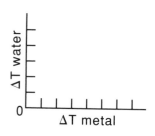

⸙2. Graph your data on the exchange of heat between the water and the metal.

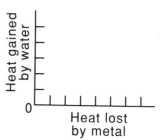

3. What are the relationships, if any, between the changes in the temperature of the water and the metal?

⸙4. What are the relationships, if any, between the amounts of heat gained and lost by the water and the metal?

5. Compare the two graphs. What are the relationships, if any, between the changes in temperature and the amounts of heat gained and lost by the water and the metal?

6. Compare your predictions with your findings of the final temperature of equal masses of cold water and hot metal put together into a calorimeter. Were your predictions accurate? Explain.

‡7. Compare your graph of the heat exchange between water and metal with your graph of Investigation 38, Exchange of Heat between Hot and Cold Water.

    a. How are the graphs similar? How do they differ?

    b. Why, do you think, are the graphs similar or different?

‡8. Suppose that the heat gained or lost by equal masses of water and metal had been determined under ideal conditions.

    a. What would you expect your results to be when a piece of metal at 80°C is put into a calorimeter containing water at room temperature?

    b. What hypothesis might explain the results of the exchange of heat between water and metal?

Challenge
1. Suppose that it were possible to determine the exchange of heat between your metal and water under ideal conditions. How many calories of heat would be necessary to raise or lower the temperature of 1 g of the metal 1°C?

2. Devise a method to determine how many calories of heat would be necessary to raise or lower the temperature of 1 g of any liquid or metal 1°C. Explain how your method works.

40. SPECIFIC HEAT AND THE IDENTIFICATION OF UNKNOWN SUBSTANCES

Background
If ideal conditions were possible for determining the exchange of heat between a metal and water, the heat lost by the metal would be equal to the heat gained by the water:

$$\text{Heat loss}_{(metal)} = \text{Heat gain}_{(water)}$$

$$M_{metal} \times \Delta T_{metal} \times \text{sp ht}_{metal} = M_{water} \times \Delta T_{water} \times \text{sp ht}_{water}$$

The ΔT of the metal always seems to be greater than the ΔT of an equal mass of water. Thus the number of calories necessary to raise the temperature of 1 gram of metal 1°C would be small compared to the number of calories necessary to raise the temperature of 1 gram of water 1°C. This is because the specific heat of a metal is small compared with the specific heat of water.

Activity
Identify unknown substances by their specific heats.

Materials
- samples of metals
- tongs
- stirring rod
- balance
- thermometer
- calorimeter
- tap water
- hot water
- apron and goggles

Procedure

CAUTION: You will use heat in this investigation. Use heat-resistant glass. Handle everything carefully to avoid burns from hot glass and metal. Wear an apron and goggles.

1. Identify each of your unknown substances. See Table 40–1 for the specific heats of some common substances. Record your procedure and observations.

2. If your unknown is a liquid, verify your identification. See Table 22–1, Physical Properties of Some Pure Substances, for other properties of the liquids. Record your procedures and your observations.

Table 40–1 Specific heats of some common substances

Name		Specific Heat (cal/g°C)
Liquids	Ethyl alcohol	.58
	Glycerin	.57
	Methyl alcohol	.60
	Water	1.00
Solids	Aluminum	.21
	Brass	.09
	Carbon steel	.10
	Copper	.09
	Glass	.12
	Iron	.11
	Lead	.03
	Silver	.06
	Zinc	.09

Challenge

1. Develop a hypothesis to explain the differences between the specific heats of different substances. Test your hypothesis.

2. What are the relationships, if any, between matter and energy?

3. What happens to the heat lost by an object when it cools? For example, what happens to heat from the ground when it cools off at night or to the heat from a cup of coffee as it cools to room temperature?

41. SOLAR HEATING PROJECT

Background

Most of the energy on Earth comes from the sun and can be measured as heat. We now attempt to apply our knowledge of the interaction of heat and matter to design a device that uses the sun's energy to heat a substance to a higher temperature.

Activity

Design a solar heating device.

Procedure

1. Design a device that uses sunlight to raise the heat content of substances.

2. If you can, construct your device and show how it operates.

3. Write an explanation of how your device operates.

Summary

1. Describe some possible applications of your solar heating device.

2. Which of the devices in your class is best?

3. Explain how you decided which device is best.

New Vocabulary for Section B

calorie
calorimeter
descriptive definition

heat
heat exchange
ideal conditions

operational definition
solar
specific heat

UNIT 1. PLANT GROWTH

Section A. Seed Germination

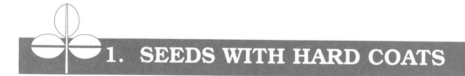

1. SEEDS WITH HARD COATS

Background
Ecology is the science that studies the interactions of plants, animals, and the physical environment. In this unit we focus on plants—how they grow and how they interact with their environments.

You already know that many plants grow from seeds. You've probably sprouted some seeds yourself, either on your own or for a science project in school. The sprouting of a seed is called *germination*.

You may have noticed that seeds germinate differently and that some take longer to germinate than others. You may also have noticed that seeds have different kinds of coats. Some seeds have hard coats that can delay or even prevent germination. We begin our study of plant growth by investigating some seeds that have hard coats.

Activity
1. Get some seeds with hard coats.

2. Observe and describe your seeds.

3. Describe the plant that grew your seeds and the environment where you found your plant.

Procedure
1. Collect some hard-coated seeds from your neighborhood or some other place. Bring them to class. Your teacher will tell you what seeds you can find in your area and how many to collect.

2. In your notebook, sketch or describe the seeds, the plants they came from, and the environment where you found them.

Summary

¶1. Look at your sketches or descriptions of the seeds.

    a.   What did the seeds have in common?

    b.   What differences did you find between the seeds?

¶2. What other kind of environment would you expect these plants to grow in?

2. SCARIFYING SEEDS

Background
Some seeds have hard coats that protect them and keep them from germinating until the environment is best for the plant to grow.

In nature the hard seed coat sometimes gets damaged or broken. Damaging the seed coat is called *scarification.* In this investigation we study what happens to the germination of seeds when we scarify their hard coats.

Problem
What effect, if any, does scarification have on the germination of seeds with hard coats?

Procedure
1. Team assignments
   Find out who your working companions are and what jobs your group has been assigned.

2. The mold problem
   Seeds that germinate in a wet place often get moldy, making them hard to count. To prevent the growth of mold, work in a clean area and use clean equipment. Wash your hands and the work area with soap and water before you begin the investigation.

3. Scarification
   In this experiment, seeds will not be scarified naturally. Some groups will scarify some seeds mechanically. Some groups will immerse seeds in hot water for different lengths of time, some in water of different temperatures, or some in acid.

4. Sorting and counting seeds

   a. Each group will need about a tablespoon of seeds from the class supply.

   b. Take out all dirt and all wormy or undersized seeds by blowing and hand-sorting.

   c. From the good seeds, count out two piles of 50 seeds each.

   d. The seeds in one good pile will have their hard coats scarified. The seeds in the other good pile will not be scarified. This second group will be used for the *control.* What happens to the controls is the basis for comparing effects of scarification on the experimental seeds.

5. The experimental seeds
   The 50 seeds in the experimental pile will be scarified. The scarifying experiments are on the following pages. Find the experiment that describes the kind of scarification your group is assigned to do. Follow the instructions carefully.

Figure 2–1 Sorting and counting seeds

Table 2–2 Reference pages for scarification experiments

Type of Experiment	Pages
Scarifying seeds by mechanical damage	155–156
Scarifying seeds by immersing them in hot water	157–158
Scarifying seeds by immersing them in 70°C water	159–161
Scarifying seeds by immersing them in acid	162–164
Preparing a greenhouse	165–167
Collecting data	168–169
Interpreting and summarizing data	170–171

6. The control seeds
   The 50 seeds used in the control pile will not
   be scarified. For the control seeds, follow the
   instructions in "Preparing a Greenhouse" on
   page 165.

EXPERIMENT A. SCARIFYING SEEDS BY MECHANICAL DAMAGE

Materials
- 2 pieces of sandpaper
- masking tape
- wood block about 5 to 6 cm wide and 10 to 15 cm long
- fingernail file or triangular file
- nail clipper
- apron and goggles

Directions

1. Scarifying by sanding

   a. Tape or tack a piece of sandpaper around a small block of wood.

   b. Tape another piece of sandpaper to the table.

   c. Put a few seeds at a time on the sandpaper taped or tacked to the table and rub them with the block until a light spot on each seed shows that the hard coat is worn through. Scarify all 50 seeds in this way. Do not use the sandpaper on the pointed tip of the seed.

   d. Symbol for greenhouse label: M–Sand

2. Scarifying by filing

   a. File each seed until a light spot shows at one place on its surface.

   b. Do not file the pointed tip of the seed.

   c. Symbol for greenhouse label: M–File

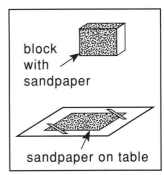

Figure 2–3 Scarifying by sanding

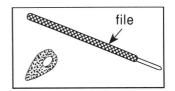

Figure 2–4 Scarifying by filing

3. Scarifying by nicking

   a.   Use a nail clipper to chip, nick, or cut one spot on the hard seed coat.

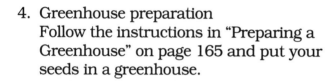

nail clipper

Figure 2–5 Scarifying by nicking

   b.   Be sure to damage only the seed coat, not the inside of the seed or its pointed tip.

   c.   Symbol for greenhouse label: M–Nick

4. Greenhouse preparation
Follow the instructions in "Preparing a Greenhouse" on page 165 and put your seeds in a greenhouse.

5. Collection of data
Follow the instructions in "Collecting Data" on page 168.

Challenge

1. Test your own ideas of ways to damage the hard seed coat. Use a different group of 50 seeds, and put your private experiment in a separate greenhouse to germinate.

2. What would happen if you cut off or damaged the tip of the seed?

3. What would happen if you cut a seed completely in two?

4. What would happen if you sanded or filed away the entire coat of the seed?

EXPERIMENT B. SCARIFYING SEEDS BY IMMERSING THEM IN WATER AT DIFFERENT TEMPERATURES

Materials
- net bags big enough to tie 50 seeds in. Use pieces of nylon stocking, netting, screening, or empty tea bags.
- string
- large beaker or pan
- thermometer
- 2 beakers
- water
- stirring rod
- watch or clock
- heat source
- apron and goggles

Directions
1. Make small bags from nylon stockings or netting material.

2. Put 50 experimental seeds in a bag and tie it securely. Leave plenty of room inside for water to swish between the seeds.

3. Attach a string to the top of the bag to use for lifting it from the hot water.

CAUTION: **You will use heat in this investigation. Use heat-resistant glass. Use care to avoid burns from hot glass or metal. Wear an apron and goggles.**

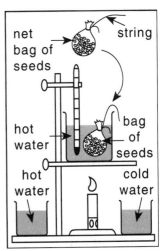

Figure 2–6 Procedure for immersing seeds in water

4. Prepare a bath for immersing your seeds. Heat a large beaker or pan of water to the temperature your group is assigned from Table 2–7. Check the temperature constantly with a thermometer. Handle the thermometer carefully. Do not use it for stirring.

5. Put hot water into one beaker and cold water into another beaker. Add a little hot water or cold water as needed to keep the bath at the desired temperature. You may also regulate the heat with the heat source.

6. Immerse the seed bags for 10 minutes in hot water at your assigned temperature. Label the bags with the right symbol from Table 2–7. For example, if you immerse a bag of seeds for 10 minutes at 30°C, label the bag "W–10–30."

7. Follow the instructions in "Preparing a Greenhouse" on page 165 and put your seeds in a greenhouse.

8. Follow the instructions in "Collecting Data" on page 168.

Table 2–7 Temperatures for hot water scarification

Temp. (°C)	Symbols for Greenhouse Labels
30	W-10-30
50	W-10-50
70	W-10-70
90	W-10-90
Boiling	W-10-B

Challenge

1. What would freezing do to the germination of hardcoat seeds?

2. What effect would soaking at room temperature overnight have on germination of hardcoat seeds?

3. If you can think of other ways to scarify seeds, test them on another set of 50 seeds in a separate greenhouse.

EXPERIMENT C.   SCARIFYING SEEDS BY IMMERSING THEM IN WATER AT 70°C FOR DIFFERENT LENGTHS OF TIME

Materials
- net bags big enough to tie 50 seeds in. Use pieces of nylon stocking, netting, screening, or empty tea bags.
- string
- large beaker or pan
- thermometer
- 2 beakers
- water
- stirring rod
- watch or clock
- heat source
- apron and goggles

Directions
1. Make small bags from nylon stockings or netting material.

2. Put 50 experimental seeds in the bag and tie it securely. Leave plenty of room inside for water to swish between the seeds.

3. Attach a string to the top of the bag to use for lifting it from the water.

CAUTION: You will use heat in this experiment. Use heat-resistant glass. Use care to avoid burns from hot glass or metal. Wear an apron and goggles.

4. Prepare a bath for immersing your seeds. Heat a large beaker or pan of water to 70°C. Check the temperature constantly with a thermometer. Handle the thermometer carefully. Do not use it for stirring.

5. Put hot water into one beaker and cold water into another beaker. Add a little hot water or cold water as needed to keep the bath at 70°C. You may also regulate the heat with the heat source.

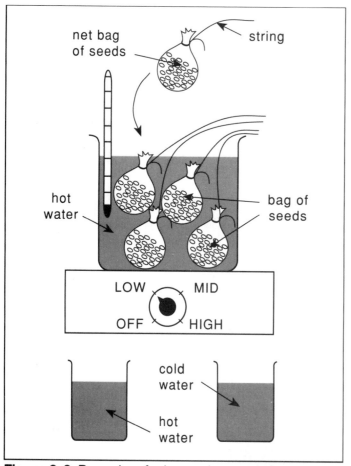

Figure 2–8 Procedure for immersing seeds in water

6. Immerse all the seed bags in 70°C water at the same time. Keep track of the number of minutes when you take each bag out of the water as shown in Table 2–9. Label each bag with the right symbol when you take it out. For example, if you take a bag of seeds out after 5 minutes, label it "W–5–70."

7. Follow the instructions in "Preparing a Greenhouse" on page 165 and put your seeds in a greenhouse.

8. Follow the instructions in "Collecting Data" on page 168.

Challenge

1. What would be the effect on germination of immersing the seeds in hot water for only a few seconds?

2. What would be the effect on germination of immersing the seeds in hot water for a long time?

Table 2–9 Time of scarification of seeds in 70°C water

Time (min)	Symbols for Greenhouse Labels
5	W-5-70
10	W-10-70
20	W-20-70
30	W-30-70

EXPERIMENT D.   SCARIFYING SEEDS BY IMMERSING THEM IN ACID

Materials
- mesh bags made of plastic screening or glass cloth. Cloth or metal mesh is not usable because acid reacts with it.
- 10 to 20-cm length of wire to attach to the bag as a handle
- acid bath
- sodium bicarbonate solution
- water
- beaker
- apron and goggles

NOTE: Your teacher has set up the acid station and will show the team how to handle the equipment.

CAUTION: Wear an apron and goggles. Use the wire handle to dip the seed bags into the beaker of acid. Do not touch the bag until it has been rinsed well in water. Strong acid reacts with cloth, wood, paper, skin, hair, and fingernails. An acid burn can leave a permanent scar.

When you handle concentrated acid, do not let any water get into the container. Keep the beaker covered with a glass except when you are putting bags in or taking them out.

If acid splashes on you or if you get acid on your fingers, apron, or goggles, report to your teacher at once. Rinse immediately with plenty of water. After long rinsing with floods of water, apply sodium bicarbonate.

Directions

1. Make small bags from plastic mesh or glass-cloth mesh.

2. Put 50 experimental seeds in a bag and tie it securely. Leave plenty of room inside for the seeds to move about freely.

3. Attach a piece of wire to the top of the bag to use as a handle for lifting it from the acid.

4. Listen to your teacher's special instructions for using the acid station.

5. Immerse the seed bags in the acid for the number of minutes you have been assigned from Table 2–11.

6. Using the wire handle, lift each bag from the acid, immerse it in the large beaker of water, and rinse it thoroughly.

7. Holding the wire handle, rinse the bag under running water in the sink for at least a full minute. Keep moving the bag to make sure all the seeds are thoroughly rinsed.

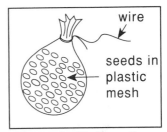

Figure 2–10 Bag of seeds for acid scarification

Table 2–11 Time of acid scarification

Time (min)	Symbols for Greenhouse Labels
10	A-10
20	A-20
30	A-30

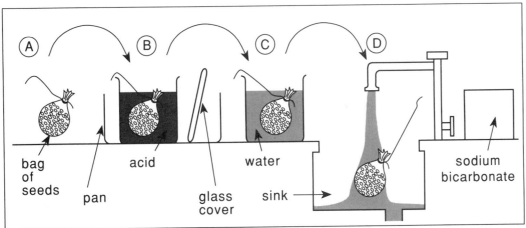

Figure 2–12 Procedure for acid scarification

8. The bag is now safe to touch. Label each bag with the proper symbols. For example, if the bag was in acid for 10 minutes, label it "A–10."

9. Follow the instructions in "Preparing a Greenhouse" on page 165 and put your seeds in a greenhouse.

10. Follow the instructions in "Collecting Data" on page 168.

Challenge

1. What might be the effect on germination of immersing the seeds in acid for different lengths of time?

2. What effects might other kinds of acid have on germination?

3. What effects might some other kinds of chemicals have on germination?

PREPARING A GREENHOUSE

Materials (for two greenhouses)
- 2 bottoms cut from 1/2-gallon milk cartons (or saucers, jar lids, or Petri dishes)
- 2 new plastic sandwich bags
- 2 identification tags
- 2 clean, absorbent paper towels
- scissors or a sharp knife
- 250-mL beaker of 50% bleach solution (equal amounts of liquid bleach and water)
- 250 mL of tap water
- 250-mL container to collect excess water
- piece of old, clean nylon stocking or fine netting material

Directions
1. With scissors or a sharp knife, cut the top off a milk carton, leaving just a rim about 1 cm high around the bottom. See Figure 2–13. This is the dish you will plant your seeds in. (You may use a saucer, a jar lid, or a Petri dish instead.)

2. Rinse your dish with fresh tap water. If you are using a milk carton bottom, rinsing will remove the last droplets of milk. If you are using another container, rinsing will remove any mold or spores clinging to it.

3. With clean hands, fold a clean piece of absorbent paper towel into four thicknesses.

4. With as little handling as possible, cut the folded paper towel to fit the dish. The fit need not be exact, but the paper towel should cover most of the bottom of the dish.

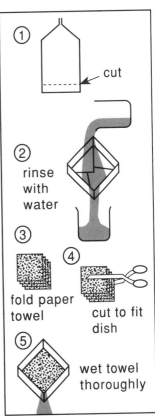

Figure 2–13 Preparing a greenhouse

5. Wet the paper towel in the dish with fresh tap water. Swish the water about until all four layers of towel are very wet. Pour the excess water into your empty container.

6. Put your 50 seeds (control or scarified) in a small net bag for rinsing in the bleach solution. Seeds scarified in hot water are already in bags. Seeds scarified in acid need not be rinsed in the bleach solution.

7. Submerge the bag of 50 seeds in bleach solution for as long as it takes you to count slowly to five. Then remove the bag.

8. Because bleach discolors silver, take off any silver jewelry before rinsing your fingertips in the bleach solution.

9. Open the seed bag and arrange the 50 seeds in rows on the paper towel in the dish so that the seeds do not touch one another. Putting seeds in rows makes them easy to count.

10. Open a new plastic sandwich bag by blowing into it. Keep your hands out of the bag to avoid contaminating it. Slide your open dish into the puffed-up bag, keeping a small dome of air over the seeds.

11. Close the mouth of the bag and tie it securely. See Figure 2–14. Attach a label showing

    a.   the treatment (control or scarified by what method)

    b.   the name of the seeds

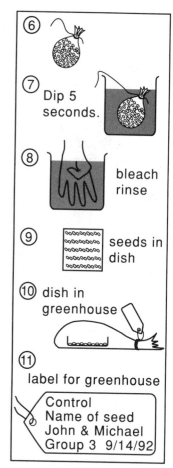

Figure 2–14 Preparing seeds for a greenhouse

c. the names of the students and the group number

d. the date

12. **Do not open your greenhouse** during the experiment for any reason, not even for counting. The moisture in the paper towels is sufficient for seeds if they are ready to germinate.

13. Put all the greenhouses in the area designated by your teacher.

14. Clean up your working area. Clean, dry, and put away all equipment but the acid bath, which your teacher will handle.

COLLECTING DATA

Directions

1. With your class, set *standards* for collecting and recording data:

   a. At what time each day will you count germinated seeds? In early morning? During noon hour? After school?

   b. When will you count the seeds as germinated? When they swell? When the white root begins to show? When the first leaves unfold?

2. Study the data table below and make sure you understand where and how to record the information in numbers and percentages each day.

3. Record data every school day until no more seeds seem to germinate. **Do not open** the greenhouses. Count by looking through the plastic bag.

Table 2–15 Germination of _____ after scarification

Treatment	Type of Count	Day 0	Day 1	Day 2	Day 3	Day 4	Day 5	Day 6	Day 7	Day 8
Control	Number germinated									
	Percentage germinated									
Experimental	Number germinated									
	Percentage germinated									

4. When you have collected all your data on germination, your teacher will explain how to graph the data.

5. Answer the questions in "Interpretation and Summary of Data on Seed Germination."

6. Answer the questions in "Analysis of Testing Procedures."

INTERPRETING AND SUMMARIZING DATA ON SEED GERMINATION

Summary
As you and your classmates discuss the questions below, write your own ideas and the group's ideas in your notebook.

1. Graph the class data on scarifying seeds with hard coats. Your teacher will explain how to set up your graph.

2. Look at the class data on controls. What was the range in the numbers of germinated seeds for the controls?

3. Which methods of scarification gave higher numbers or percentages of germination than the controls? Which method gave the highest number or percentage? What hypothesis might explain why these seeds germinated better than the controls?

4. Did some scarified seeds germinate in the same percentage range as the controls? If so, what does this mean?

5. Did seeds in any of the greenhouses not germinate at all? Have you any ideas that might explain why?

6. Did any of your experiments produce "no results"? Explain what you mean by "no results."

7. Which greenhouses had seeds that sprouted sooner than others? Have you any idea why? How many days did it take most greenhouses to reach maximum germination?

8. Some seeds in the **same** greenhouse sprouted sooner than others, and some may not have sprouted at all. What hypothesis might explain the difference?

9. How does a seedling look when it first sprouts? How does it look as it grows? Use words or sketches to answer this in your notebook.

10. Do you think **all** seeds (beans, corn, and so on) should be scarified before planting? Why or why not?

11. What is the function of the hard seed coat?

12. What is inside a seed?

13. If the seeds you worked with became rare and you had only 10 seeds left for reproducing the species, would you scarify the seeds before planting? If so, what method would you use? Why?

14. If the seeds you worked with were plentiful and you were a farmer with three bushels of seeds to plant, which scarification methods, if any, would you use? Why?

ANALYZING TESTING PROCEDURES

Summary

Continue to write your own ideas and those of your classmates and teacher in your notebook.

1. What are the reasons for using controls in an experiment?

2. Why did the class have to make so many control greenhouses? Would one or two control greenhouses for the whole class have been enough?

3. What is the value of showing the germination range of the controls (the shaded area) on the graph? Why not just show the average number or percentage of germination of the controls?

4. How many times should an experiment be repeated to obtain believable results? Did the class do enough replications for each type of scarification? If not, what use can be made of the results?

5. Why did we compare percentages of germination instead of numbers of seeds germinated?

6. Why were 50 seeds put in each greenhouse instead of 100 seeds or 10 seeds or just one seed?

7. What other places or containers or methods could be used for germinating seeds? What advantages and disadvantages would each way have?

8. Why did you not have to add water to the plastic bag during germination? What caused fog droplets to form in the bag?

9. A plastic bag used as a greenhouse is sometimes called a controlled micro-environment. What is controlled and what is "micro" about it?

10. Did you have much trouble with mold? Did the dip in bleach solution control mold well enough for you to count your seeds? If not, how else might you control mold? What would happen if you did nothing to control the growth of mold?

New Vocabulary for Section A

control
ecology
environment
experimental
germination
greenhouse

replication
scarification
seed coat
standard
valid experimental design

Section B. Plant Propagation

3. PROPAGATING PLANTS

Background

Getting a plant to make more plants is called *plant propagation*. In this section you will try ways of starting new plants and make observations as they grow.

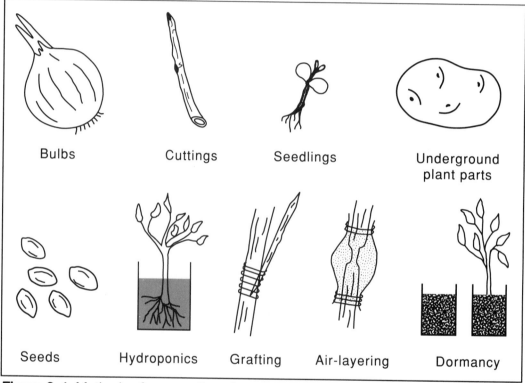

Figure 3–1 Methods of propagating plants

Activity

1. Select one or more ways to propagate plants.

2. Using the method you select, do one or more of the suggested investigations.

Procedure

1. Read the information and the suggestions in the reference booklet "Plant Propagation."

2. Choose one or more ways to propagate plants.

3. Choose one or more of the suggested investigations to work on.

4. Make a plan for your investigation. Write it in your notebook, along with rough sketches. Include the following information:

   a. Which method of planting you will use

   b. Which question you will investigate

   c. Who will do the investigation

   d. What kind of plants you will use

   e. Where you will get the plants or seeds

   f. How you will set up a control

   g. What materials you will need (soil, tools, etc.)

   h. How many pots or cans you will need

   i. How you will carry out the investigation (Make a flow diagram.)

   j. What kind of data you will collect (Draw a blank data sheet.)

   k. Where you will keep your experimental plants

5. As soon as your teacher approves your written plans and sketches, begin your investigation.

Summary

Report your findings. Refer to Section C, Scientific Reporting, for information on how to present an oral scientific report and how to prepare a written scientific report.

New Vocabulary for Section B

air-layering	grafting	seedlings
bulbs	hydroponics	thinning
cuttings	loam	transplanting
dormancy	plant propagation	underground plant parts
flow diagram		

4. ORAL SCIENTIFIC REPORTS

Background

By now you understand your equipment and have some data and some ideas about the method you used in your investigation. Your classmates may have investigated other phenomena, used other organisms, and found other information. Now it is time to share information with one another.

Communicating information is a skill that takes practice. This activity will give you a chance to practice your communicating skills. You can learn from your classmates as well as contribute ideas to the class.

Activity

1. Prepare an oral report on your investigations.

2. Make your report to the class.

3. Listen to the reports of others and contribute your ideas about their investigations.

Procedure

1. Speak loudly and clearly, looking at the faces of people in the group.

2. State the problem you worked on. Write it on the board to help listeners follow your presentation.

3. Tell how you decided to investigate the problem.

4. Show pictures or actual samples of your equipment and your work.

5. Show the tables and graphs of your results on large charts or on an overhead projector. Point out the data that seem most important.

6. Explain the meaning of your results.

7. Point out your successes and show how the results led to your conclusion.

8. Note any difficulties or failures you had and explain what caused them if you can.

9. Ask your colleagues (classmates) for comments, criticisms, suggestions, and ideas.

10. Lead the group in discussion. Try to give everyone a fair chance to speak. Defend your work, but be open to suggestions and new ideas.

    Encourage your listeners to critique your presentation. These are some of the questions they may ask:

    a. Can these tests lead to other possible answers?

    b. Were enough tests made?

    c. Were there sufficient controls?

    d. How do the data support the conclusion?

    e. Are you claiming more than the data allow?

f. Does your conclusion answer the problem statement? If not, can you explain why it does not?

g. Do your tests show points other than the ones you mentioned?

h. What other investigations do you think should be done now?

5. WRITTEN SCIENTIFIC REPORTS

Background

In science as in other areas of human effort, work done by one person is often valuable to other people. Your work may be useful to students in other classes or to students next year. They may want to try the same experiments, carry your investigation a step further, verify your work, or try to solve problems you encountered.

Scientists have a way to share their experiences. They report their work in scientific journals. They follow a standard style of reporting. The style of scientific reports differs among the sciences and from one journal to another, but the general structure is much the same.

The guidelines given here for reporting in science are from the style manual of the American Institute of Biological Sciences (AIBS). For other subjects you may be asked to write your report in a different style.

Activity

Write a report of your investigation following the procedures used by biological scientists.

Procedure

Write the sections of your report in this order:

1. Title. Write a short descriptive phrase of about three to ten words telling precisely what the experiment is about. For example:

   Effect of Light on Germination of Bidens
   Growth of Geranium Cuttings in Different Soils
   Rate of Growth of Weed Seedlings

2. Table of contents. List the topics, tables, and illustrations (sketches, photos, graphs) with their page numbers, like this:

Contents

Tables

Illustrations

3. Introduction. The introduction has two parts: (a) your statement of the problem and (b) information about your topic from books and articles. You can be reading about the topic and writing this section while you are setting up and running your experiment. In your reading you may find information you can use in your experiment.

As you read, record the author, date, title, publisher, and page numbers of each book or article from which you take information. A good way is to write the information for each source on a separate file card. (See procedure 7, Bibliography.) Do this as you read so you won't have to go back and look for the books and articles when you assemble your bibliography.

Include the following in your introduction:

a. State your problem in one sentence.

b. Give the scientific and common names of the plant or animal you used in your experiment if you know them. Include a sketch or picture.

c. Describe the plant or animal; tell about its life requirements; explain any of its special characteristics.

d. Briefly describe experiments similar to yours that you read about.

4. Materials and methods. In this section list the materials you used and the methods you followed in your experiment. Give detailed instructions, including sketches and diagrams. Describe amounts, concentrations, weights, conditions, construction of apparatus, and sources of supplies. Describe your method so clearly that another person could repeat your experiment.

5. Results. Report and explain the data you collected. Include the following:

a. Make neat copies of your data tables. Give every data table a number and a title.

b. Make graphs of your data. Give every graph a figure number, a title, and an explanation of what the graph shows.

c. Report your observations in your own words.

6. Discussion and conclusion. Interpret your findings and write your conclusions about the experiment.

  a. Describe what your data and graphs show and do not show.

  b. Comment on why you think things did or did not turn out as you expected.

  c. Draw a conclusion about your experiment. The conclusion should answer the problem you stated in your introduction.

7. Bibliography. List the books and articles you used for references.

  a. Take out the file cards or the list of references you read while you were writing the introduction and working on your experiment.

  b. List the references in alphabetical order by the **last names** of the authors.

  c. List each reference in this order:

    1) The author's last name, followed by first name and initial.

    2) The year the book was published.

3) The title of the book or article. Capitalize only the first word and proper names. Do not underline the title or put quotation marks around it.

4) For a book, name the publisher and city of publication, like this:

> Harms, Lawrence S. 1967. Growing winter bulbs. Random House. New York.

5) For an article in a journal, name the author, the title of the article, and the journal with the volume number, the issue number, and the page numbers, like this:

> Minota, Sydney R. 1970. Transplanting tomatoes and other seedlings. Journal of American Botany 10:6, 252–273.

UNIT 2. THE PHYSICAL ENVIRONMENT

Section A. Soil

6. SOIL COMPOSITION

Background

One important component of the physical environment is soil. Because it is so important, many scientists have spent their lives studying types of soil and ways to use them. Soil affects the kinds of plants that can be grown, their rate of growth, and even how houses should be constructed.

Problem

What is the composition of soil?

Procedure

1. Before doing any test on soil in your location, predict what its composition might be. Record your predictions in a table like Table 6–1.

Table 6–1 Composition of soil

Predictions	Summary of Tests

2. Perform Soil Tests A, B, and C as described on the following pages. You may also wish to perform other tests of your own design.

3. Identify the kinds of materials and estimate the proportions or percentages of each kind of material in your soil samples.

4. Summarize the results from Soil Tests A, B, and C in a table like Table 6–1. Compare the results with your predictions.

Summary

⸙1. What is your definition of soil?

2. Is your definition of soil one that could be used to describe any soil in any location? (In science, such a definition is called a *universal definition*.) How might you determine whether your definition of soil is a universal one?

SOIL TEST A. THE SHAKE JAR

Materials
- spoon or small digging instrument
- quart or liter jar with tight lid
- hand lens
- metric ruler
- watch or clock

Directions
1. Collect half a jar of soil from your schoolground or some other place.

2. Add water almost to the top of the jar.

3. Screw the lid on tight. Shake hard for about 1 minute.

4. Let the mixture stand for about 10 minutes. In your notebook, record your observations of what is happening. You may wish to use a hand lens to make close observations.

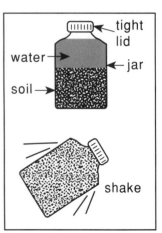

Figure 6–2 The shake-jar test on soil

5. After about 10 minutes draw your jar and its contents as shown in Table 6–3. Label the contents of the jar on your drawing.

6. Save your jar of soil and water for Soil Test B.

7. Develop a hypothesis to explain why particles are floating or sinking to different depths in the shake jar. Test your hypothesis.

Table 6–3 Observations of the shake jar

Diagram of Jar and Contents	Other Observations

SOIL TEST B. EXAMINING CONTENTS OF THE SHAKE JAR

Materials
- jar of soil and water from Soil Test A
- spoon
- thick layer of newspaper
- empty glass jar
- hand lens

Directions
1. Spread a thick layer of newspapers on your desk.

2. Unscrew the lid of the shake jar. Skim off the particles floating on top. Put them in a pile on one spot of the newspaper. Label this pile "scum."

3. Pour the water off the soil into another jar and set it aside for later observation.

4. With a spoon carefully separate the soil material in the shake jar. Put a sample of each kind in a separate pile on the newspaper. Mark on the newspaper the level in the jar where each sample came from (top, middle, and bottom or measured depths).

5. In your notebook make a table like Table 6–5.

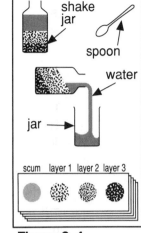

Figure 6–4
Examination of contents of shake jar

Table 6–5 Observations of composition of soil

Location of Sample in Jar	Observations of Samples with Hand Lens	Feeling of Samples When Wet	Observations of Samples after Drying (Test C)	Other Observations
Scum				
Layer 1				
Layer 2				
Layer 3				

6. Examine the materials with a hand lens. Can you see differences in the particle size? Is there evidence of plant or animal life? Record your observations in your data table.

7. Feel the wet material in each pile. Describe how the wet material feels. Record your description in the data table.

8. Observe the jar of water you set aside. Record your observations.

9. Save your soil samples for Soil Test C.

SOIL TEST C. DETERMINING SOIL TEXTURE

The size of soil particles gives soil a quality called *texture.*

Materials
• small piles of wet soil from the shake jar

Directions
1. Pick up a small amount of wet material from one of the piles you made in Soil Test B. Roll it into a marble-sized ball.

2. Hold the ball between your thumb and forefinger. Push forward and down with your thumb to roll or flatten the ball. Using the following descriptions, determine the texture of your soil.

Figure 6–6 Rolling soil into marble-sized ball

> **Clay** feels sticky and slippery. The ball rolls out into a smooth ribbon.
>
> **Silt** feels floury and smooth. The ball crumbles and will not roll out into a ribbon.
>
> **Sand** feels rough and grainy. The ball crumbles.

3. Repeat this procedure for each pile.

4. Record your observations in the data table you made for Soil Test B.

5. Make some more balls from each layer. Put the balls on a piece of paper or a dish. Label the balls. Either let them dry overnight or dry them in an oven.

6. After the balls have dried, check the texture of each pile. Pick up the soil balls and apply pressure to each. Use the following descriptions to confirm the texture of your soil samples. Record your observations in a table like Table 6–5.

> **Clay** stays together in a hard ball even under pressure.
>
> **Silt** crumbles into a fine powder when handled.
>
> **Sand** falls apart as soon as it is touched—or sooner.

7. COMPARING SOILS

Background

We have observed the composition and texture of just a few samples of soil. Do you suppose all soils are the same?

Problem

Does soil from different places have the same composition and texture?

Procedure

1. Discuss in class whether you think soils are alike or different everywhere. Consider what you and your classmates mean by "alike," "different," and "everywhere."

2. Either alone or in a small group, plan a way to make tests and collect evidence to support your opinion about soil.

3. Obtain evidence for your point of view. Use Soil Test A, B, C, or tests you design yourself. You may also use library references to support your argument.

Summary

1. Compare the results of tests on the composition and texture of many soil samples.

   a. How are soils similar?

   b. How are soils different?

2. Judging from everyone's laboratory tests and reading in reference books, is there a consensus in the class on whether soils from different places are alike or different?

?3. What is your universal definition of soil?

8. SOIL AND ROOTS

Background

When we think about plants growing in soil, we assume that the soil benefits the roots. But do roots also have an effect on soil?

Problem

Is soil affected by plant roots? If so, how?

Procedure

1. Predict the effects of plant roots on soil.

2. Perform Root Tests A and B described on the following pages. You may also perform other tests of your own design.

Summary

1. Look at the results of Root Tests A and B. What conclusions can you draw about the effect of roots on soil?

2. Compare the results of Root Tests A and B with your predictions. Were your predictions successful? Explain.

3. Compare the amount of water and effort needed to wash soil off fine roots with the amount of water and effort used to wash soil off other objects. How can you explain any differences?

4. How might the holding power of roots on soil affect other events or conditions in the environment?

Challenge

1. Does the presence of dead roots have the same effect on soil as the presence of living roots has?

2. Does the effect of roots on soil depend on the shape of the roots? Design and perform experiments to investigate this problem.

ROOT TEST A. ROOT BALL TEST

One effect of roots on soil can be tested by comparing the rates at which clumps of soil break up and scatter in water. Breaking up and scattering of particles is called *dispersion*.

A tight clump of soil containing living roots is called a *root ball*. The root ball test is a way of comparing the rate of dispersion of soil particles from a root ball with the rate of dispersion of a clump of soil with no roots in it.

Materials
- digging tool
- root ball
- clump of soil without roots
- 2 wide-mouth jars
- 2 baskets made of chicken wire or coarse screen to fit about halfway into the jars
- watch or clock
- apron

Directions
1. Make two wire baskets, each to fit about halfway into each jar. See Figure 8–1.

2. Dig up a small clump of soil containing many roots. A section of lawn or a well-rooted potted plant may be used. Put the clump in one of the wire baskets.

3. For a control, find a lump of similar soil with no roots growing in it. If you cannot find one, make one by gathering some similar soil and wetting it slightly to form a moist ball. Put this clump in the other wire basket.

4. Fill the two jars nearly to the top with water and set the screens into the jars.

5. Gently lower both baskets into the water.

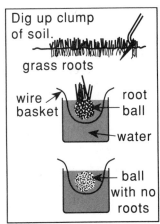

Figure 8–1 Procedure for root ball test

6. Time the dispersion of the two clumps of soil into the water. If the soil disperses too slowly to observe completely during class, you can either shake both baskets gently or let them stand overnight. Record your observations.

ROOT TEST B. SOIL AND FINE ROOTS

Materials
- root ball or potted plant
- garden hose
- hand lens
- forceps
- apron

Directions

1. Lay your root ball on a paved surface. Holding the stem of the plant in one hand, wash out all the soil you can from the roots. Alternatively, dip the root ball repeatedly into a bucket of water to wash off as much soil as possible.

2. Record your observations.

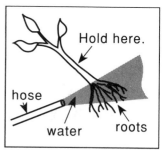

Figure 8–2 Washing soil off roots

3. Using the same method, wash the soil off your hands or off a nonliving object such as a rock, a shovel, a stake, or the hose.

4. Record your observations.

New Vocabulary for Section A

clay	proportion	silt
composition	root ball	soil
dispersion	sand	texture
holding power		

9. ABSORPTION AND PERCOLATION OF WATER IN SOIL

Background

Soil consists of particles of many sizes with small spaces called *pores* between them. The pores may be filled with air, water, roots, tiny worms, molds, bacteria, dissolved minerals, and other substances.

The process by which water enters the pores and stays there is called *absorption.* But water may also go into the soil and move downward through it. The process by which water enters and moves downward through soil is called *percolation* or seepage. In the next few tests we will investigate the ways water and soil interact.

Activity

1. Perform the Soil-and-Water Tests on absorption and percolation.

2. Do one or more of the suggested investigations.

Procedure

1. Soil-and-Water Tests A, B, and C are three methods for measuring absorption and percolation. Instructions for the tests are on the following pages. Before starting, try out the tests to practice using the equipment.

2. Look over the suggested investigations below and select one to do.

   a. How do the amounts of water absorbed and the amounts of water percolated through different soils compare? Which kinds of soil absorb most? Absorb least? Which kinds percolate most? Percolate least?

b. How do the rates of percolation compare among soils?

c. Is the soil that absorbs the most water the same soil that absorbs water the fastest? Does the "slowest" soil allow more or less water to percolate than "fast" soil does?

d. How do absorption and percolation rates compare in soils with and without plant roots in them?

e. Do soils of different textures (different-sized particles) differ in absorption and percolation? For example, how do sand, silt, and clay compare in rates and amounts of absorption and percolation?

f. How do the amounts and rates of absorption and percolation compare in fine sand and coarse sand?

g. Does the rate at which water is poured on soil make any difference in the amount of water percolated or absorbed? Does soil absorb more water from a downpour or a drizzle?

h. How does the packing of soil affect the amount and rate of water absorption and percolation?

i. Propose and investigate your own question about absorption and percolation.

3. After selecting your investigation, decide on standards for your comparisons. Consider these points:

a. The kinds of soil samples to be tested

    1) Where will the samples be collected?
    2) Should the same soil be used for all tests?
    3) Should the soil be tested as a complex mixture or be separated into its clay, silt, and sand layers and tested separately?
    4) Should soil be used if it has plant roots in it?

b. The packing of the soil

    1) Should the samples be packed or loose?
    2) Should the samples be packed the same as in the ground?

c. The amount of moisture

    1) Should the soil samples be dry, moist, or wet at the start of the test?
    2) Should all samples have the same amount of moisture?

d. The way the water is poured

    1) Should the water be added all at once?
    2) Should the water be poured slowly? How slowly?
    3) Should the water be sprinkled or drizzled like rain?

e. The number of samples to test

1) Should several tests be made on only one kind of soil?
2) Should only one test be made on several kinds of soil?
3) Should several tests be made on several soils? How many?

f. The soil test to use

1) Should the same method be used for all the investigations?
2) Should different amounts of soil be used in the samples?
3) If different methods are used for testing, how can the results be compared?

g. The amount of soil

1) Should every test use the same amount of soil?
2) Should the mass of the soil be measured?
3) Should the volume of the soil be measured?

4. Make a data table for recording the information collected during the tests. See Table 9–1 for a sample. Include only the items you plan to test. Leave enough space to record your data.

Table 9–1 Sample data table for tests of absorption and percolation of water in soil

Title:	Soil Sample		
Name _____ Date _____	1	2	3
Source of soil sample			
Type of soil			
Amount of moisture at the beginning of the experiment			
Test method used			
Test A and/or B: Amount of soil in sample			
Amount of water poured into soil			
Amount of water percolated			
Amount of water absorbed			
Test C: Time test ended			
Time test began			
Time it took water to percolate			
Other test information			

Summary

ϙ1. Make bar graphs showing the amounts of water measured in the absorption and percolation tests. Compare the results and record your conclusion in your notebook.

ϙ2. Make a bar graph showing the rates of percolation through different soils. Compare the results and record your conclusions in your notebook.

3. What effect would you expect absorption and percolation of water in soil to have on living things such as ants, worms, plant roots, and other things that inhabit the soil? Would you expect living things in the soil to have any effect on absorption and percolation?

4. Why, do you think, percolation tests are required in many places before a house may be built?

SOIL-AND-WATER TEST A. MEASURING ABSORPTION AND PERCOLATION BY VOLUME

Materials
- 2 graduated cylinders
- funnel
- filter paper

Directions

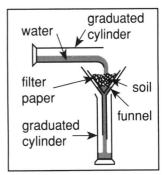

Figure 9–2 Soil-and-Water Test A

1. Set up the equipment as shown in Figure 9–2.

2. Measure the volume of water you pour into the funnel.

3. Measure the volume of water that percolates through the soil into the graduated cylinder.

4. Calculate the volume of water absorbed by the soil.

5. Empty the soil out of the funnel to see whether **all** the soil got wet.

SOIL-AND-WATER TEST B. MEASURING ABSORPTION AND PERCOLATION BY MASS

Materials
- large jar
- can with holes in the bottom
- beaker or jar

Directions

1. Set up the equipment as shown in Figure 9–3.

2. Measure the mass of water you pour into the jar.

3. Measure the mass of water that percolates through the soil into the jar.

4. Calculate the mass of water absorbed by the soil.

5. Empty the soil out of the funnel to see whether **all** the soil got wet.

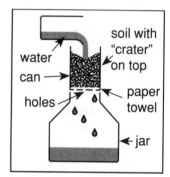

Figure 9–3 Soil-and-Water Test B

SOIL-AND-WATER TEST C. FIELD TEST ON RATE OF PERCOLATION

Materials
- 1-gallon can
- large juice can
- watch or clock

Directions

1. Remove the tops and bottoms from both cans.

2. Set up the cans in soil in the ground as shown in Figure 9–4. Set the smaller can in the ground first; then set the larger can around the smaller can.

3. Fill the large can with water.

4. **Immediately** fill the small can with water and begin timing as soon as the can is filled.

5. Time how long it takes the water in the small can to percolate into the soil.

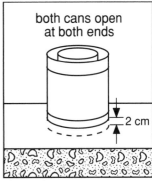

Figure 9–4 Soil-and-Water Test C

10. CAPILLARITY OF WATER IN SOIL

Background
In percolation, water moves downward through soil. But water can also move sideways and upward through soil. Movement of water sideways and upward through small spaces (pores) in soil is called *capillary action,* or just *capillarity.*

Problem
How fast is water carried upward in soil by capillary action?

Materials
- marking pencil
- metric ruler
- clear plastic drinking cup at least 10 cm tall
- small pan or dish
- dry soil samples
- nail
- flame for heating nail
- watch or clock

Procedure
1. With a heated nail melt a few small holes in the bottom of a plastic cup.

2. Pack a soil sample into the cup.

3. Set the cup of soil in a pan. Add 1 or 2 cm of water to the pan and start timing.

4. Watch the water rise through the soil in the cup.

5. After 5 minutes, use a marking pencil to show the level to which the water has risen in the cup. Continue to mark the height every 5 minutes for 30 minutes.

6. Remove the cups of soil from the water. Do not discard the soil.

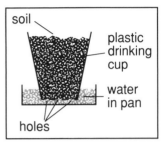

Figure 10–1 Apparatus for testing capillarity of soil

7. Repeat the procedure with different soil samples. Test some of the soils you tested for absorption and percolation so that you can compare results.

Summary

1. Line up all the cups of soil by the height to which water rose in 30 minutes.

   a. Which soils, if any, got wet all the way to the top?

   b. Which soils, if any, show almost no capillarity?

   c. Which soils had the fastest capillarity? Which had the slowest?

2. What quality or characteristic of the soil samples could account for capillarity? Does capillarity seem to be related to the texture of the soil? The degree of packing? Some other factors?

3. Let the cups of soil stand overnight **without** water in the pan. Observe them the next day.

   a. Predict what will happen to the level of water overnight.

   b. Mark the level of water the next day.

   c. Explain your observations.

Challenge

1. How high will water rise in soil? If you make the soil column as high as you can and have unlimited time, at what height will capillarity stop? Will it ever stop?

2. In what ways is capillarity like the movement of fluids in a Torricelli tube? How is it different?

11. EVAPORATION OF WATER FROM SOIL

Background
Water in soil can be absorbed, percolated downward, or moved upward or sideways by capillarity. We know from experience that soil surfaces wet by rain or by capillary action often become dry. This drying up of water from wet surfaces is called *evaporation*.

Problem
Can you get 200 grams of wet soil dry in less than 10 minutes?

Procedure
1. You may use any kind of soil, but it must be thoroughly wet.

2. At the end of the experiment all the soil must be dry to the touch.

3. You may use any method you can think of to dry the soil, but you must be able to explain your method.

NOTE: Before you begin, think about all the factors that may affect evaporation. How can you use each factor to the best advantage? Consider which kind of soil might give the fastest results and why.

Summary
¶1. Which types of soils and sets of conditions seem to speed up or slow down the evaporation process?

2. What might happen to water in each of these environments?

    a. Water deep under desert soil

    b. Water under garden soil

    c. Water in soil under a forest

    d. Water on grass

    e. Surface water after a heavy rain in a desert

    f. Surface water after a heavy rain in a garden

Challenge

Without adding water, can you prevent 500 grams of wet planting medium (soil or other garden mixture) in an open container from drying completely when left out for a month?

At the beginning your sample should be thoroughly wet but not dripping. The open surface area of the container may be no less than 10 cm^2. Explain your method.

New Vocabulary for Section B

absorption
capillarity
capillary action
evaporation
percolation
pores

12. WATER VAPOR IN THE AIR

Background
We have seen that water gets into the air by evaporation from wet surfaces. Water in the air is called *water vapor*. The amount of water vapor in the air is called *humidity*. The amount of humidity in the air is measured in grams per cubic meter (g/m^3).

Air can hold different amounts of water vapor at different temperatures. The actual amount of water vapor in the air compared with the maximum amount of water vapor the air can hold is called *relative humidity*.

Activity
Determine the changes in relative humidity in the following problems.

Procedure
1. Read the information below on relative humidity.

    a. At 30°C, 1 m^3 of air can hold a maximum of 30 g of water vapor (H_2O).

    b. If 1 m^3 of air contains 30 g of water vapor (H_2O) at 30°C, the relative humidity (RH) is 100%. See Air Parcel 1 in Figure 12–1.

    c. If 1 m^3 of air contains only 15 g of water vapor at 30°C, the relative humidity is 50%. See Air Parcel 2 in Figure 12–1.

    d. If 1 m^3 of air contains only 7.5 g of water vapor at 30°C, the relative humidity is 25%. See Air Parcel 3 in Figure 12–1.

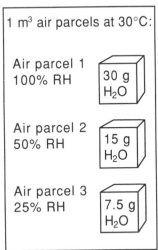

Figure 12–1 Relative humidity of air parcel at 30°C

e. In Air Parcels 4, 5, and 6 in Figure 12–2, the temperature has changed to 10°C. At 10°C, 1 m³ of air can hold only 10 g of water vapor. Look at the parcels and note how the relative humidity changes with different amounts of water vapor in the air.

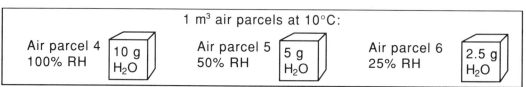

Figure 12–2 Relative humidity of air parcel at 10°C

2. Referring to the six parcels of air, fill in the missing information in a table similar to Table 12–3.

Table 12–3 Examples of relative humidity calculations

Example	Volume of Air (m³)	Temperature (°C)	Mass of Water (g)	Relative Humidity
a.	1	10	5	
b.	1	10	1	
c.	1	10		80%
d.	1	10	10	
e.	1	30	10	
f.	1	30		10%
g.	1	30	20	

3. Graph your data for Air Parcels 1–6. Use the horizontal axis for mass of water vapor and the vertical axis for relative humidity. For each temperature (10°C and 30°C) draw a line or curve through the data points for that temperature.

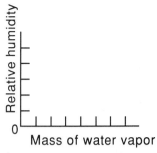

Summary

1. The relative humidity of a parcel of air is 100%. If the temperature rises, what will happen to the relative humidity?

2. The relative humidity of a parcel of air is 50%. If the temperature rises, what will happen to the relative humidity?

3. The relative humidity of a parcel of air is 50%. If the temperature falls, what will happen to the relative humidity?

4. The relative humidity of a parcel of air is 100%. If the temperature falls, what will happen to the relative humidity?

Answers

2.a. 50%; 2.b. 10%; 2.c. 8 g; 2.d. 100%; 2.e. 33+%; 2.f. 3 g; 2.g. 67%.

13. MEASURING RELATIVE HUMIDITY

Background
Water vapor is an invisible gas in the air. To detect its presence, we must use instruments.

Several kinds of instruments are used to measure humidity. We will study the ones called *hygrometers* and *psychrometers.*

Problem
How does relative humidity vary in and around your school?

Procedure
1. Get the reference booklet "Weather Instruments" and find the pages that describe humidity-measuring devices.

2. Choose one of the devices to use in this investigation. Obtain or construct the device.

3. Decide where to make your measurements. Choose sites and times that can be compared. For example:

   a. The basketball court at noon and after school

   b. The cafeteria in the morning and during lunchtime

   c. Inside the classroom and outside the building at the same hour

d. In the parking lot and under a low, dense tree or bush

  e. At school and at your home

 4. Plan to make measurements that will give you data useful for answering the questions about the places and circumstances you choose.

Summary

 1. How does the humidity vary among the sites and times you investigated?

 2. How can you explain any differences in humidity?

 3. What factors or conditions seem to affect the relative humidity of a certain area or place?

14. WATER DROPLETS IN THE AIR

Background
We said earlier that water vapor is an invisible gas. But under certain conditions, water vapor in the air condenses to form liquid droplets that are visible. Collections of tiny water droplets buoyed up in the air are called *clouds*.

Activity
Observe the appearance and movement of clouds.

Procedure
1. Read the summary questions before you make your observations.

2. Find a comfortable spot on the lawn or the beach on a clear day when there are just a few clouds in the sky. Lie on your back and watch the sky. Try to keep the horizon or a ridge of land in view. Lie still and watch the clouds.

3. Try this experiment at different times of day or night or different times of the year and compare your observations.

4. When you finish your observations, meet together as a class. Share your observations and opinions on the summary questions.

Summary
¶1. What shapes do clouds have? Sketch the shapes of some clouds you watched.

2. How do clouds change in shape and size?

3. In what direction do clouds move?

4. What colors are clouds?

¶5. Do clouds seem to float at different heights?

    a.   If they do, how can you tell?

    b.   How can you account for the fact that clouds float in the sky?

    c.   How can you account for their floating at different heights?

6. In what part of the sky do you find the most clouds?

7. Do clouds near the horizon seem different from clouds directly over your head? If so, how? Why?

8. As clouds approach or leave ridges, do they change?

¶9. Do clouds above an industrial smokestack look different from other clouds?

10. What other special things did you notice in the sky?

11. Share your experiences with snow, hail, lightning storms, and other weather phenomena. What were the experiences like?

12. Share your descriptions of how clouds look from an airplane.

13. Share your descriptions of clouds near the ground. A cloud near the ground is called *fog*. How does fog feel or look as you drive through it?

Challenge
Use reference materials to find answers to these questions.

1. What names are given to different types of clouds?

2. Do clouds contain anything besides water droplets?

3. Under what conditions do water droplets form in the air?

4. How do rainbows form? What causes double rainbows? Where is the sun relative to the arch of a rainbow? Why?

New Vocabulary for Section C

cobalt chloride	humidity device	relative humidity
fog	hygrometer	water vapor
humidity	psychrometer	

Section D. The Air around Us

15. MAJOR GASES IN THE AIR

Background
The layer of air just above Earth's surface is called the *atmosphere*.

Problem
What are the **major** gases that make up the atmosphere?

Procedure
1. Make a table like Table 15–1. List all the gases that you think are in air.

2. Predict the quantity or percentage of each gas you think is in the air. Record your predictions in the table.

Table 15–1 Major gases in air

Predictions		Reference:	
Name of Gas	Percentage of Air	Name of Gas	Percentage of Air
		Trace components	1

3. After you have written your predictions, look in a reference book to find the amount or percentage of each major gas in the air.

a. List the gases in order from most to least abundant in Table 15–1. Do not list any gas under 1%. They are included in the term *trace components* in the table.

b. Record the author, title, year of publication, city, publisher, and page number of the book you used.

4. The quantity of major gases in the air can be expressed in several ways:

a. Percentages (%): the number of parts of a component in 100 parts of air.

b. Parts per million (ppm): the number of parts of a component in a million parts of air.

c. mL/100 mL: the number of milliliters of a component in a 100-mL sample of air.

For example, if one gas makes up 20.95 percent of the air, that amount may be expressed in any of the following ways:

20.95% = 209,500 ppm = 20.95 mL/100 mL

5. Set up a table with columns for name of gas, percentage (%), ppm, and mL/100 mL.

a. Convert the percentage of each major gas in the air to milliliters per 100 milliliters.

b. Convert 1% into ppm and mL/100 mL.

Summary

¶1. How did the actual percentage of each gas in the air compare with your predictions?

2. Compare the percentage of each gas other students found with the percentage you found.

   a.   How might the differences, if any, be accounted for?

   b.   Check the dates of publication for each reference you use. How much, if at all, have the percentages of gases in the air changed in recent years?

¶3. Do you think the gases in the air are the same all over the world?

   a.   How might the gases over Alaska and Egypt compare? Give reasons for your answer.

   b.   How does the mixture of gases differ with altitude? Explain.

   c.   How might the components of air differ in each of these places?

      1)   Over open ocean
      2)   Over dense forest
      3)   Over a high mountain
      4)   Over a large city
      5)   Over a desert

¶4. What factors in the environment might tend to keep the mixture of gases in the air the same?

Challenge

1. Prepare a report complete with sketches or diagrams showing how far the atmosphere extends beyond the surface of Earth. Use references to find whether air composition changes with altitude.

2. Show where each object listed in Table 15–2 would be located on your sketches.

Table 15–2 Altitudes of various objects

Object	Height in Miles	Height in Kilometers
Cumulus clouds	1–2	1.61–3.22
Highest-flying birds	4–5	6.44–8.05
Peak of Mt. Everest	5.5	8.86
Jet airliners	5–7	8.05–11.27
Jet stream	2–8	3.22–12.88
Peak of Mauna Kea	2.61	4.20

3. Explain these terms:

   a. stratosphere

   b. troposphere

   c. ambient air

   d. ionosphere

   e. atmosphere

   f. inert gases

   g. gas

   h. vapor

   i. trace components

16. THE TRACE COMPONENTS OF AIR

Background
Substances found in very small amounts in air are called *trace components* of air. All trace components add up to less than 1% of the total composition of air.

Problem
1. What are the trace components of clean, dry air?

2. How might the trace components of air vary?

Procedure
1. Make a table like Table 16–1. Predict which gases are trace components in clean, dry air.

Table 16–1 Proportions of trace components in the air

graduated cylinder →

| 100 |
| 90 |
| 80 |
| 70 |
| 60 |
| 50 |
| 40 |
| 30 |
| 20 |
| 10 |

1% or
10,000 ppm or
1 mL/100 mL

Name of Trace Component	Percentage	ppm	mL/100 mL

2. Look in different references to find the amount of each trace component in air. Express the amounts in percentages, parts per million, and milliliters per 100 milliliters. Record the publication information of each reference you use.

3. Describe how each of the following might affect the quantities of trace components in air. List your references with their publication information.

   a. volcanic eruptions

   b. pollen from plants

   c. gases from plants

   d. rain

   e. wind over land

   f. wind over ocean

   g. forest fire

   h. animal life

   i. other factors

4. Put an asterisk (*) before the name of each trace component on your list that might vary in quantity at different times or in different places.

Summary

¶1. Compare your list of trace components in clean, dry air with other students' lists. Try to form a definition of *clean, dry air*.

↑2. What trace components do natural phenomena put into the air?

↑3. How much does human activity affect the quantity of trace components in the air?

4. How might the quantity of trace components in air vary from time to time or from place to place?

Challenge

1. Explain each process listed below. Give examples of how each process might affect the quantity of trace components in air.

   a. combustion

   b. friction

   c. evaporation

   d. decomposition

   e. respiration

   f. photosynthesis

2. How might changes in the quantities of trace components in air affect plants, animals, or the physical environment?

17. WEATHER STATIONS

Background

Weather affects our decisions about where to go, what to wear, and what games to play. We often wish we could predict weather so that we could plan our activities. The science of weather prediction is called *weather forecasting*. Forecasting is based on understanding weather patterns and the causes of changes.

Scientists at the National Weather Service study phenomena and collect data from many stations. Many amateurs help the Weather Service. They keep records of rainfall in their yards and of other weather changes in their areas, then send their data to the Weather Service each week or month.

Weather is the word for day-to-day conditions of the atmosphere. The average or normal trend of weather over a long period is called *climate*.

Next we'll make some simple instruments and use them to make measurements about weather phenomena.

Activity

Set up a weather station at school or at home.

Procedure

1. Choose a spot for your weather station. Read "Preparing a Weather Station" on the following pages and study the figures. Then follow the instructions to build your weather station.

2. Find the reference booklet "Weather Instruments" and read the information on the weather instruments.

Table 17-1 Sample data sheet for daily weather report

Name of reporter _____

Location _____

Height above ground _____

Reporter's initials _____

Time daily readings are taken _____

Date	Rainfall	Temperature	Wind Direction	Wind Speed	Humidity	Barometric Pressure	Clouds	Visibility
Total for Week		Highest ____ Lowest ____ Average ____	Usual Direction ____	Highest ____ Lowest ____ Average ____	Highest ____ Lowest ____ Average ____	Highest ____ Lowest ____ Average ____	Summary Statement	Summary Statement

3. Decide which instruments your class will use.

4. Set *standards* for collecting data.

    a.   What time each day will you make observations and record data? (The National Weather Service reads rain gauges every morning between 6:00 and 9:00.)

    b.   How long will you collect data? Two weeks is a good span of time. You might like to choose one week during a stormy season and a second week during clear weather.

    c.   Which measuring system you will use, the U.S. customary system or the metric system? (The Weather Service reports data in both.) For international comparisons or for computer recording, use the metric system.

5. Prepare data sheets like Table 17–1 and Table 17–2. Include only the items you need. Make the columns wide enough for your data.

On each data sheet show the site of your weather station, its height above ground, and the time you record your daily readings. Be sure to write both your name and your initials in the proper blanks on the data sheet. You will use the initials later to identify your station.

Table 17–2 Sample data sheet for long-term observations

Long-Term Observations		
Device	Time of Exposure	Results
Dustfall jar	30 days	
Sticky-tape can	7 days	
Nitrogen dioxide indicator fabric	30–90 days	
Sulfur dioxide indicator fabric	30–90 days	
Ozone indicator	30 days	

Summary

Describe the construction of your weather station.

PREPARING A WEATHER STATION

A *weather station* is a box or platform that holds weather instruments. Stations should be in easy-to-reach places at home or at school. One station should be in your class study area. See Investigation 29, The Physical Environment of the Class Study Area.

Materials
- meterstick
- a box that won't be damaged by rain or wind
- a strong, steady post or other support for the box

Directions
1. Select a site for your station.

    a. The station should be at least 1 meter above the ground or on a roof.

NOTE: The Weather Service sets its rain gauges about 1 meter above the ground. It puts its wind instruments about 10 meters above ground, or high enough to be well above nearby obstructions. It puts its other instruments wherever conditions are best for the purpose.

    b. Put your station as far from trees and buildings as you can. Trees and buildings affect wind patterns and rainfall.

2. Make a site map showing your weather station. See Figure 17–3.

   a. Draw a map of the site with your station at the center.

   b. Pace off the distance in eight compass directions to things higher than 1 meter. Write their height and distance on the site map.

   c. Keep your site map with your data sheet. The site map shows what objects might affect your data.

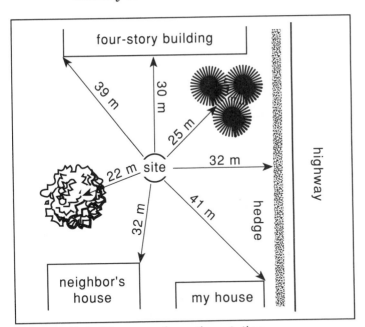

Figure 17–3 Site map of weather station

3. Build your weather station. Figure 17–4 shows two designs. You may think of a design better for your site and the instruments you plan to use.

a. The station's top surface should be open to the sky for rain gauges and a wind vane.

b. Each station should have a section that protects other instruments from rain and sun but lets air through.

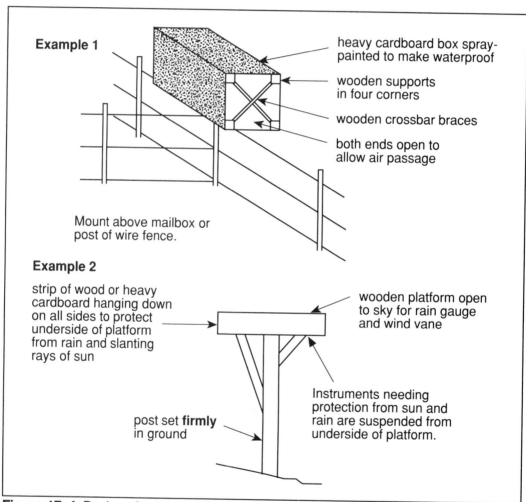

Example 1

heavy cardboard box spray-painted to make waterproof

wooden supports in four corners

wooden crossbar braces

both ends open to allow air passage

Mount above mailbox or post of wire fence.

Example 2

strip of wood or heavy cardboard hanging down on all sides to protect underside of platform from rain and slanting rays of sun

wooden platform open to sky for rain gauge and wind vane

Instruments needing protection from sun and rain are suspended from underside of platform.

post set **firmly** in ground

Figure 17–4 Designs for two weather stations

18. WEATHER MAPS

Background

We have collected a lot of atmospheric data. Now we must put the data into forms that can be interpreted and compared. One way to do this is to plot the data on maps with numbers or symbols.

With numbers, readings of the same value can be connected with lines called *isograms*. Isograms on maps are named by the type of data they represent:

> Isobars connect sites with equal barometric pressures.
> Isohyets connect sites with equal amounts of rainfall.
> Isotherms connect sites with equal temperatures.

Figure 18–1 is a map of the island of Oahu, Hawaii, showing mean annual rainfall—the average rainfall for a year. Study this map to see how rainfall and other weather data can be plotted on a map.

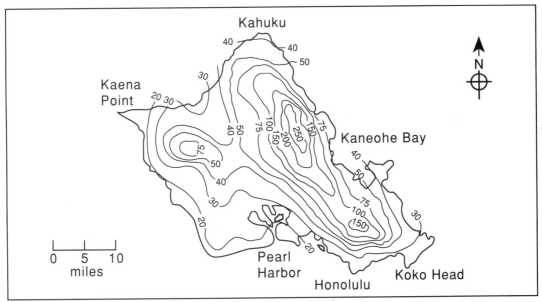

Figure 18–1 Isohyets showing mean annual rainfall in inches on the island of Oahu (Map prepared by William Taliaferro, National Weather Service, Pacific Region.)

Problem
What are the weather patterns in the area where your class collected data?

Materials
- contour map of area covered by weather stations
- plastic sheets for making transparencies

Procedure
1. Copy a map of the area covered by the class's weather stations onto a transparent plastic sheet.

2. Mark the site of each weather station on the transparent plastic sheet. Write students' initials at the location of their station on the area map. This is the master map.

3. Divide into groups. Each group will be responsible for summarizing a different kind of weather data according to the directions on the following pages.

4. Display all the data sheets from all the weather stations in a place where each group can copy the data it needs.

5. If you wish to compare the class data with official data, get a Weather Service map of your area. Before comparing data, check to see whether the Weather Service map records yearly averages or covers a shorter period.

6. When reviewing the data, try to find pairs of maps that show similar patterns. For example, compare the rainfall map to see whether it shows the same high and low areas as the temperature map. Try all kinds of combinations.

Summary

Drawing on the comparisons of pairs of maps, discuss these questions:

1. How does each type of data relate to the elevations on the elevations map?

2. What pattern, if any, can you find between wind direction and the collection of windblown particles?

3. If two or three maps show similar patterns, how might you explain the similarities? Could it be coincidental? Make a statement about the kinds of data that seem to vary together.

4. Is there a pair of maps that **do not** match in any way? How might you explain the differences?

5. How do your data compare with Weather Service data?

6. Look at your data sheets for notes on clouds and other observations not reported in numbers.

   a. How do these help you interpret some of the maps?

   b. How do these observations fit with or explain some of the data on the maps?

7. If you took data during a week of stormy weather and a week of fair weather, what differences, if any, did you find?

WEATHER MAP ASSIGNMENTS

Map Group A. Elevation

Directions

1. Make a transparent copy of the master map.

2. Lay your transparent map on top of a contour map of the area you are studying.

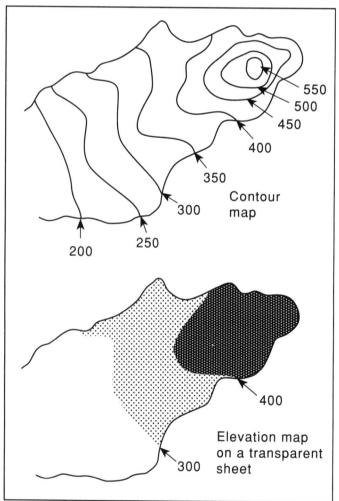

Figure 18–2 Preparation of elevation map

3. Find the highest and lowest elevations in the area. Subtract the low number from the high number to get the range of elevation for your area.

4. Divide the range of elevation into three equal parts. Find the contour line that marks off each third:

   a. Suppose your area map looks like the one in Figure 18–2. The highest elevation shown is 550 m, and the lowest elevation is 200 m. The range of elevation is 350 m.

   b. Find the contour line at 300 m and the one at 400 m. These lines separate the lower, middle, and upper thirds of the map.

   c. Draw the contour lines between the high, medium, and low elevations on your transparent map.

5. Devise a way to shade the elevations. For example, you could make the highest elevation a medium shade, the middle elevation a lighter shade, and leave the lowest elevation unshaded.

Map Group B. Rainfall

Directions

1. Make a transparent copy of the master map.

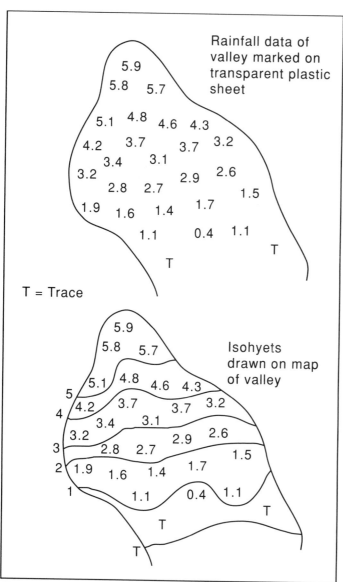

Figure 18–3 Preparation of rainfall map

2. Find out the total rainfall at each station during the sampling time by referring to the data sheets posted in the room. Write the rainfall total on your transparent plastic map at the site of each station.

3. Draw lines connecting areas of nearly equal rainfall:

   a. Suppose your mapping area is a valley with 25 stations. Your map showing rainfall numbers might look like the one in Figure 18–3.

   b. The lines on the map define areas that have about the same amount of rainfall. These are *isohyets.*

4. On your transparent map find which areas have heavy, moderate, and light rainfall.

5. Devise a way to shade these rainfall areas. Areas of light rainfall can be left unshaded.

6. If you took data during a week of stormy weather and a week of fair weather, make a map showing rainfall for each week.

Map Group C. Temperature, Wind Speed, and Barometric Pressure

Directions
1. Follow all the directions for Map Group B but record the average temperature, average wind speed, or average barometric pressure for the period.

2. Put each type of measurement on a separate map.

3. Draw the isograms for each type of measurement.

4. Show the areas of the high, moderate, and low intensity of the factor measured.

Map Group D. Wind Direction

Make a transparent plastic map of the study area. On it draw arrows showing the usual direction of the wind at each station.

Map Group E. Particles and Gases

Directions
Because it takes longer to collect data on particles and gases, you may have to make your map and compare it with other maps later in the year.

1. Follow all the directions for Map Group B but record the total particle count or a thirty-day average for the period. For gases, prepare a map using the scale you devised to show the relative amounts of gases detected.

2. To map the data from the sticky-tape can, draw an arrow at each site showing the direction **from which** most particles seem to come. See Figure 18–4. The *N* in Figure 18–4 shows that most particles came from the north.

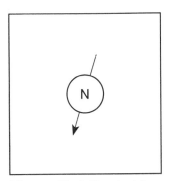

Figure 18–4 Symbol for particle map group

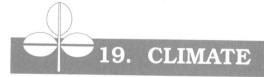

19. CLIMATE

Background

Weather is the word for daily atmospheric conditions. Weather averaged over long periods is called *climate*. The same factors that affect weather regulate climate.

Problem

What factors regulate the climate of the area where you live?

Procedure

1. Read "Climate Factors" on the following pages and discuss the factors that regulate the world's climates.

2. Decide which factors affect the climate in your area.

Summary

1. Describe the climate where you live. What factors regulate it?

2. Explain how a difference in temperatures over ocean and nearby land produces diurnal winds.

CLIMATE FACTORS

Latitude

Our Earth is heated by light and radiation from the sun. The location of an area determines the amount of solar radiation it gets. For example, in the tropics—latitudes near the equator—the sun shines directly down, so each square kilometer gets large amounts of solar radiation. But in latitudes nearer the poles, sunshine comes in at an angle, so each square kilometer gets less radiation than a square kilometer near the equator does. The angle is due to the tilt of Earth's axis and the curve of Earth's surface. The angle of the sun's rays and the length of time the sun shines each day determine the average temperatures of an area.

Temperature is the major factor affecting climate. Figures 19–1 and 19–2 show how the angle of the sun's rays changes during the seasons of the year. Notice that the tropics receive almost vertical rays of sunshine throughout the year. The diagrams also show why each hemisphere is warmer in summer than in winter and why one hemisphere is having winter while the other is having summer.

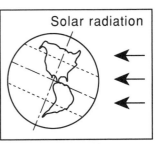

Figure 19–1 Summer in the northern hemisphere comes between June and September, when the sun's rays fall on the entire hemisphere sometime during the day.

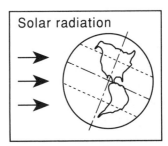

Figure 19–2 Winter in the northern hemisphere comes between December and March, when the sun's rays fall on only part of the northern hemisphere during the day. Winter in the northern hemisphere is summer in the southern hemisphere.

Figure 19–3 shows how the angle of the sun's rays determines the amount of solar radiation on the Earth's surface. Because vertical rays are concentrated in a smaller area, they produce higher temperatures than slanted rays, which spread their heating radiation over a larger area.

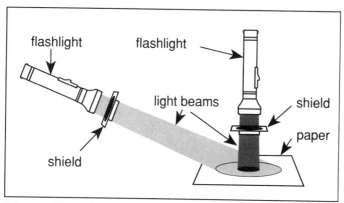

Figure 19–3 Comparison of area of illumination of vertical and slanted rays of light

Oceans and Other Large Bodies of Water

Large bodies of water, especially the oceans, affect the temperature of nearby areas. The *specific heat* of water is higher than that of land. That means it takes more heat to raise the temperature of water 1°C than it takes to raise the temperature of the same mass of rocks or soil 1°C. Water heats up and cools down more slowly than land does. The result is that nearby oceans tend to keep land areas cooler in summer and warmer in winter than they would otherwise be.

In coastal areas, land and ocean temperatures differ from day to night. The difference in temperatures between the water and the land produces diurnal winds, commonly called sea breezes and land breezes. *Diurnal* means "twice a day."

Using figures like 19–4 and 19–5, show which way the wind blows by day and by night. Show where the air parcels move and use arrows to show wind direction.

Ocean Currents

Currents or streams of water in the oceans also affect climate by keeping an area warmer or cooler than it would otherwise be. Some currents are warm, some cold. Their effect is especially noticeable in places such as northwestern Europe, Japan, and Alaska, where the warm currents originating in the tropics keep temperatures higher than normal for their latitudes.

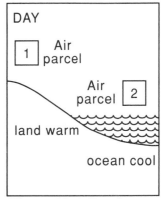

Figure 19–4 Daytime movement of air near water

Water Vapor

Oceans, lakes, and forests are major sources of *water vapor,* which ultimately condenses as rain, snow, or hail. Radiation falling on bodies of water results in *evaporation,* which often makes areas near oceans quite humid.

Great quantities of water vapor are also released by plants through *transpiration,* which can make air in a forest feel humid.

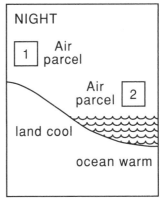

Figure 19–5 Nighttime movement of air near water

Prevailing Winds

The direction from which winds most often blow affects the amount of moisture reaching an area. Prevailing winds passing over oceans, lakes, and forests pick up moisture and carry it with them. Winds passing over grassland and deserts tend to remain dry and contribute less precipitation to a given area. The amount of moisture carried to an area by moving air masses in part determines how much rainfall an area gets.

Altitude

Mountains block air movement, forcing clouds to move up, then over or around them. The vertical movement of air affects the rainfall and temperature of an area.

Using Figures 19–6 and 19–7, trace the movements of a parcel of air arriving on the windward side of a mountain. The numbers in the figure show the points of passage of a single parcel of air.

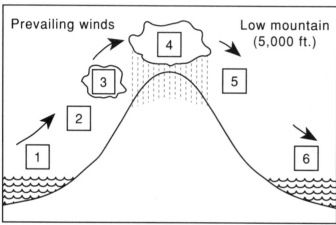

Figure 19–6 Air moving up and over a low mountain

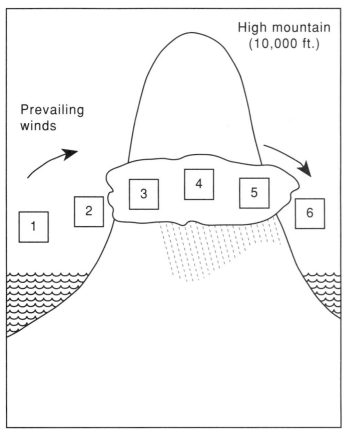

Figure 19–7 Air moving up and around a high mountain

At point 1 in Figures 19–6 and 19–7, an air mass approaches a mountain—a low mountain in Figure 19–6 and a high one in Figure 19–7. The parcel is moving at 10 to 15 miles per hour, or 4.5 to 6.5 meters per second. The humidity in the parcel is high because the air has taken up water evaporated from an ocean surface. The barometric pressure of the air is about 760 mm at sea level.

At point 2 the air parcel begins to climb the windward slope of the mountain. As the parcel moves up the slope, the air is channeled by the ridges and valleys and picks up speed. **As the air rises, _barometric pressure_ falls, and the air**

expands. Its density decreases as it expands. The rising air cools 1°C for each 100 meters it rises. This rate of cooling is called the *adiabatic lapse rate.* **As the air cools, relative humidity rises**. Can you recall any experiments that demonstrated some of these phenomena?

At point 3 the same air parcel is at several thousand feet elevation. Its temperature has dropped to the *dew point,* and clouds form. The clouds usually stay near the same altitude on the mountainside where they form, but the air from which they condensed keeps moving. As new parcels of moisture-laden air arrive, more moisture condenses at the same altitude.

Point 4 shows the air carried **over the top** of a relatively low mountain but **around the slopes** of a high peak. The upsweep of the wind does not carry the clouds to the summit. The clouds release much of their moisture as rain. Mt. Waialeale (pronounced Wye-ah-leh-ah-leh) on Kauai, Hawaii, is the wettest spot on Earth. If you left a rain gauge on top of Mt. Waialeale for a year, you'd need a can nearly 40 feet deep—taller than a four-story building—to hold the water! The Koolau range on Oahu, Hawaii, gets about 300 inches of rain a year. How many feet or meters is that?

At point 5 the air begins to move down the *lee slope* of the mountain. **As the air moves downward, barometric pressure rises, and density increases as the air compresses.** The descending air has the same adiabatic lapse rate as the ascending air, warming about 1°C for each 100 meters it falls. **As air warms, relative humidity falls,** and the clouds evaporate.

At point 6 the warmer air moves away from the mountain, drier than when it arrived because the moisture fell as rain on the mountain.

Local Conditions and Subclimates

Local climate conditions in an area create *subclimates.* Subclimates are especially evident in mountains in the tropics, where conditions change rapidly. Local topography, plants, and manmade factors often make local climates differ somewhat from the general climate of an area. Large inland lakes such as the Great Lakes in the United States moderate the temperatures and add to the rainfall of nearby areas. Plants, especially forests, regulate local climate through transpiration and their effect on wind patterns.

Tall buildings and large paved areas in cities cause temperatures to change more rapidly in cities than in the surrounding countryside. Rapid shifts in temperature cause changes in the winds. Cities also tend to have lower humidity because they have few open areas where water evaporates into the air. This drier air gives big cities what is called the *city desert climate.*

Someone driving up a mountain in the tropics could pass through many climates. At sea level there could be tropical rain forests. On the slopes, people might be growing fruits, flowers, and vegetables typical of temperate zones. Higher up, cattle might graze in alpine meadows. Still higher, fog would cover the road through the cloud belt, and the air would be colder.

Finally, if the mountain were high enough, the driver would come to clear, crisp, cold air above the timberline. Shrubs and clumps of grass would thin out, then disappear. Only crevices between rugged rocks would hold any soil. From bottom to top, the altitude of the mountain produces a variety of subclimates.

New Vocabulary for Section D

adiabatic lapse rate
anemometer
barometric pressure
city desert climate
climate
dew point
diurnal winds
evaporation

isobar
isogram
isohyet
latitude
lee slope
parts per million
solar radiation
specific heat

subclimate
trace components
transpiration
tropics
Weather Service
weather
weather map

20. RAINDROPS

Background

To form a raindrop, water vapor must condense around a *nucleus*—a dust particle, a salt crystal, or some other speck of matter. This process is called *nucleation.* It happens during high humidity when water vapor condenses on particles in the air and becomes raindrops. Sometimes humid air can be artificially "seeded" from airplanes with tiny crystals of silver iodide or dry ice. The crystals act as nuclei for raindrops.

From 1898 to 1905, a Vermont farmer named Wilson Bently studied raindrops. With no schooling in science and no scientific equipment, he invented some tests still used today by scientists. Bently's tests are the basis of the raindrop tests we do next.

Problem

1. What size are raindrops?

2. How many raindrops fall in a given area during a shower?

3. How do showers compare in size and number of raindrops?

Procedure

1. Read about the three raindrop tests on the next few pages.

2. Select one test or more to investigate raindrops. Assemble the equipment you need.

3. Keep your equipment ready so you can make the tests the next time it rains during class. You may also do the tests at home so that you can compare rains in different places.

4. Plan to do your tests during several rains. In a hard rain you may need to reduce the time of exposure; in a light rain you may extend the time. You must determine the number of drops per second to get a basis for comparison.

5. Agree on the size of the area you will use for your tests. One possibility is for everyone in the class to use pie pans or other objects having the same surface area.

6. After you do the tests, calculate the number of raindrops per area per second. Measure and record the diameters of raindrops in each test.

Summary

1. What is the largest raindrop you measured? The smallest? What is the distribution of sizes?

2. How many raindrops per second fall in a rain? What were the highest and the lowest numbers recorded? What was the average?

3. What is the relationship, if any, between the size of raindrops and the number of raindrops per second?

4. What shapes were the raindrops in the flour test?

5. Knowing the number of raindrops falling in a second and their size, how could you calculate the amount of rain that would fall in 10 minutes? What other information, if any, would you need?

RAINDROP TEST A. FLOUR TEST

The flour test measures the number, diameter, and shape of raindrops.

Materials
- 2 aluminum pie pans of the same size
- flour
- sifter or piece of screening
- oven or drying box with light bulb
- metric ruler

Directions

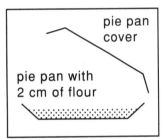

Figure 20–1 Flour test for raindrops

1. Sift flour into one pie pan to about 2 cm depth.

2. Cover it with the other pie pan.

3. When it rains, take the covered pan out to a spot away from trees or buildings.

4. Uncover the flour for just 3 seconds—the time it takes to say "one thousand, two thousand, three thousand." Then cover it.

5. Bring the covered pan indoors. Remove the cover and dry the flour in a warm oven or in a box with a light bulb. It may take an hour or overnight to dry.

6. Sift out the "raindrops." The smaller pellets are the size and shape of actual raindrops. Larger raindrops form pellets that flatten on impact.

7. Observe and describe the shape of the flour "raindrops."

8. Measure and record the diameters of the flour "raindrops."

RAINDROP TEST B. NYLON STOCKING TEST

Because large drops splash, their shapes are hard to measure from the marks they make. In Raindrop Test B the drops fall on a surface open enough that the drops fall through, leaving a mark about the size of their falling diameter.

Use the nylon stocking test to measure the size and number of raindrops.

Materials
- a nylon stocking that has been washed at least once (New nylon does not work well because it repels the coating in this test.)
- a flat, open frame onto which the nylon can be stretched (You can use a can, a large-mouth jar, an embroidery hoop, or a clothes hanger bent into a circle.)
- powdered sugar (confectioner's sugar)
- sifter or piece of screening
- pie pan or stiff paper large enough to cover the frame
- metric ruler

Directions
1. Stretch the nylon stocking over the frame.

2. Put a very light coating of powdered sugar on the nylon. The sugar should be barely visible.

3. Cover the nylon. When it rains, take the nylon outdoors to a spot away from trees or buildings.

4. Uncover the nylon for 3 seconds—the time it takes to say "one thousand, two thousand, three thousand." Then cover it.

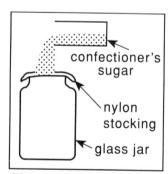

Figure 20–2 Nylon stocking test for raindrops

5. Back in your classroom, count the marks the raindrops left in the sugar coating as they fell through the nylon.

6. Measure and record the diameters of the imprints.

RAINDROP TEST C. COLORED PAPER TEST

In this test, raindrops fall on colored construction paper, leaving permanent marks that are easy to count. But because water spreads when the drops strike, this method cannot be used to measure the diameters of drops.

Materials
• colored construction paper that spots from water drops
• pie pan or stiff paper large enough to cover the colored paper

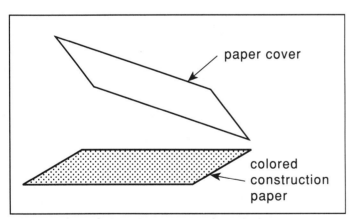

Figure 20–3 Colored paper test for raindrops

Directions

1. Cover the colored construction paper with the pie pan or stiff paper.

2. When it rains, take the covered paper out to a spot away from trees or buildings.

3. Uncover the paper for 3 seconds—the time it takes to say "one thousand, two thousand, three thousand." Then cover it.

4. Back in your classroom, count the splash marks left by the raindrops.

21. THE RAIN WALK

Background

Walking in the rain can be interesting and fun. But remember to dry off thoroughly afterward to avoid catching cold. Keep a raincoat and hat or some old clothes handy to wear for walking the next time it rains hard after school or on a weekend.

Activity

Take a walk in the rain. Report your observations.

Procedure

Here are some things to observe during your rain walk. Read the list carefully **before** you go so that you will remember what to watch for.

1. Smell the air.

2. Stand quietly in the rain, feeling the sky and the earth and the trees and the whole rainy world. How does it differ from the sunny world?

3. Listen to the rain. Does it drum out a rhythm for you?

4. Watch raindrops as they strike the sidewalk or pavement. Can you see the splash? How high and wide is the splash? (Sometimes you can tell from mud marks on building walls how high the raindrops splashed in earlier showers.)

5. When puddles form, can you see the patterns that raindrops make on their surface? Do the patterns change when the wind falls or rises? Do they change when the rain lets up or pours harder?

6. Walk under some trees. Does rain come through the leaves and branches? If so, does it fall through all trees the same way?

   a. Can you see water running down the stems or trunks?

   b. Look under the thick branches of low bushes. Is the ground wet? If so, how did the water get there? If it is dry or only slightly wet, what happened to the water that fell on the top branches?

   c. Look at the leaves on trees and other plants. Do they look different in the rain? Have any leaves folded?

7. If you can see any insects or animals or birds, observe how they behave in the rain.

8. Look for slopes—one with a hard soil or a paved surface, one with a grass cover, and one with overhanging trees or shrubs. Does water run down the slopes and form little streams or *rivulets?*

   a. Is the water in the rivulets clear or muddy? Does the surface of the slope— hard soil or paved surface or grass cover—make a difference in the amount and muddiness of the rivulets? Is the water more or less muddy at the beginning, middle, and end of the rain?

b. After the rain stops, how long does water keep running down the slope? Does the rivulet leave a "fan" of mud where it stops at the bottom of the hill? If some rivulets differ from others, and if some slopes have no rivulets at all, can you see reasons for the differences?

9. If there is a stream or a drainage canal nearby, look at its width, speed, and muddiness. Does it seem different in the rain than it does on a sunny day?

10. If you stroll along a beach, look at the colors of the water and the shapes of the waves near shore and farther out. Do they look different in the rain than they do in sunny weather?

a. What differences do you see in the beach in the rain? Is there a difference in the way the waves lap the sand? Where are the crabs?

b. If you see any birds, observe how they behave in rainy weather.

11. What color is the sky? Does it change during a shower? Can you see the sun? Is there a rainbow?

Summary

1. After you are dry and warm, reread the questions above and write your observations. Perhaps you noticed things not covered by these questions. Write those observations too.

2. Perhaps you would like to write a poem or paint a picture to express the feeling of the rain or the mood it put you into.

3. If you didn't notice some things in the questions, go out in the rain again and complete your notes. You might visit the same places so that you can compare your observations.

22. WATER UNDER THE GROUND

Background

All the water that falls as rain has to go somewhere. Each year the Earth gets about 150 million m³ of rain. About 75% of it falls on the oceans, the rest on land. A third of the rain that falls on land doesn't sink into the ground but runs off through streams and rivers into the oceans within a few weeks. The remaining 24 million m³ of water percolates into the soil. Water that soaks into the soil is called *groundwater*.

Problem

What happens to water under the ground?

Procedure

1. See Figure 22–1. Match the letters and numbers on the figure with the following comments:

   E   Water evaporates from ocean and land, increasing the relative humidity of the air.

   W   Prevailing winds carry the moist air up the slopes of a mountain.

   R   As the moist air rises, it cools. Water vapor condenses to form clouds. The clouds continue to receive moisture from the incoming winds, dropping the excess on the tops and slopes of the mountains. This area, which is usually forested, is called the *watershed area*.

1   Leaves and spongy topsoil in the watershed area hold the water, keeping it from running downhill and letting it soak into the ground.

2   Water percolates through porous soil and rocks, seeping deep into the ground.

3   The water continues to seep through soil and rock until it reaches *nonporous* rock or clay, which it cannot pass through. It begins to fill every available crack and pore of the soil.

4   The water builds up in the soil above the nonporous layer, forming a large underground *reservoir.*

5   The top level of the water reservoir is called the *water table.* The depth of the water table below the surface at any point depends on the conditions of the soil, the slope of the land, and other factors. The depth of the water table also changes during wet and dry seasons.

6   Where the water table meets the ground surface, a *spring* forms. At the surface, water flows freely from the spring, but it may stop flowing if the water table drops during a dry season.

7   Streams carry run-off water down the slopes and eventually return it to the ocean.

8 A hole dug or drilled below the water table fills with water and becomes a *well.* Water can be pumped from the well; if conditions are favorable, it may flow from the well as a result of underground pressure. A free-flowing well is called an *artesian well.*

2. Trace the flow of water from the ocean through the atmosphere and back to the ocean. This recurring flow is called the *water cycle.*

Summary

1. What is the water cycle? What changes of state does water go through during the cycle?

2. What source of energy drives the water cycle?

3. Where does the water in your school come from? The water in your home?

4. Where and how do cities and farms in your area get pure drinking water?

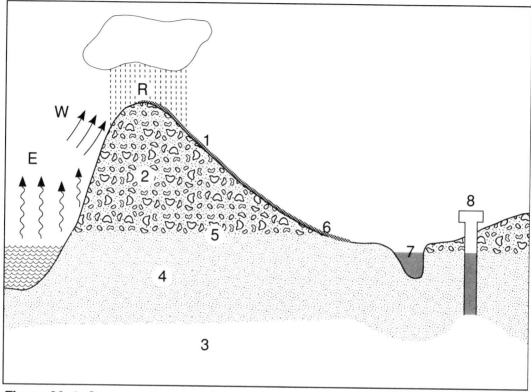

Figure 22–1 Cross-section of land area showing water cycle

Challenge

1. In what ways can water become polluted in the water cycle? How can water pollution be controlled or eliminated?

2. What does your community do to keep drinking water pure?

3. What does your community do to treat sewage?

New Vocabulary for Section E

artesian well   nucleus   water cycle
groundwater   rivulets   water table
nonporous   saturate   watershed area
nucleation   spring   well

Section F. Water Out of Plants

23. PLANTS AND WATER

Background
Plants take in water through their roots. Have you ever wondered what happens to this water? Do plants store it? Do they perspire? Does any water come out through leaves or other parts of a plant?

Problem
Does water come out of plants?

Procedure
1. Devise an experiment to show whether water comes out of plants. In your design include a control, set standards, and provide for replications to ensure that your results are reliable.

2. Carry out your experiment.

Summary
What evidence, if any, did you find that water comes out of plants?

24. THE CASE OF THE LEAKY LEAVES

Background

In this experiment we look at leaf surfaces through a microscope to see whether they have holes too small to see with the unaided eye.

To be seen through a compound microscope, objects must be thin enough for light to pass through. A leaf is too thick. One way to examine a leaf is to make slices thin enough for light to pass through. Another way, the way we will use, is to make a thin, transparent *cast* of the leaf surface and view the cast.

Activity

1. Make a cast of a leaf surface.

2. Examine the cast of the leaf surface under a microscope.

Materials

- compound microscope
- 2 or 3 microscope slides
- 2 or 3 cover slips
- small bottle of clear or pale nail polish
- forceps

Procedure

1. Get a fresh green leaf. The leaf may or may not be attached to a plant.

2. Using clear or pale nail polish, paint a section of the leaf about the size of the blunt end of your pencil. Make a fairly thick coating, not a glob. The polish makes an exact cast of the leaf surface.[1]

nail polish

Figure 24–1 Making a leaf cast

---

[1] Johnson, B. and Brun, W. H. 1965. "Stomate density and responsiveness of banana fruit stomates." *Plant Physiology* 41:99.

3. Let the nail polish dry for about 20 minutes. When it is thoroughly dry, it will peel off easily. If it is rubbery, it is not yet dry enough.

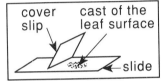

Figure 24–2 Cast on microscope slide

4. Using the tip of the forceps, peel off the cast and put it on a microscope slide.

5. Put a cover slip over the cast.

6. Get directions from your teacher for focusing and using the compound microscope.

7. Put the slide on the microscope stage. Focus under low power; then change to high power. Look for openings in the cast of the leaf surface.

8. Follow the instructions below for measuring and counting the tiny openings in the surface.

Summary

Tiny openings in the surface of leaves are called *stomates.*

1. How do stomates compare in size with other tiny objects? Could water molecules pass through stomates?

2. Draw the shapes of stomates of different kinds of plants in your notebook. If you can, name the plant having each shape of stomate.

3. Predict the environmental conditions associated with closed stomates and with open stomates.

Challenge

Prepare thin slices of a leaf or a peeling of epidermis to view under the microscope. Can you see stomates? What differences, if any, are there between the appearance of stomates in a leaf peeling and a leaf cast?

MEASURING STOMATES

Leaf surfaces have tiny holes called *stomates* (*stomata* in Latin, with stress on the first syllable: *STOmata*). One hole is a *stomate*. Stomates are exceedingly small, visible only under the high power of a compound microscope.

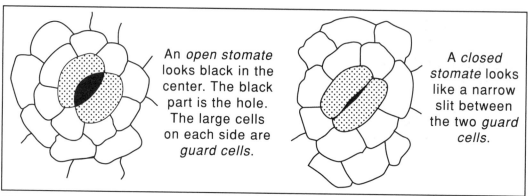

An *open stomate* looks black in the center. The black part is the hole. The large cells on each side are *guard cells*.

A *closed stomate* looks like a narrow slit between the two *guard cells*.

Figure 24–3 Stomates

Are stomates large enough to let water molecules through?

Directions

1. Prepare a cast of a leaf surface showing stomates.

2. Focus on the stomates under the high power of a compound microscope.

3. Without changing the power of the lens (you may adjust the focus), move the slide to one side and insert a single strand of human hair under the lens.

   a. Observe the diameter of the hair.

   b. Move the slide so you can observe the stomates, then the hair, then the stomates again, comparing their sizes.

4. Compare the sizes of the stomates and other tiny items such as a dust particle or the dot made by a sharp pencil.

5. Compare the size of the stomate with the size of a water molecule. Your teacher can give you information on the size of water molecules.

COUNTING STOMATES

Stomates are only a few microns across. A *micron* is one one-thousandth of a millimeter (1/1,000 mm), smaller than a pinpoint, but this opening is enough to let water molecules through. It has been said that a forest puts as many water molecules into the air as a lake does. If that is true, there must be an enormous number of stomates in the leaves of trees.

How many stomates do leaves have on their upper and lower surfaces?

Directions

1. Look at the number of stomates per square centimeter reported for the plants listed in Table 24–4.

Table 24–4 Number of stomates on leaves per cm²

Species	Upper Surface of Leaf	Lower Surface of Leaf
Shower tree (Acacia)	11,200	11,200
Bean	4,000	28,100
Cabbage	14,100	22,600
Corn	5,200	6,800
Geranium	1,900	5,900
Tomato	1,200	13,000
Coleus	0	14,100
Water Lily	46,000	0

2. Get a leaf of one or more of the plants listed in the table. Make a cast of the leaf's upper or lower surface or both. Examine the stomates under the microscope at high power. These will be your standards for comparing "unknowns."

3. Prepare casts of some "unknowns"—leaves of unlisted plants whose stomate count you don't know. You may want to use some of the plants you tested with cobalt chloride. Many plants are unknowns whose stomates have never been counted.

4. Using the same power of the microscope (you may adjust the focus), look at your standard, then at your unknown. Keep looking at each in turn until you can decide how their stomate counts compare. You can use such phrases as "half as many as tomato," "twice as many as corn," or "about the same as corn." Record your observations in your notebook.

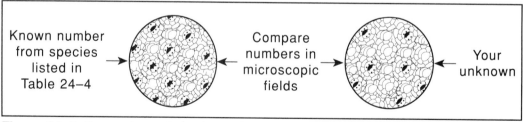

Known number from species listed in Table 24–4 → ← Compare numbers in microscopic fields → ← Your unknown

Figure 24–5 Comparison of numbers of stomates on surfaces of leaves

25. TRANSPIRATION

Background

Plants need huge amounts of water. A single acre of sugarcane needs about 20,000 tons of water a year. An acre of cane weighs about 100 tons. The 100 tons of cane yield about 10 tons of sugar. So it takes about 2,000 pounds (1 ton) of water to make 1 pound of sugar. The mystery is, what happens to the rest of the water? It is not easy to lose 20,000 tons of water!

Sugarcane is not the only plant that needs huge amounts of water to grow. Scientists who investigated 1 acre of corn in Illinois through one growing season reported that the corn took in 2,000 tons of water. Only 5 tons of that water was used within the plants. The rest of the water—1,995 tons—was *transpired.*

Transpiration is the process by which plants release water vapor into the air. The amount of water transpired by trees is so large that a forest puts as much moisture back into the atmosphere as the surface of a lake of about the same size does.

You have done tests showing that water does come out of leaves. Getting a measure of how much water is transpired requires an instrument called a *potometer.* The potometer measures the water that goes into a stem. To demonstrate transpiration, you need a potometer and some cobalt chloride paper.

Experiments have measured the transpiration in different plants. The line of reasoning for such an experiment is this:

1. Potometer measurements show that a given number of plants take in 100 tons of water during their life span.

2. During this time the plants gain 1 ton in mass.

3. So at least 99 tons of water must have passed into and out of the plant during this time.

4. A simple cobalt chloride paper test shows that water comes out from leaf surfaces.

Activity
Use a potometer to investigate transpiration.

Procedure
1. Decide which of these suggested investigations your group or class will do:

   a. Does the *micro-climate* affect transpiration? The micro-climate is the set of conditions surrounding the leaf.

   b. Does transpiration affect the micro-climate?

   c. Do plant stems transpire? Do both top and bottom leaf surfaces transpire? Do flowers transpire?

   d. Do different kinds of plants transpire equally under the same conditions?

   e. Does the area of the leaf surface affect the amount of water transpired? For instructions on measuring surface area, see "Measuring the Area of Irregularly Shaped Objects" on page 275.

f. Does the age or condition of the leaves affect transpiration? Test some of the following:

young leaves
dusty leaves
old leaves
wet leaves
wilted leaves
dead leaves
colored leaves
single leaves detached from stem
stems and leaves freshly picked
stems and leaves picked the day before

2. Decide how many tests to do, what controls to use, and what conditions to set for getting your data.

3. Read the descriptions of potometers on the following pages. Study each device and choose the one that is best for your experiment. You may also design your own device.

Summary
Make an oral report on your investigation. Follow the procedure and format in "Oral Scientific Reports" on page 177.

PREPARING PLANTS FOR A POTOMETER

In plant stems, water moves through tubes in the *cambium layer*. See Figure 25–1, parts a. and b. Water in the tubes is under tension, like a stretched rubber band. When you cut a stem, the water "jumps" back into the tube, leaving an air space or *air lock* in the water column near the cut. See Figure 25–1, part c.

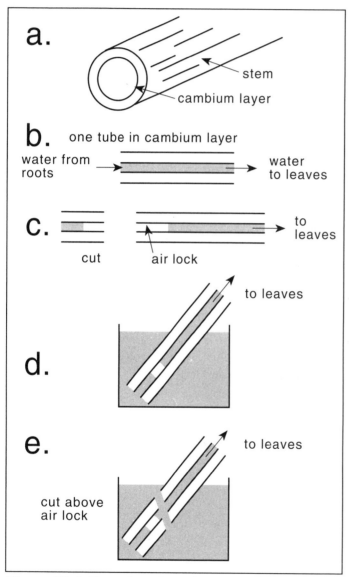

Figure 25–1 Preparing plants for potometers

Air locks prevent water from passing to leaves. When you put the end of an air-locked stem in water, water will enter, but the air acts as a plug. See Figure 25–1, part d.

You can prevent air locks by keeping the entire stem under water while you cut it. The water in the stem will form a continuous column traveling up the stem quickly and smoothly. Doing this when you arrange cut flowers will make them last longer.

Make the new cut on a slant to make a larger opening for water to enter the plant stem. See Figure 25–1, part e.

MEASURING THE AREA OF IRREGULARLY SHAPED OBJECTS

To estimate the area of a leaf, trace your leaf as shown in Figure 25–2. Then follow the steps below. Refer to Toolsheet 3, Introduction to Graphing, and Toolsheet 5, Metric Area Measurement, in Appendix 1 for more information on using a metric area grid.

Sample Calculation
Calculate the area of your leaf by counting the squares it covers on a metric area grid.

1. Number of cm² covered by leaf   33 ×   1   = 33.0

2. Number of half cm² covered by leaf   8 × $^1/_2$ =   4.0

3. Number of quarter cm² covered by leaf   10 × $^1/_4$ =   2.5

4. Number of three-quarter cm² covered by leaf 6 × $^3/_4$ =   4.5

5. Total cm² of leaf area   44.0

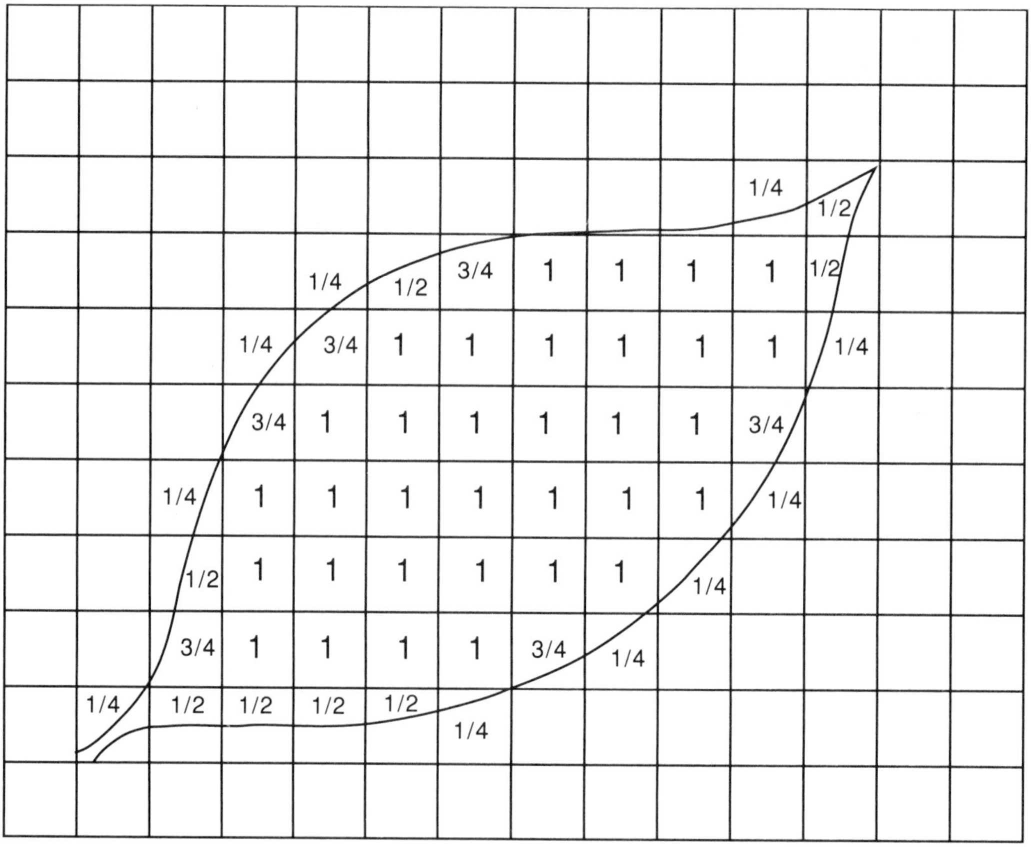

Figure 25–2 Estimating area with a metric grid

DEVICE A. COMMERCIAL-MODEL POTOMETER

Follow these instructions for setting up a potometer with valves and parts modeled after a commercial potometer.

Materials
- beaker or jar
- medicine dropper
- rubber tubing to connect parts
- capillary tube
- T-tube
- clamp
- funnel
- thistle tube or syringe barrel
- one-hole stopper to fit thistle tube to syringe barrel
- watch or clock
- plant

Construction

1. Assemble the apparatus as shown in Figure 25–3. Make sure all connections are leakproof, especially around the plant stem and the one-hole stopper.

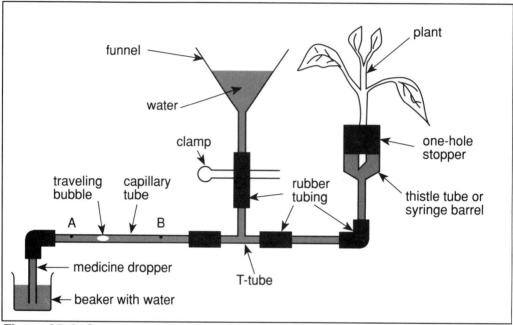

Figure 25–3 Commercial-model potometer

a. Make sure the stem of the plant is completely covered with water and all openings are sealed so that the only way water can get out of the potometer is through the plant's stem. See Figure 25–1.

b. The traveling bubble measures how fast water goes through the stem.

2. Fill the entire system with water. To make sure there are no visible air bubbles, assemble the apparatus under water.

Using a Commercial-Model Potometer

1. As the plant begins to transpire, water will flow through the capillary tube toward the plant, drawing water from the beaker. Lift the medicine dropper out of the water in the beaker for a moment and shake off a drop of water to put an air bubble into the dropper.

2. Return the dropper to the beaker of water. As the plant transpires, the air bubble will move through the capillary tube toward the plant.

3. Note the time when the air bubble enters the capillary tube at point A. Time its trip to point B.

4. As soon as the bubble reaches point B, open the clamp slightly to let more water into the system and drive the bubble back to point A.

5. You can move the apparatus to different places—in sunlight, in shade, in still air, in wind—and time the movement of the air bubble to get a rapid comparison of the rate of transpiration under each condition.

DEVICE B. SYRINGE POTOMETER

Materials
- ring stand
- clamp
- syringe barrel
- rubber tubing
- motor oil
- plant
- watch or clock

Construction
1. Assemble the apparatus in style 1 or style 2 as shown in Figure 25–4. Assemble the parts under water to prevent an air lock in the system.

2. Make sure all connections are leakproof, especially those around the plant stem.

3. Put a thin layer of motor oil on the water in the syringe barrel to prevent water evaporation.

Using a Syringe Potometer
1. Note and record the water level in the syringe barrel at the start. Note and record the time at the start.

2. Measure the amount of transpiration by recording the number of milliliters of water lost from the syringe barrel.

3. Leave the equipment set up for 24 hours or more. Record the total time of the experiment. Calculate the amount of water transpired in an hour.

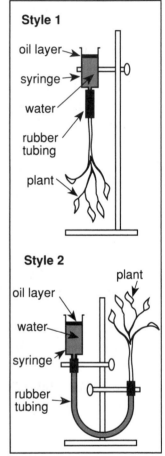

Figure 25–4 Syringe potometers

4. When the water level gets low, refill the syringe barrel. Be sure to keep the cut end of the plant under water.

5. You can move the apparatus to other places and measure the amount of transpiration under differing conditions—in sunlight, in shade, in still air, in wind.

DEVICE C. GRADUATED-CYLINDER POTOMETER

This is the only design that lets you test a plant with roots. But you can also use it with a cut stem.

Materials
- graduated cylinder
- one-hole stopper to fit the graduated cylinder
- motor oil
- plant
- watch or clock

Construction
1. Assemble the equipment as shown in Figure 25–5. To support the stem of the plant, split a one-hole stopper down one side. Put the plant in the hole and hold it in place with tape or a rubber band. Or make a stopper out of cotton.

2. Put the plant root or stem in the water in the graduated cylinder.

3. Put a thin layer of motor oil on the water in the graduated cylinder to prevent evaporation.

Using a Graduated-Cylinder Potometer
1. As water is taken in by the plant, the water level in the cylinder drops. Read the water level in the cylinder. Measure the amount of transpiration by subtracting the reading at the end of your test from the reading at the start of your test. Time the water loss. Calculate the amount of water lost per hour.

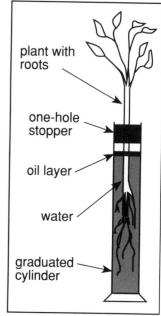

Figure 25–5
Graduated-cylinder potometer

plant with roots

one-hole stopper

oil layer

water

graduated cylinder

2. You can move the apparatus to other places and measure the amount of transpiration under differing conditions—in sunlight, in shade, in still air, in wind.

DEVICE D. FLASK POTOMETER

Materials
- Erlenmeyer flask with side arm
- two-hole stopper to fit the Erlenmeyer flask
- small beaker or jar
- capillary pipette
- two 6-cm lengths of glass tubing
- 2 syringes
- one-hole stopper to fit the syringe
- watch or clock

Construction
1. Assemble the apparatus as shown in Figure 25–6. Make sure all connections are leakproof, especially around the plant stem and the one-hole stopper.

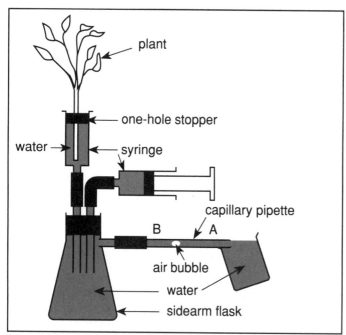

Figure 25–6 Flask potometer

a. Make sure the stem of the plant is completely covered with water and all openings are sealed so that the only way water can get out of the potometer is through the plant's stem. See Figure 25–1.

b. The traveling bubble measures the rate of transpiration. The syringe measures the water that flows through the stem.

2. Fill the entire system with water. To make sure there are no visible air bubbles, assemble the whole apparatus under water.

Using a Flask Potometer

1. As the plant begins to transpire, water will flow through the capillary pipette toward the plant, drawing water from the beaker. Lift the pipette out of the water in the beaker a moment and shake off a drop of water to put an air bubble into the pipette.

2. Return the pipette to the beaker of water. As the plant transpires, the air bubble will move through the capillary pipette.

3. Note the time when the air bubble enters the pipette at point A. Time its trip to point B.

4. As soon as the bubble reaches point B, press the syringe plunger to force more water into the system and drive the bubble back to point A. The amount of water added to the system from the syringe is the measure of water transpired.

5. You can move the apparatus to different places—in sunlight, in shade, in still air, in wind—and time the movement of the air bubble to get a rapid comparison of the rate of transpiration under each condition.

DEVICE E. COLD-WATER POTOMETER

The cold-water potometer is sometimes used to measure water coming out of leaves.

Materials
- beaker
- 2 rubber bands
- dish or pan
- leaf

Construction
1. Set up the apparatus as shown in Figure 25–7.

   a. Fill the beaker with ice water.

   b. Using two rubber bands, secure a leaf to the outside of the beaker so that the tip and about half of the leaf are in close contact with the beaker but the stem and other half of the leaf stand free of the beaker.

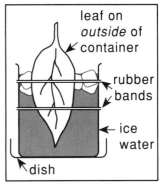

Figure 25–7 Cold-water potometer

2. Let the apparatus stand for a few minutes. Observe water droplets forming and record your observations.

Using a Cold-Water Potometer
1. Water transpired from the leaf will fall into the dish. Empty the water from the dish into a graduated cylinder to measure the amount of water transpired.

2. You can move the apparatus to other places and measure the amount of transpiration under differing conditions—in sunlight, in shade, in still air, in wind.

New Vocabulary for Section F

acid

base

cambium layer

cobalt chloride paper

epidermis

guard cells

indicator

leaf cast

litmus

micro-climate

micron

potometer

stomate

transpiration

UNIT 3. ANIMAL CARE

26. CARE OF AN ANIMAL IN THE LABORATORY

Background

Ecology is the science that studies the interactions of plants, animals, and the physical environment. In Unit 1 we worked with plants. In Unit 2 we studied the physical environment.

In this unit we will study animals. To learn how to best care for them, we will study these topics:

1. The normal behavior of animals

2. The relationships among animals, plants, and the environment

3. The relationship of animals to humans

Activity

Take care of an animal in the laboratory for several weeks or through one life cycle.

Procedure

1. Choose an animal you think you would like to care for from the class study area or from the list your teacher gives you.

2. Consult books, read last year's animal reports, or ask friends and neighbors what kind of cage or tank your animal should have. Find out what it eats and what else it needs to keep it alive and healthy. Refer to the reference booklet "Animal Care" for basic information on types of animals, their food and water needs, and the construction of cages for them.

3. Make a chart showing your animal's food and cage needs. Prepare observation sheets with blanks for writing dates and recording your observations. Put the chart in a sturdy folder and keep it near the cage so that others can consult it to find out what to do for your animal if you are absent.

4. Prepare the cage or tank and get the food and water ready for the first day.

NOTE: Do not go on to procedure 5 until you have completed procedures 1, 2, 3, and 4.

5. Obtain your animal.

6. Care for your animal.

    a.   Check on your animal every day. Replenish its food and water and keep its cage clean.

    b.   As often as you can, spend time watching your animal. If you can, play with it. Laboratory animals that are handled gently and frequently, especially when they are young, usually become tame and easy to work with.

7. Keep dated notes on everything you observe. Make the following observations about your animal:

    a.   Its *life cycle*

        1)   How it is born or hatched
        2)   How fast it grows

3) How it changes in shape, color, size, and so on as it grows
4) How long it takes to become an adult
5) How long it takes to reproduce and how many offspring it has

b. Its life requirements

1) Its food and water requirements
2) The *habitat* (kind of place) it normally lives in
3) The kind of nest, shelter, or hiding place it likes
4) Its preferred temperature
5) The amount of light, air, and space it needs

c. Its ecological *niche*

1) What it feeds on and what feeds on it
2) What other animals eat the same things it does
3) How many different animals eat the animal
4) What *parasites* and *disease germs* the animal may get
5) What effect the animal has on the area it lives in

d. Its behavior

1) What it does when it is alone
2) What it does when it is with other animals of the same species
3) What it does when an animal of the same kind but the opposite sex is near

4) What it does when it is hungry,
       thirsty, content, in danger, or in pain
    5) Whether it can learn, and if it can,
       how much and how fast

e. Its relationship to humans

    1) How it relates to people
    2) Whether it lives as a pet, is raised for
       food, or lives by scavenging, and so
       on
    3) Whether it is dangerous
    4) How humans should act toward it

Summary

Make a report on your animal, oral or written or both, as your teacher directs. Follow the procedure and format explained in "Oral Scientific Reports" and "Written Scientific Reports" on pages 177-184.

New Vocabulary for Unit 3

disease germs	interdependence	parasites
habitat	life cycle	scavenger
interaction	niche	species

UNIT 4. FIELD ECOLOGY

Section A. Field Survey

27. THE INITIAL SURVEY

Background

Ecological relationships are the ways that things in an environment interact with each other. There is no way to study all the ecological relationships of the entire world, or even a single island, so we select small parts of the environment and specific relationships to study. The area we will study we call the class study area (CSA).

Before doing measurements and observations in our study area, we must get acquainted with it by learning its general characteristics and main features.

Activity

Make an initial survey and sketch of the class study area.

Materials (per team)

- 10-m length of string
- note pads and pencils
- large sheet of blank paper

Procedure

1. Before making the initial survey, learn how to pace distances in meters. Work in teams.

   a. Stretch out 10 meters of string in a straight line on the lawn or sidewalk. Mark the two ends of the 10-meter distance.

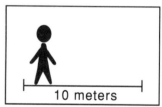

Figure 27–1 Learning to pace distance

   b. Count the normal-sized paces you use to walk 10 meters. Repeat three times.

c. Find the average number of paces you use to walk 10 meters. Each of you must determine your own pace.

d. Calculate how many centimeters there are in one of your normal paces.

2. Make a graph for converting paces into meters. Use the vertical axis for the number of meters, the horizontal axis for the number of paces.

   a. Find the intersect of 10 meters and the average number of paces it took you to walk 10 meters. For example, the graph in Figure 27–2 shows that it took someone 14 paces to walk 10 meters.

   b. Draw a line from the origin (0) through this intersect.

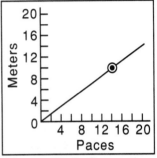

Figure 27–2 Converting paces into meters

   c. By interpolation or extrapolation you can now convert any number of paces into meters by reading the graph. For example, we can see from the graph that it takes 8 paces to walk 6 meters.

3. For the initial survey, form five groups as shown in Table 27–3.

Table 27–3 Groups and assignments for initial survey of CSA

Group Name	Number of Students	Chief Job
Boundary group	3–8	Outline area on map
Plant group	4–8	Survey plants
Animal group	4–8	Survey animals
Physical environment group	4–8	Note features of physical environment
Human factors group	4–8	Note influence of humans on area

4. Survey the class study area (CSA) by following the directions for your group on the following pages.

Summary

1. When you finish the initial survey, post your maps and your lists of observations on the bulletin board. Use them to guide your decisions about where and what to measure.

2. Discuss the general characteristics and important features of the CSA. Which characteristics and features have the greatest influence on the ecology of the area? Suggest ways that objects in the CSA might affect its ecology.

GROUP ASSIGNMENTS FOR THE INITIAL SURVEY

Group A. Boundary

1. Pace off the boundaries of the study area.

2. Draw the outline of the area on a large sheet of paper and sketch in the major features. You do not need exact measurements.

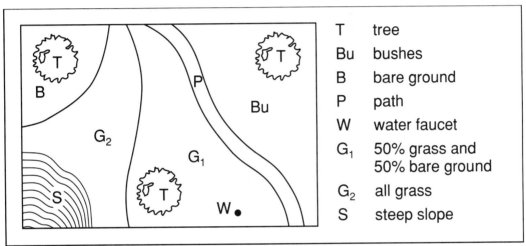

Figure 27–4 Sample map prepared by boundary group

Group B. Plants

1. Look at the types of vegetation in the class study area.

2. Pace off the distances between trees and mark their locations on the map prepared by the boundary group. See Figure 27–4.

3. On the map sketch these features:

   a.   Hedges, bushes, and other vegetation

b.   Grassy and weedy areas

    c.   Areas of bare ground or pavement

4. Take notes on any special vegetation you think might make a good subject for later study.

Group C. Animals

1. Look for animals or evidence of animals in the class study area.

2. List your observations of the following:

    a.   Animals or insects you see

    b.   Bird nests, insect nests, ant hills, spider webs, and homes of other animals

    c.   Droppings from lizards, cockroaches, toads, and other animals

    d.   Any other evidence of animal life

3. Mark the locations of your observations on the map prepared by the boundary group.

Group D. Physical Environment

1. Observe the physical environment, including these features:

    a.   Terrain (level, sloping, hills, bumps, holes)

    b.   Soil (sandy, rocky, muddy, dusty, soft, hard, wet, dry)

c. Sunlight (sunny, light shade, heavy shade, rough proportion of the area in shade)

d. Open water (pond, stream, drainage ditch, and so on)

e. Other prominent objects

2. Mark the locations of these features on the map prepared by the boundary group.

Group E. Human Factors

1. Look for evidence of human effects on the class study area.

2. List your observations of the following:

a. Buildings (location, estimated height, possible effect on wind and shade)

b. Paved areas (roads, sidewalks, playing courts, parking places)

c. Litter (paper, bottles, cans)

d. Things built or installed by humans (bridges, fences, water pipes, and so on)

3. Mark the locations of your observations on the map prepared by the boundary group.

28. ECOLOGICAL CHANGES IN A SMALL AREA

Background

Two important characteristics of life are change and growth. All living things change, but their rates of change differ. The physical environment also changes. An insect moves noticeably within milliseconds. The sun and shadows move noticeably within an hour. A spider spins a web in a day; flowers bloom and die within a week; streams rise and fall with the seasons; trees and people grow in years; soil and rocks erode in centuries.

To watch changes, select a small part of the class study area for intense study. Select a small patch of vegetation, an insect's nesting site, or something else that is likely to change within the school year. A small patch of ground selected for study is called a *quadrat*. See the reference booklet "Sampling Methods" to learn about quadrats.

Activity

1. Make an inventory of a quadrat in your class study area.

2. After several weeks or months, make a second inventory of the same quadrat.

3. Report on the changes in the ecology of that quadrat.

Materials

- small quadrat frame (see the reference booklet "Sampling Methods")
- notebook

Procedure

1. First inventory

   a. Work in pairs. One person measures and the other records.

   b. Make a quadrat frame according to the directions in the reference booklet

"Sampling Methods." The quadrat may be anywhere in the class study area. The size depends on the size of the things studied. For a study of tiny plants use a quadrat 10 cm on a side. For weeds or grasses use a quadrat 20 to 40 cm on a side. Place your frame over your quadrat.

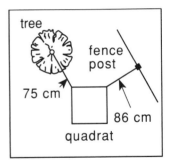

Figure 28–1 Diagraming the location of a quadrat

c. In your notebook, diagram the exact location of your quadrat so that you can find it later. Measure from at least two **permanent** landmarks.

d. Make a careful inventory of the quadrat. Measure and count everything you see. (A camera would help.) Include the following in your inventory:

1) Types and numbers of plants
2) Shapes and numbers of leaves and/ or branches
3) Estimated weights of plants
4) Colors, flowers, buds, and seeds
5) Percentage of bare ground
6) Quality of the soil and objects found on its surface
7) Insects, other animals, or evidence of their presence
8) Any other features you observe

e. Record all the data you collect.

f. Keep your notebook and quadrat frame in a safe place. You will need them for another inventory in a few weeks or months.

2. Second inventory

A good time for the second inventory is after a period of change in weather, such as heavy rain or a long drought.

a. Find your quadrat by using the landmarks and measurements you wrote in your notebook. Place your frame over the same spot.

b. Repeat the observations in procedure l.d. If something new has appeared, add it to the list.

c. Decide on a good time to do a third inventory of your quadrat. Do the inventory when the times comes.

Summary

1. Compare the observations of the first inventory with the observations of the second and third inventories.

a. How have the plants changed? How much? Have any died?

b. Have insects, other animals, or their nests changed? How?

c. Has the soil surface changed? How?

d. What else changed?

2. What may have caused the changes during the periods between the three inventories?

3. Compare inventories with students in nearby quadrats. How are the results similar? How are they different?

4. How do changes in your quadrat reflect general changes in the area?

29. THE PHYSICAL ENVIRONMENT OF THE CLASS STUDY AREA

Background
The physical environment is essential to all living things. Conditions there control the survival and affect the success of all organisms.

Activity
Describe the physical environment in and around the class study area.

Procedure
1. Study the physical environment of the class study area (CSA). Describe physical features that could affect organisms living there. Include these features:

   a. Terrain (level, sloping, hills, bumps, holes)

   b. Soil (see Unit 2, The Physical Environment, for soil tests)

   c. Sun and shade (amount of each at different times of day)

   d. Open water (pond, stream, drainage ditch, and so on)

   e. Weather (see the data from the weather station in the CSA)

   f. Physical barriers (fences, buildings, hedges, trees)

2. Record your description of each feature on a card. Add the cards to your bulletin board next to the map of the CSA.

30. MAPPING THE CLASS STUDY AREA

Background
Using a small quadrat lets you observe and measure changes over a span of time.

Ecologists must often study large areas to observe populations and examine their interrelationships. The first steps in a detailed study of the ecology of an area are mapping it and identifying its physical features and populations.

Activity
1. Make a scaled map of your class study area.

2. Make a detailed inventory of the living organisms in the area.

Procedure
1. Refer to the reference booklet "Field Mapping." Two plans for mapping are described. Look at your initial survey map to see which plan is better for your class study area (CSA).

2. Map the CSA according to the plan you choose.

Summary
Post your map on the bulletin board. Mount the cards with sketches of the plants and animals next to the map. This map will be your reference for later investigations.

New Vocabulary for Section A
contour lines	interaction	organisms
ecologists	interdependence	pace
elevation	interrelationships	quadrat
ground cover	inventory	scale
		survey

Section B. Sampling Techniques

31. METHODS OF SAMPLING POPULATIONS

Background

Your observations of plants and animals in your class study area so far have been *qualitative;* that is, you have described the kinds of plants and animals that are in the area. You have not yet made *quantitative* measurements; that is, counts of each kind of organism in the class study area.

Organisms of a particular kind living in a given area are called a *population.* To study the ecology of an area, scientists must know the size of populations of organisms living there. Counts of organisms can show whether a population is increasing or decreasing, whether a new species has moved in, or whether an old one is dying.

The size of a population shows something about its success as a species in that location. The population size also affects other species and the physical environment itself. For example, it makes a difference in all the relationships in an area whether there are two trees or fifty trees, whether there are two grasshoppers or half a million grasshoppers.

One way to find out how many organisms of each kind live in an area is to count them one by one. Can you imagine counting every ant on your CSA one at a time? There must be an easier way.

Can you think of ways to find the size of the following "populations" without counting each member one by one or asking someone?

1. The number of leaves on a tree

2. The number of hamburgers eaten at the corner drive-in during the school year

3. The number of birds living on your campus and the number of birds that visit the campus but nest elsewhere

4. The number of ants on your campus

For estimating the size of those "populations," you may have decided that you need more than one method because the method you use depends on the kind of population.

Scientists have had the same difficulty in finding ways to estimate population sizes. They have devised methods of sampling them—that is, estimating the size of a population by counting a small portion or sample of it. A list of some of the methods of sampling is shown in Table 31–1. You may have already thought of a number of these same ideas yourself.

Table 31–1 Methods of sampling populations

Type of Population to be Counted	Tools and Techniques Used	Example
Population of sparse or rare species	Count the individuals	Rare birds Trees having more than 1 meter diameter
Fairly evenly distributed population	Random sampling using quadrats or nets	Weeds in a lawn Mosquitoes in a swamp
Clumped, unevenly distributed population	Quadrats, traps, nets used in the population areas	Schools of tuna fish Ant hills Morning glory
Populations of rapidly moving organisms	Traps, pits, nets, tags, bird bank, fur marks, capture-recapture, visual counts	Flying insects Birds Other animals
Two or more overlapping populations in a transition area	Transect	Intertidal area Weedy area between a garden and a pasture

Activity

Using scientific sampling methods, determine the size of populations of organisms in the class study area.

Procedure

1. Select one or two populations in the class study area to sample.

2. Read about sampling tools and techniques in the reference booklet "Sampling Methods."

3. Select the tools or techniques that seem best. Determine the size of each population you have chosen.

4. Prepare the tools you need to sample each population. The reference booklet "Sampling Methods" describes some standard tools and ways to use them.

5. Learn how to determine *density* and *frequency* of populations from your teacher.

Summary

Write the information about each population on a card. Add the cards to your bulletin board next to the map of the class study area (CSA).

New Vocabulary for Section B

clumped population
cover
density
frequency

population density
population frequency
qualitative

quantitative
sample
sampling

32. THE ECOLOGY OF THE CLASS STUDY AREA

Background
Ecology is the study of the interactions among plants and animals and the physical environment. Every population affects and is affected by other populations and by the physical environment in which they all live. Nothing can exist by itself.

Some time ago you made a map of your class study area. Since then you have learned techniques of sampling and of using sampling tools. Now you are ready to identify some of the ecological interactions in your area and identify the populations that interact.

Activity
1. Look for interactions in your class study area among plants, animals, and the physical environment.

2. Identify the populations that interact.

3. Investigate the interactions you identify.

Procedure
1. Using the map and inventory cards as guides, look for interactions in your class study area. You might investigate questions such as these:

   a. Observation: Are some populations of plants or animals clumped?

   Possible investigation: Why are they clumped? Are there special physical or biological conditions where they are found?

b. Observation: Do some populations of plants and/or animals seem to stay together?

Possible investigation: Is there a relationship between them? Does one eat the other? Does one benefit from the other? Does one harm the other?

c. Observation: Are there moving populations in your area?

Possible investigation: How mobile are they? Is your area their home? Their feeding ground? Why are they in your area at all?

d. Observation: Is there evidence of human influence?

Possible investigation: What are the influences? How are population types, densities, and frequencies affected by human pressures?

3. Read Examples A, B, and C of class study areas on the following pages. Reading about other areas may help you recognize and think about interactions in your own area.

4. Plan your investigation.

a. Background: Write why you chose your investigation and what you expect to accomplish.

b. Problem: Write a clear statement of the problem or problems you will investigate.

c. Populations and sampling techniques: After you read up on sampling methods, select the best sampling techniques and tools for determining the size of the populations you will study. Describe the techniques.

d. Materials: List the tools you need for your investigation.

e. Procedure: Write the steps you will follow in your investigation.

4. Investigate the ecological interactions you have chosen.

5. Prepare a report using the form in Table 32–1.

Summary

ʔ1. Hold a class seminar to discuss the interactions and the meaning of the data that have been collected. You may wish to use the oral scientific report format for this seminar.

ʔ2. Prepare a written report. Use the format for written scientific reports. File your report for future classes in your school to use.

Table 32–1 Example of a class study area report form

THE ECOLOGY OF _____ CLASS STUDY AREA
 (location)

_____ ,19 , _____ SCHOOL
 (month)   (name)

<u>Background</u>

<u>Problem</u>

<u>Populations Involved and Sampling Techniques to be Used</u>

<u>Materials</u>

<u>Procedure</u>

<u>Results and Conclusion</u>

EXAMPLES OF CLASS STUDY AREAS

Example A. Wikiwiki School

At Wikiwiki School grass was widely distributed in the class study area. It grew to different heights and thicknesses in different places. There was no grass at all under some trees, but under two kiawe trees it grew taller and thicker than in any other place.

The class decided to study the interaction of the environment and the grass. The students did quadrat sampling of the grass and measured its coverage and height in relation to many features of the physical environment, other organisms, and even human trampling.

Example B. Kulawaena Intermediate School

At Kulawaena Intermediate School the class study area had a hedge that was badly eaten by insects. The students didn't know which insects were eating the hedge, whether they ate other things, whether several kinds of insects were eating the hedge, whether they lived in the hedge or came there only to eat, or whether it was a large population of insects or just a small population with a big appetite.

One group decided to investigate the problem. The group divided the work of collecting the insects, trying to raise them on different foods, and finding their range in the neighborhood. They measured the amount of leaf one insect ate in one day or one night, and they explored what enemy ate that insect. They made population counts of the insect and its enemies.

Example C. Koolau Academy

In the class study area at Koolau Academy there were many shells of tiny garden snails in the surface litter, but the students never noticed any live snails.

One group in the class investigated snails, using an animal-collecting funnel and capture-recapture trapping. They found where live snails lived, how many there were, what environmental conditions they preferred, whether they harmed the environment, what they ate, and what time of day they were active.

New Vocabulary for Section C

ecology
interaction
interdependence
relationship

UNIT 1. AIR POLLUTION

1. EVIDENCE OF AIR POLLUTION IN THE COMMUNITY

Background

In the Ecology strand of this course we investigated the interactions of plants and animals with their immediate environment. In the Physical Science strand we investigated properties of matter and changes of state in matter.

In this strand you use your knowledge of the environment and of the properties of matter to study a community issue: the pollution of the atmosphere.

To investigate such a huge problem, we must not only extend our scientific knowledge but also identify and discuss social, political, economic, and technological aspects of this human-created problem. We must examine the issue from the perspectives of many people—scientists, politicians, economists, technologists, and, most important, good citizens.

How clean is the air you breathe? Is the air polluted where you live? How does air quality in your community stack up with air quality in other communities?

We begin to study air pollution by seeking answers to some of these questions.

Figure 1–1 Possible sources of air pollution

Problem

What evidence of air pollution, if any, can you find in your community?

Materials

- Ringelmann Smoke Chart
- map of your area
- data from pollution-detecting devices in your weather stations

Procedure

1. List evidences of air pollution that you have
   noticed in your community.

2. During the next few days locate sources of smoke in your community. A *source* is a starting place. In air pollution studies it refers to anything that releases pollutants into the air. Add the sources you find to your class list.

3. Measure the pollution from sources in your community.

   a. Get a copy of the Ringelmann Smoke Chart.

   b. Read the reference booklet "Air Pollution" for directions on how to use the chart and record smoke observation data.

   c. Carry the Ringelmann Smoke Chart with you. Make and record observations whenever you see smoke.

4. Prepare a class *Air Pollution Source Map* of your community.

   a. Get a map of your community.

   b. Record on the map the location of each source you have seen emitting pollutants into the air. *Emitting* means releasing. *Emissions* are the substances released from sources. Devise symbols to represent the kinds of sources you find in your community.

   c. Record Ringelmann Smoke Chart measurements on your map.

5. Refer to the weather maps the class prepared in Ecology Investigation 18, Weather Maps.

a. Find the data and maps displaying the data from the pollution-measuring devices used in the weather stations. Include data from your dustfall jar, sticky-tape can, gases in the air, pH of rain water, and observations of the atmosphere.

b. Check the maps to be sure they show the location of each weather station and the amount of pollution measured there. These maps will be called *Air Pollution Measurement Maps.*

c. If you have not already done so, draw the isograms on each Air Pollution Measurement Map.

Summary

1. What evidence of air pollution did you find in your community?

2. Compare the Air Pollution Source Map with the Air Pollution Measurement Maps. Does there seem to be any relationship between the locations of the sources and the amounts of air pollution you measured? If so, describe the relationship. If not, describe the differences between the maps.

3. How polluted is the air?

a. What is the highest Ringelmann Smoke Chart measurement recorded by members of the class? The lowest measurement?

b. Prepare a bar graph showing how many times each Ringelmann Smoke Chart grid was reported by members of the class.

c. What information do you need to further investigate how polluted the air is?

14. Review your measurements, using the Ringelmann Smoke Chart.

    a. What does it measure? What does it not measure? What does "visible emissions" mean?

    b. What kinds of problems did you have in using the chart to make measurements?

    c. Why can only trained inspectors submit Ringelmann data as legal evidence of violations?

Challenge

1. Predict which air pollutants are the most common and possibly the most dangerous in your community.

2. Prepare a presentation with slides, photos, or drawings showing evidences of air pollution in your community.

3. Start a file of articles about air pollution in your community. Clip and post the daily Air Pollution Index from your local newspaper.

4. Coordinate a study of air pollution with another class or a nearby school. Combine your data on air pollution and prepare a series of air pollution maps.

5. Coordinate a study of air pollution with a school in another community. Compare data on air pollution over the same span of time.

6. Compare your study of air pollution in your community with studies done in previous years. What changes, if any, do you find? How do you account for any changes?

2. AIR POLLUTANTS

Background
Air pollutants include hundreds of substances released into the atmosphere. Major air pollutants are the ones that are most common and most abundant in *ambient air*—the air that surrounds us outdoors.

Problem
1. What are the major air pollutants?

2. What are the properties of the major air pollutants?

Procedure
1. Using library references, find and record names and descriptions of the major air pollutants. For each one include the following:

   a. Its name and chemical formula

   b. Its physical properties

   c. Its source—where it comes from and what causes its release into the air

   d. The damage it can cause to plants, people, other animals, and nonliving things

2. Record the title, author, and publication date of each reference you use.

Summary
⸮1. What is an air pollutant?

12. Which are the major pollutants? What are their sources?

13. Identify the major air pollutants and these properties of each one:

    a. Visibility

    b. Odor

    c. Solubility in water

    d. Density in relation to air

14. What kind of danger do air pollutants present to these groups?

    a. Humans

    b. Other animals

    c. Plants

    d. Nonliving things in the environment

3. EFFECTS OF AIR POLLUTANTS

Background

An air pollutant can damage property and harm plants, people, and other animals. The *effects* of a pollutant are the changes that exposure causes in living and nonliving things. *Acute damage* comes from short-term exposure, often to high concentrations of pollutants; *chronic damage* comes from prolonged exposure, often to low concentrations of pollutants.

The damaging effects of air pollutants on plants can be determined by exposing test plants to pollutants in *environmental chambers*—containers in which the environment can be controlled and measured. Determining the effect of a substance on an organism or an object is called *effects sampling*.

Figure 3–1 shows two environmental chambers. One is for testing effects of *volatile liquid pollutants*. Volatile liquids produce vapors by evaporation at room temperature. The other chamber is for testing effects of gaseous pollutants.

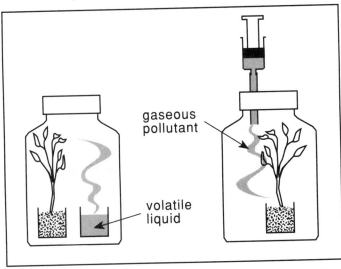

Figure 3–1 Environmental chambers made from gallon glass jars

Problem
What are the effects of air pollutants on plants?

Procedure
1. Refer to the reference booklet "Air Pollution." Read the parts about effects sampling.

2. Design an experiment to test the effects of one air pollutant on one type of plant. In your design consider the following:

   a. The kind and concentration of pollutant to use

   b. The kind and number of plants to use

   c. The standards and controls to use

3. Have your teacher approve your design before you start your test.

4. Carry out your test. Record your observations every day.

Summary
1. Explain the design of your experiment. Describe the standards and controls you used.

2. How do the test plants compare with the control plants?

   a. What effects did putting plants in a closed chamber without a pollutant have on them?

   b. What signs, if any, did the experimental plants show of damage caused by exposure to the pollutant?

3. How can you be sure the effects you observed were caused by the pollutant? What else might have caused them?

14. Which concentrations of pollutants were too low to have quick and noticeable effects on the plants? What kinds of less visible damage might these low concentrations have caused?

15. How valid is this kind of experiment? How do the concentrations of pollutants in ambient air compare with the concentrations you used in your experiment?

Challenge

1. Find out how much damage air pollution does to crops in the United States each year. Which crops have been damaged most? What does this damage cost in lost food yields? In dollars?

2. Air pollution also harms people. Consult references to learn about one or more of the pollution *episodes* listed below. Plan a dramatization or other kind of presentation of the events.

   a. Meuse Valle, Belgium (December 1930)

   b. Donora, Pennsylvania (October 1948)

   c. London, England (December 1952)

   d. New York, New York (1953)

3. If a farmer asked you for help in finding out whether air pollution was stunting plant growth and reducing crop yields, what would you do? What would you recommend to reduce the damage?

4. A COMMUNITY POLLUTION INVENTORY

Background

People who work at reducing pollution need to know what substances are being released and in what quantities. One way to find out is to prepare an *air pollution emission inventory*—a study of pollutants released from all sources within a given area during a certain period.

An inventory may be prepared for a nation, a state, or a community. The information may be presented in tables, graphs, or maps and charts. Table 4–1 uses a bar graph to display changes in air pollution emissions over a 10-year period.

Table 4–1 Comparison of 1970 and 1988 emissions (EPA, 1988)

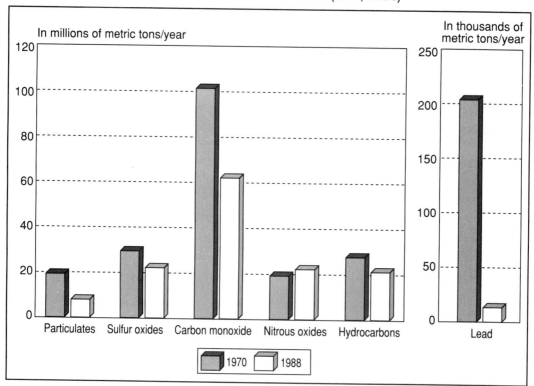

Activity
Prepare a partial air pollution emission inventory for your community.

Procedure
1. Get pollution inventory data for your state from the regional office of the Environmental Protection Agency, the American Lung Association, the state agency responsible for air quality, or an environmental group. Record the information in your notebook in a pie graph like Table 4–2.

Table 4–2 Air pollution emissions for the state of _____ , 19__
(total mass _____ tons)

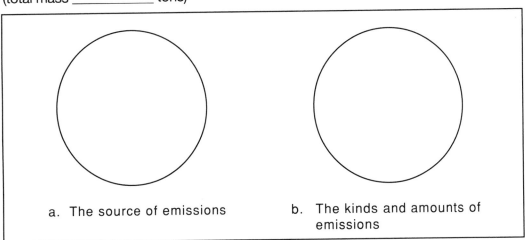

    a. The source of emissions   b. The kinds and amounts of emissions

2. From the information in Table 4–1 and Table 4–2, predict the air pollution emission inventory for your community. Sketch your predictions in pie graphs.

3. Use Sampling Techniques A, B, and C on the next few pages to prepare a *partial* air pollution emission inventory for your community.

Preparing a complete air pollution emission inventory is difficult and time-consuming. Using the sampling techniques to estimate emissions will show you how a complete pollution inventory for your community could be prepared.

Summary

1. Describe the partial air pollution emission inventory for your community.

    a. Which source emits the most pollutants? What kinds of pollutants does it emit?

    b. Which pollutant is the largest by percentage of total? What sources emit this pollutant?

2. Compare the pie graphs of emissions for the nation and the state.

    a. How are the graphs similar? How are they different?

    b. Suggest some factors that might account for differences.

3. How could statewide totals of emissions from all sources be estimated for a state air pollution emission inventory?

4. How could an inventory of emissions be used for making a plan to control air pollution in your community?

5. Display the findings at your school or some public place in your community such as a library or a mall or a grocery store.

SAMPLING TECHNIQUE A. AIR POLLUTION SOURCE REGISTER

An *air pollution source register* lists all known or possible sources of air pollution in an area. Such a register describes each source but does not tell the kinds or amounts of pollutants each one emits.

Table 4–3 shows the kinds of information listed in a source register.

Table 4–3 A source register card

Item	Data
a. Description of source:	*Speedy Brothers, a two-story dry cleaning plant*
b. Location of source:	*1973 Hawaii Street*
c. Description of surrounding area:	*Light industrial zone, some commercial and business buildings*
d. Operating times:	*Mon. through Fri. 8 a.m. to 5 p.m.*
e. Type of source (circle one):	

Motor vehicle   Other transportation   (Stationary source)

Power plants   Solid waste disposal   Industrial process loss   Agriculture

Directions

1. Prepare an air pollution source register for a selected area near your school. Record the information on cards like Table 4–3. Make the list as complete as you can.

2. Using symbols for types of sources, record the locations of all sources on the air pollution measurement map you prepared in Relational Study Investigation 1.

3. Suggest what other information is needed for estimating the kinds and amounts of pollutants emitted from each source.

SAMPLING TECHNIQUE B. EMISSION FACTOR TABLES

After preparing an air pollution source register (Sampling Technique A), the next step in developing an air pollution emission inventory is to estimate the kinds and amounts of emissions released from each source listed in your register.

The costs of sensitive equipment and skilled technicians make it expensive to measure emissions from all sources, so researchers rely on estimates shown in tables of emission factors.

Table 4–4 is a table of emission factors showing about how many grams of pollutants an automobile emits for each gallon of gasoline it uses. (Similar tables are available for all major types of sources.) In preparing a partial air pollution emission inventory for the community, focus on one source—automobiles.

Directions
1. Using method (a) or (b) below, calculate how many gallons of gasoline your family car uses in one week.

    a. Measure the quantity of gasoline used. Start with a full tank at the beginning of the week. Refill the tank at the end of the week. Record the number of gallons needed to refill the tank.

    b. Determine the number of miles traveled by recording the mileage on the odometer at the beginning and end of a week and subtracting. Divide the number of miles by 15 to get the number of gallons of gas. (If you know how many miles your car gets per gallon of gasoline, divide by that number instead.)

2. Determine the total amount of pollution emitted in one week from all the family cars in your class. Calculate the average amount of pollution emitted by one car in one week.

3. Using the emission factors in Table 4–4 (Sampling Technique B), estimate the total grams of each pollutant emitted by all the cars in your community. Convert grams to kilograms.

4. Discuss how tables of emission factors can be used in estimating the total quantity of pollutants emitted from all cars in a community. Suggest what other information, if any, is needed to make such an estimate.

Table 4–4 Factors for estimating pollutants in automobile emissions

Kind of Pollutant Emitted	Grams of Pollutant Emitted per Gallon of Gas Consumed
Carbon monoxide	1,321
Hydrocarbons	238
Nitrogen dioxide	51
Sulfur dioxide	4
Particulates	5

SAMPLING TECHNIQUE C. TOTAL EMISSION ESTIMATES

A pollution emission inventory estimates total pollutants released from all sources within an area. Environmental officials determine the emission rate and the kinds of pollutants from each source. They then add all their estimates to get an estimate of total emissions in the area.

A source register (Sampling Technique A) can't give information on every automobile driven in a community, but it can estimate total emissions from all the automobiles there. Researchers can get the number of automobiles from licensing records; they can find the amount of gas sold from records of gas taxes.

Directions

1. Try to find how much gasoline is consumed by automobiles in your community. If you can't get the information, use your knowledge of sampling techniques to estimate the number of gallons used. For example, you might sample people in your community to find out how much they drive within the community and outside it.

2. Using the emission factors in Table 4–4, estimate the total grams of each pollutant emitted from all cars in your community. Convert grams to kilograms.

5. AIR POLLUTION AND THE PHYSICAL ENVIRONMENT

Background

Once a pollutant is emitted, its fate in the air depends on weather and topography. *Topography* refers to the surface features of the area—hills, valleys, rivers, buildings, and so on.

Because you are now an expert on weather patterns and sources of air pollution, you will be asked to serve on a committee of the Air Pollution Task Force in your community. The task force must study the effects of weather and topography on air pollution, then recommend where new community facilities should be built.

Activity

1. Prepare a study describing how local weather and topography can affect the distribution of air pollutants emitted from sources in the community.

2. Recommend the best locations in the community for an *incinerator*.

3. Recommend the best locations in the community for pollution-monitoring stations.

Procedure

1. Divide the class into committees as shown in Table 5–1 to study factors in the physical environment affecting air pollution.

2. Learn as much as you can about your topic. Read the reference booklet "Air Pollution" for information and suggested investigations. Consult other sources, including your teacher, for more information or for help in understanding what you read.

Table 5–1 Factors in the physical environment for investigation by task force

Com-mittee	Factors
1	Wind
2	Sunlight
3	Water and soil
4	Topography
5	Urban land use
6	Rural land use

Summary

¶1. Make a brief oral report to the class on what your committee learned about how the factors it studied may affect air pollution in the community. Relate your findings to the weather data the class collected earlier.

¶2. After hearing all the reports, call a meeting of the Air Pollution Task Force.

    a. Using the information assembled by the committees, decide where and when to expect the highest and lowest pollution concentrations.

    b. Show these locations on a topographic map of the community.

¶3. Recommend the best locations for a pollution-monitoring station and a new incinerator.

    a. List the factors to consider in making the decision.

    b. Identify information the task force needs before it can recommend sites.

Challenge

1. Plan a class study on how your community is handling problems in disposing of solid waste.

2. Explain how changes in disposal methods could affect air quality.

6. AIR POLLUTION CONTROL

Background

Air pollution control refers to efforts to limit or reduce emissions to preserve the quality of ambient air. Passing laws and using technologies are the major methods of controlling air pollution.

The U.S. government in 1970 passed laws setting national standards for air quality. The standards specified the maximum or highest concentration of each major pollutant legally allowed in the air. Each state must meet these standards or set stricter standards of its own.

Air pollution control technology uses scientific information about the kinds and amounts of pollution. Scientific information on (1) the physical and chemical properties of pollutants and (2) the processes that create pollutants is essential to pollution-control efforts.

Activity

1. Find out what laws regulate air pollution in your community.

2. Show how technology could be used to reduce air pollution.

Procedure

1. Consult references on air pollution for information on these topics:

   a. Air pollution laws enacted by the U.S. government, including

      1) The Clean Air Act of 1955
      2) The Air Quality Act of 1967
      3) The Clean Air Act Amendments of 1970
      4) The Clean Air Act Amendments of 1990

b. Ambient air quality standards adopted by your state

    c. Emergency plans for preventing an air pollution episode in your community

2. Devise and carry out a demonstration of how technology might be used to control some aspects of air pollution.

    a. Read the information and suggested investigations for air pollution control in the reference booklet "Air Pollution."

    b. Select an investigation or devise your own way to demonstrate a device for controlling air pollution.

    c. Complete the investigation and perform the demonstration for the class.

Summary

1. What is air pollution control? What are the purposes of air pollution legislation?

2. How do air quality standards for your state compare with federal standards?

3. What is being done to control air pollution in your community? What actions are planned in case the quantity of a pollutant exceeds the standards?

4. How can the physical and chemical properties of a pollutant be used to control it?

5. How is technology being used to control air pollution?

Challenge

1. Prepare a report describing efforts to reduce emissions from automobiles. Include the following:

   a. A summary of laws to control emissions

   b. Types of devices and engines designed to reduce emissions

2. Explain how planning for an emergency could prevent a tragedy in your community.

3. Find out how much money the utility companies and major industries in your area are spending to install pollution-control devices or to find low-polluting fuels. Report your findings to the class.

7. AIR POLLUTION IN THE FUTURE

Background
It's the year 2020. The air is clean and clear because the people of your community began to solve their pollution problems back in the 1990s. Everyone is proud of what has been accomplished.

Activity
Prepare a historical documentary telling how your community cleaned the air and kept it clean.

Procedure
Be imaginative in planning your documentary.
Include as many ideas as you can. Consider doing the following:

1. Describe the air as it was in the 1990s when efforts to control pollution began.

2. Tell what laws were enacted between 1990 and 2020 to control air pollution.

3. Describe the technological changes that were made.

4. Explain what people did and how they worked together to control air pollution.

Summary
Share your ideas and information for your documentary.

Challenge

1. Find out what each citizen can do now to control air pollution. List the ideas on a large chart. Type the list, make copies, and give them to others.

2. Take your own advice. Carry through one of your suggestions faithfully for at least two weeks. At the end of the time, report what you did to help control air pollution. Describe how it felt to change your behavior for those two weeks. Explain why you would or would not recommend that others follow your example.

New Vocabulary for Unit 1

acute damage
air pollutant
air pollution episode
air pollution index
air pollution inventory
air quality standards
ambient air
chronic damage
dispersion
effect

effects
emissions
emitting
environmental chamber
evaporate
gaseous
incinerator
major pollutants
physical properties
polluted air

rural
sampling
source
task force
topography
urban
vapor
volatile liquid

UNIT 2. WATER RESOURCE MANAGEMENT

Section A. Water in My Community

8. THE WATER CYCLE

Background

In the Ecology strand of this course we investigated the interactions of plants and animals in the class study area, the movement of water through soil and air, and water coming out of plants in transpiration. Wherever we look in the environment, we seem to find water.

In the Physical Science strand we did experiments on the buoyancy of water, on its changes of state in boiling, freezing, melting, and condensing, and on its movement in the presence of pressure and vacuums. We found that water can change state as it moves through the environment.

In this unit we will use our knowledge of the properties of matter and interactions in the environment to study a community problem—water resource management. For such a study we must apply and extend our knowledge of science, and we must identify and discuss the social, political, economic, and technological aspects of this problem.

We will look at water resource management from the viewpoints of scientists, technologists, politicians, economists, and—most important—citizens of the community.

First we will review what we already know about water relationships. Then we will investigate some questions: How is water used in the community? How is it distributed through the community? What happens to water after we use it? How clean is the water we use? How can water be purified? Who controls the use of our water?

We will begin by describing the *hydrologic cycle*—the flow of water through the environment.

Activity

Trace the flow of water through the environment.

Materials
• Water Game
• materials for projects

Procedure
1. Organize the class into groups of three or four students each.

2. Review Ecology Investigations 8 through 25. Also review Physical Science Investigations 18 through 33.

   In your group discuss the flow of water through the environment. Base the discussion on what you learned in your investigations and experiences.

3. Using the diagram below as a guide, trace the flow of water through the environment. Identify as many pathways as you can. A copy of the diagram is in the Student Record Book.

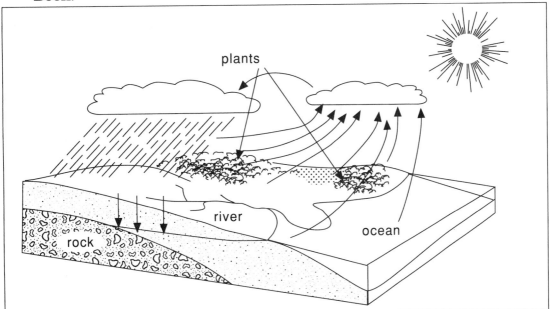

Figure 8–1 Tracing the hydrologic cycle

4. Play the Water Game in your group. Your teacher will give you the materials and directions for the game.

5. Choose one of the projects below to illustrate the water cycle. Plan and carry out the project with your group.

   a. Write a story about four raindrops each taking a different path through the environment until they rejoin in a new rainfall. Illustrate your story. Share it with the class.

   b. Create a skit that shows the flow of water through the hydrologic cycle. Perform your skit for the class.

   c. Write a poem about the water cycle. Share it with the class.

   d. Make a collage using pictures from magazines and newspapers to show the water cycle. Post the collage in the classroom.

   e. Set up a closed terrarium to show the hydrologic cycle. Refer to the reference booklet "Animal Care" for information on setting up a terrarium.

   f. Begin a news file of articles or reports about local water issues. Keep the file in the classroom so that others can add to it.

Summary

¶1. Share your project on the hydrologic cycle with the class.

¶2. What are the sources of energy that drive the water cycle?

Challenge

1. How could water in the hydrologic cycle become polluted?

2. What other cycles in nature can you identify? Try to name and describe at least two cycles other than the hydrologic cycle.

3. In some places agricultural crops are being grown in the desert with fossil water. What does "fossil water" mean? Try to find information about this practice, including the amounts of water used, its source, and its effect on raising food crops.

9. USES OF WATER

Background

Hydrology is the study of the movement and distribution of water on Earth. In nature, water circulates through the *hydrologic cycle*. Heat from the sun makes surface water evaporate and change to water vapor. When water vapor in the atmosphere cools, it condenses, forming clouds. When sufficient liquid or solid water collects in clouds, it falls in the form of rain, snow, sleet, or hail, collectively known as *precipitation*. When water reaches the ground, it may seep or flow into lakes and oceans. Eventually, water works its way to the surface, evaporates, and begins the cycle anew.

Water is a vital resource. We use it for drinking, cooking, cleaning, grooming, manufacturing, growing food, and disposing of wastes. Water is used in homes and hotels, on farms and golf courses, in factories and public buildings—in fact, wherever humans live and work. With so many people needing water, is there enough to go around?

Problem

How much water do you use?

Materials

- chart paper
- graph paper
- colored pens

Procedure

1. Divide the class into groups of three or four.

2. In your group create a concept map on water uses.

   a. Write WATER USES in the center of a large sheet of paper and build a concept map of your group's ideas.

   $$\boxed{\text{WATER USES}}$$

   b. Think about water. What do you know about it? How do we use it? Where does it come from?

   c. Write words on the map to name the uses, sources, properties, and anything else that affects the use of water. Draw lines to show connections. Label the lines.

3. Prepare a class list of water uses.

   a. Organize the list into groups of similar kinds of uses.

   b. Identify the uses of water that affect you personally.

4. Estimate how much water your family uses in a day.

   a. Use Table 9–1 to estimate the amounts of water you use in family activities. Determine whether your family members are normal or conservative users of water.

Table 9–1 My family's daily water usage

Type of Use	Average Amount of Water Used (gallons)		Number of Uses per Day	Estimated Total Water Used per Day (gallons)
	Normal	Conservative		
Showering	25	4		
Bathing	36	12		
Brushing teeth	10	0.5		
Shaving	20	1		
Dishwashing by hand	30	5		
Dishwashing automatic	16	7		
Washing hands	2	1		
Flushing toilet	5	4.5		
Washing clothes	60	27		
Watering lawn by hand	10/min.			
Watering lawn automatic	500			
Washing car	150	50		
Cleaning sidewalks	10			
Cooking				
Drinking				

Number of people in my family ____

b. Add other uses from your concept map.

c. Observe and record the amount of water you drink in one day as well as the amount of water required by your additional uses in 4.b.

d. Calculate the total amount of water your family uses in a day.

e. Calculate the average amount of water each person in your family uses in a day.

f. As an alternative to completing Table 9–1, or as a comparison, get a recent water bill from your family. Locate the total amount of water used. Calculate the average amount of water used per person each day in your family.

5. Compare your daily consumption of water with others in the class.

a. Prepare a class graph showing the amount of water used by each person in the class per day. Post the graph in the classroom.

b. Calculate how much water is used by the whole class in a day, a week, a month, and a year.

c. Calculate the average amount of water used per person in your class.

d. Estimate the amount of water used by students and staff in your school in a day, a week, a month, and a year.

Summary

1. How much water have you used in your lifetime? How did you make your estimate?

2. Check with school officials or the community water department to find out how much water your school uses in a month.

3. Where else is water used in your community other than in homes and schools? Which uses of water in your community are essential?

↑4. How can the amount of water available to your community be increased?

↑5. How can the amount of water used be reduced?

6. Refer to your concept map on water uses. Make a class collage on water uses. Post it in the classroom near your graph of water use.

Challenge

1. What are some uses of water not common 50 years ago that are common today? How has the amount of water used per person changed in the last 50 years?

2. Plan and carry out a water conservation project in your home, school, or community. Report on the results of your project.

10. DISTRIBUTION OF WATER

Background

We all use water in many ways, but we need to have fresh, clean water for drinking and cooking. The two main sources of fresh water are groundwater and surface water.

Groundwater seeps through soil or through cracks and cavities in rocks. *Surface water* flows over land, then collects in lakes, rivers, streams, and reservoirs.

Groundwater

Groundwater lies below the surface of the earth. It is the source of water for wells and springs. About 35% of the public water supply in the United

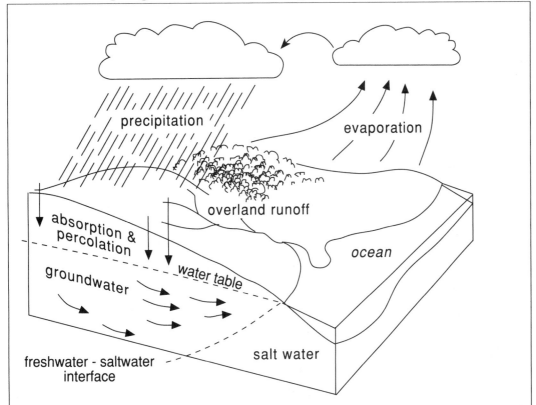

Figure 10–1 Groundwater in the hydrologic cycle

States comes from groundwater. Most rural areas and some cities depend heavily on groundwater to meet their needs.

Most groundwater comes from rain that filters through the soil by *percolation*. (Recall your studies of the interactions of water and soil in Ecology Investigations 9 and 10 on absorption, percolation, and capillarity.) Water settles into pores and cracks in underground rocks and into spaces in sand and gravel. A layer or bed of porous material that holds useful amounts of groundwater is called an *aquifer*. Wells drilled down to an aquifer draw groundwater to the surface.

The top level of groundwater, called the *water table*, drops when more water is withdrawn than is replaced. In places that have little rainfall or large human populations, the groundwater supply is sometimes used up faster than it is replaced. This lowering of the water table causes problems in coastal areas when salt water from the ocean enters the aquifer.

Water is constantly on the move in the hydrologic cycle. As you can imagine, the rates of movement differ. See Table 10–2.

Table 10–2 Rates of movement and distribution of water

Location	Rate of Movement per Day	Percentage of Water Supply
Atmosphere	100s of kilometers	.001
Land surface	10s of kilometers	.019
Below land surface	meters	4.120
Ice caps and glaciers	centimeters	1.650
Oceans	—	93.960

Surface Water

River, stream, brook, rivulet, freshet, arroyo, bayou, creek, slough, rill, runnel—these are some of the dozens of names for flowing water. Hydrologists usually refer to smaller bodies of flowing water as *streams* and larger bodies of flowing water as *rivers*. When streams join with other streams, they form a branching network called a *river system.* The river system is fed by rain and snow and by groundwater seeping from aquifers.

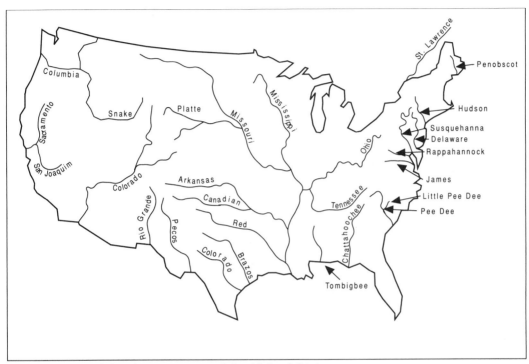

Figure 10–3 Major river systems of the United States

Most rivers don't start out big. Instead, they grow as their *headwaters* — the streams that flow into the river—begin to join together. The area of land that draws rainfall and snowmelt from headwaters into a river system is called a *watershed.*

Rivers differ not only in the rate of water flow but also in the composition of their bottoms and in the forms of life they have in them. Near their headwaters rivers may flow fast, grinding out canyons and creating rapids and waterfalls. Currents are swift in these clear, cold, highly aerated waters, yet the volume of water is low. Trees, shrubs, and grasses shade the water, bind streambank soil with their roots, and provide food for stream life.

Plants and animals living in these rivers are adapted to the fast-moving water and generally rocky bottom. Many animals have claws or suction cups on their feet for hanging on; some have flattened bodies for squeezing under rocks; others have strong appendages for bracing themselves against the forceful flow of water.

Figure 10–4 River life

As more streams flow into a river, it gets wider and wider. When the water reaches flatter land, its rate slows. As sediment is carried downstream and accumulates on the bottom, the channel widens. As the river slows, flat stretches of land called *flood plains* form on either side. During storms, rivers may overflow onto the flood plain. Then as the water recedes, it leaves deposits of rich sediment behind, making the flood plains fertile and productive.

These larger, slower rivers support diverse communities of algae, catfish, turtles, dragonflies, and other plants and animals that thrive in oxygen-poor waters. These rivers can also support a diverse shore community of kingfishers, herons, otters, raccoons, and other creatures that depend on the river for food and water.

Wide, slow-moving rivers carry huge volumes of water. Along their shores *marshes* and *swamps* form. At an "old" river's *mouth*, most often a lake or ocean, the flow of water slows even more and dumps most of the leftover sediment. This sediment creates new land, called a *delta*. Where a river meets the ocean, salty water mixes with fresh water, creating an *estuary*—a rich habitat for life and a productive nursery for young shrimp, crabs, ocean fish, and other animals and plants.

Wetlands

Wetlands—swamps, marshes, bogs, and prairie potholes—are land areas saturated with or covered by water at least part of the year. Wetlands can form where water collects in depressions in land or where soil, plant matter, and animal matter collect in ponds or along rivers. As sediments settle out, the water becomes shallow. Plants adapted to such conditions gradually establish themselves here.

Many people believe that wetlands are the most productive natural systems on Earth because they support a rich variety of plant and animal life. Wetlands also protect against flood damage by absorbing large volumes of water, thereby protecting lives and property downstream.

Swamps are wetlands where trees grow. Swamps support hundreds of species of birds, mammals, reptiles, amphibians, fish, and insects. Some swamps contain *bayous*, which are slow-moving streams. Bayous can be so narrow that mosses hanging from trees on opposite sides meet in the air above the water.

Figure 10–5 Swamps are wetlands with trees

Salt marshes are the coastal nurseries of the ocean. Many nearshore and offshore organisms begin life here. The ocean food web begins in marshes where outgoing and incoming tides create unique conditions for life. As tides go out, they carry leaves and dead matter from the marsh to the ocean, where it becomes food for many ocean animals. When tides come in, they carry ocean minerals and salts that become nutrients for plants growing in the marsh.

This exchange of food and nutrients constitutes one of the most productive ecosystems in the world. Many marine animals spend part or all of their lives in marshes. Seven of the ten most economically valuable fish and shellfish—shrimp, salmon, oysters, menhaden, crabs, flounder, and clams—need marshes for breeding. Of the ten, only tuna, lobster, and haddock neither breed nor live part of their lives in marshes. Two thirds of the fish harvested from the Atlantic and Gulf coasts and a third of those taken from the Pacific depend on these wetlands for breeding.

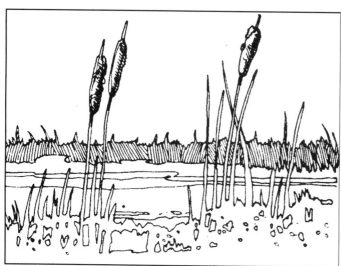

Figure 10–6 Marsh

Bogs usually form in glacial and mountain lakes that have no outlet. The water is cold and still. Because it is low in oxygen and high in acid, few plants and animals live there. But there are lots of insects and insect-eating plants such as bladderworts, pitcher plants, and sundew. These plants usually grow in a thick layer of peat moss called sphagnum. The moss looks sturdy enough, but because it sometimes shakes when someone walks on it, it is often called a "quaking bog."

Figure 10–7 Quaking bog

Prairie potholes are miniature marshes found in Iowa, Minnesota, Montana, Nebraska, and the Dakotas. They are the most important breeding grounds for waterfowl in the United States. These small marshes formed where glaciers left shallow depressions in the earth. Some prairie potholes hold only a few centimeters of water for just a few weeks in the spring. Others hold water up to 6 meters deep during the rainy season. Waterfowl use prairie potholes for breeding; they use wetlands of all kinds for feeding and resting.

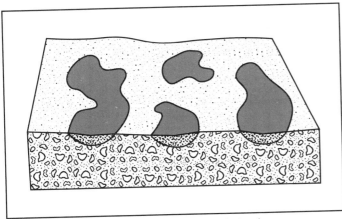

Figure 10–8 Prairie potholes (aerial view)

Problem
Where does our water come from?

Materials
- audiotape player
- tape of Bedrich Smetana's *The Moldau*
- topographic map of area
- tracing paper

Procedure

1. Before you begin this investigation, listen to the sounds of moving water. Get a tape of the musical composition *The Moldau* by Bedrich Smetana. Listen to the tape in class.

   Smetana, a composer who lived from 1824 to 1884, was proud of his home country in what is now Czechoslovakia. He wrote music to represent different parts of it. Of his compositions, one of the most famous is *The Moldau,* which he wrote to depict the longest river in his country.

   a. Listen to the musical sounds of the movements of the river. Try to picture the images the composer is trying to interpret in the music. Your teacher will give you descriptions of parts of the Moldau River.

   b. Listen to other compositions about water, such as Respighi's *Fountains of Rome* or Handel's *Water Music.*

2. Divide the class into groups of three or four. In your group make a map of your watershed.

a. Get a topographic or highway map of your region that shows the streams or rivers flowing through your community.

b. Using tracing paper, trace all the rivers and streams shown on the map.

c. Outline the drainage area that forms the watershed for your community.

d. Compare your group's watershed map with maps made by other groups. Make a large class map of your community's watershed.

3. Using your map, find the main water source for your community. Find out whether your community relies on surface water or groundwater.

4. Find out how water is distributed from its source to where it is used in your community.

a. The pipes delivering water to your home or school are usually buried. Look for evidence of the water distribution system such as fire hydrants, buildings, sprinklers, and other water distribution points. Imagine how the water distribution system works in your community.

b. Make a large-scale drawing showing the distribution system from the water source to your school.

5. Find out how water gets to classrooms in your school.

    a.   Go outdoors and find the following:

- water valves
- water meter
- water main leading into the school
- water fountains or sprinkler heads
- fire hydrants

    b.   Inside the school locate the following:

- drinking fountains
- water pipes under sinks
- source of hot water (check the cafeteria or the central heating system)

    c.   From the information you gather make a scale drawing of the water distribution system in your school.

    d.   Compare your drawings with actual plans or blueprints obtained from the office or the custodian.

Summary

1. Discuss the scenes depicted in the music of water movement.

    a.   Can you draw or sketch the images the music created in your mind?

    b.   How does the movement of water affect your feelings?

2. Refer to the class map of your watershed area.

    a.   What other communities are affected by your watershed area?

    b.   What kinds of industry or agriculture are in your watershed area? How might they affect the quality of your water?

    c.   What other communities might be affected by sewage or wastes going into streams in or near your community?

3. How do urban areas affect what happens to rain that falls there?

4. Who is responsible for maintaining the water distribution system in your community?

    a.   Who pays the costs of maintaining the system?

    b.   Who makes decisions affecting the water distribution system?

    c.   How large a population can the water distribution system serve?

Challenge

1. Invite an engineer from your water department to speak to the class about the water distribution system in your community.

2. Find the meaning of the following:

   - normal peak demand
   - per capita consumption
   - water pressure
   - pumping station
   - gravity distribution

3. Make a scale drawing of the water distribution system in your home.

4. Make a model of the water distribution system of your school or home. Share your model with your class.

11. LOCAL ISSUES

Background
We have investigated the natural water system around our community and the ways we use water. Now we turn to local issues of water resource management, trying to answer such questions as who owns the water, how the supply is regulated, how demands for clean water are changing, and what steps are being taken to keep our water clean.

Problem
1. What are the local issues of water resource management?

2. How are these issues being resolved?

Materials
- newspaper articles
- class scrapbook or newspaper files
- chart paper
- colored pens
- regional atlas
- census data on local population size

Procedure
1. Refer to your local newspaper for information on current local issues in water resource management. Newspaper articles often identify and give thorough information about controversies.

   a. Begin a newspaper file on water resource management issues. Review old newspapers for articles on water resource management in the last year and collect new articles.

b. Analyze each article for the following information:

- What does the article say about water? Does it describe uses, amounts, costs, or quality?
- What is the position or opinion of the person who wrote the article?
- Are several opinions expressed? What are they?
- Is a conflict mentioned, either directly or indirectly? What is it?

c. Keep the articles in a class scrapbook. Write a summary of each article and put it in the scrapbook with the article.

2. Using an atlas, an encyclopedia, geography books, or other sources, find the amount and distribution of each of the following in your state:

a. Annual rainfall

b. Agricultural areas

c. Population centers

d. Industrial centers

e. Major rivers

3. Make a large class map of your region. Using different colors, show the information your class gathered in procedure 2. Post the map in the classroom.

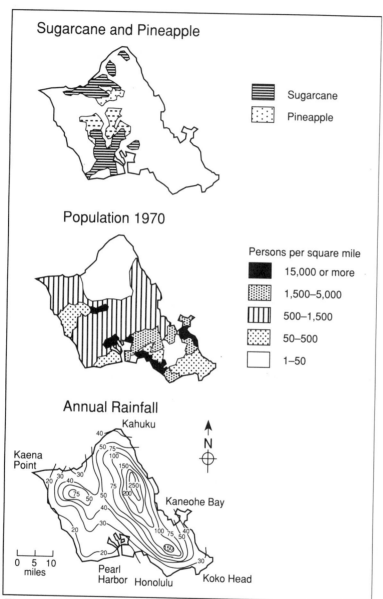

Figure 11–1 Sample distribution maps

4. Find out how the population of your region is changing. Population size has an effect on the demand for water.

    a.   Find out what the population of your community is now.

    b.   How has the population size changed in the last 50 years? What is happening to the population size now?

    c.   Refer to your data from Investigation 9, Uses of Water, on the average amount of water used per person in your class. Estimate the amount of water needed by your community in one day and in one year.

5. From your newspaper file and other information you have gathered, find out who controls water use in your community.

Discuss these questions in class:

- Who owns the water in your community?
- Are there some community members who do not pay for water?
- Who regulates the amount and cost of water used in your community?
- How are members of the regulatory agency selected? Who pays them?
- Whose interests do members of the regulatory agency represent?

6. Divide the class into two teams. Prepare and carry out a debate on the issue below or another issue chosen by the class. One team should support the statement while the other team challenges it.

ISSUE: Water should be free for all to use as much as they want.

You may want to have some classmates videotape the debate and role-play a television news team covering this community event.

Summary

1. Analyze your map of rainfall, rivers, population centers, industrial areas, and agricultural areas.

    a.   Why do you think the population centers are where they are?

    b.   What problems or issues related to water use might arise from these distributions?

2. Explain the water resource management issues in your community in one of the following ways:

- Plan and put on a skit about an issue.
- Write a research paper on an issue.
- Write and perform a song, poem, chant, or rap about an issue.
- Create a poster highlighting an issue.
- Create and record a TV commercial representing different interests in an issue.
- Conduct a mock newspaper or TV interview of interest groups' positions on an issue.

Challenge

1. Attend a hearing or a community meeting on a water resource issue. Report your experience to the class.

2. If you were going to build a new community, how would you select a place for it? What points would you consider? What would be the most "logical" place for people to live?

3. Find out what federal laws affect water quality in your community.

4. Prepare summary reports of water issues in your community. Share your reports with students in other classes, schools, states, or countries. How are the issues similar? How are they different?

New Vocabulary for Section A

aquifer
bayou
bog
delta
estuary
flood plain
groundwater

headwaters
hydrologic cycle
hydrology
marsh
percolation
prairie pothole
river

river system
salt marsh
stream
surface water
swamp
water table
watershed

12. TESTING WATER QUALITY

Background

Water is vital. All living things depend on it. Without water, they die.

But when we use water, we contaminate it with substances that make it unhealthy for living things. Used water, called *wastewater* or *sewage*, from homes, businesses, and industries may contain bacteria, suspended solids, phosphates, nitrates, and a host of other chemicals. Such contaminated water may be low in oxygen, making it impossible for some organisms, such as fish, to live in it. But other organisms, such as algae, thrive in such an environment, where they create foul-smelling, polluted water.

Human use isn't the only source of water pollution. A *source* is a starting place, thing, or process. In water studies a source is anything that releases pollutants into the hydrologic cycle. Agriculture is a source of pollution when fertilizers and pesticides enter our water or when soil erosion and runoff add silt to streams, rivers, and lakes, clogging or choking water flow.

Industries also use large quantities of water, but they do not usually need water of high quality. Some industries dump waste that contains solids, chemicals, or radioactive substances. Water used for cooling machinery gets hot; if it is dumped into a stream or lake, it too affects the lives of organisms.

Problem

What evidence of water pollution, if any, can you find in your community?

Procedure

1. Refer to the class map of the watershed of your community or region that you made in Investigation 10, Distribution of Water.

a. Prepare a Water Pollution Source Map of your community. Locate possible sources of pollutants on the watershed map.

There are two kinds of sources of water pollution. A *point source* is a well-defined spot such as a place where a pipe from a factory enters a stream. A *nonpoint source* is a large area such as grazing land, a logging area, a construction site, an abandoned mine, and gardens, lawns, and streets in cities. Pollution from a nonpoint source doesn't enter the water system at a single point.

Sediments are the major component by weight of nonpoint source pollution. Other nonpoint source pollutants include fertilizers and animal wastes from agriculture, septic tank breakouts, and runoff from urban gardens, lawns, and landfills.

b. Invent a color key to mark different kinds of sources on your map. Then color the sources on the class map.

c. Post your color key for sources next to the map, which we will call a Water Pollution Source Map.

d. Add other information to the map as you complete the investigations in this unit.

2. Arrange to go to a nearby water study area— a stream, lake, pond, or wetland—to collect water samples and test them. If possible, you should sample and test water several

times before drawing conclusions. Alternatively, bring water samples to class for testing. If possible, compare water samples from several sites.

3. Divide the class into six teams of three to five. Each team should conduct one or more of the tests shown in Table 12–1. The tests are described on the following pages.

Table 12–1 Team assignments for testing water quality

Team Name	Chief Job	Page
A. Environment	Sketch and describe the water study area; measure depth, velocity, and temperature of water.	375
B. Dissolved substances	Measure acidity and salinity.	379
C. Dissolved gases	Measure carbon dioxide and oxygen content of water.	384
D. Nutrients	Measure nitrate and phosphate content of water.	388
E. Suspended solids	Measure total suspended solids and turbidity.	391
F. Living organisms	Note biological indicators, odor, plankton, bacteria.	394

Summary

¶1. Summarize all your data in a form similar to Table 12–2. Use a separate form for each site where you tested water. Post the forms next to your Water Pollution Source Map.

¶2. Each team should prepare a report for the class on its findings.

   a. After the reports are complete, discuss with the class the general quality of the water in the water study area.

b. Decide what steps to take to maintain or improve the water quality.

c. Prepare a plan for carrying out the decisions.

13. Share your reports and your plans with classes in your city, state, or even another country.

a. How are the reports and plans similar?

b. How do they differ?

Challenge

1. How can a hydrometer be used to measure the salinity of water?

2. Design an experiment to test the effects of acid rain or other pollutants on plants.

a. Write your plans for your experiment. Include a flow diagram.

b. Get your teacher's approval and support before you start your project.

c. Carry out your experiment and report on the results.

Table 12–2 Water quality report form

WATER QUALITY REPORT FORM

Water station location _____ Date _____

Reporter _____ Time _____

Measurements made

1. Water depth _____   2. Rate of flow _____

3. Water temperature _____   4. Air temperature _____

5. pH _____   6. Salinity _____

7. Dissolved oxygen _____   8. Dissolved carbon dioxide_____

9. Nitrates _____   10. Phosphates _____

11. Total suspended solids _____   12. Turbidity _____

13. Bacterial count _____

Visible pollutants

14. In sample _____   15. At site _____

Other observations

TEAM A. ENVIRONMENT

A dynamic, thriving community depends on the interactions of the physical and biological factors in the environment. The chief job of the Environment Team is to sketch the water study area and describe some of the factors that influence and help us interpret water quality measurements.

Materials
- large sheet of map paper
- several stringed metersticks
- thermometer
- stopwatch
- 2 stakes
- weighted string
- long pole
- hammer
- orange, ball, or similar floating object

Directions
1. On a data table similar to Table 12–4, sketch the water study area. See Ecology Investigation 27, The Initial Survey, for information on making an initial survey map of an area.

   a. Pace distances to prominent objects and plants. Locate these on your sketch.

   b. Estimate the width of the water study area.

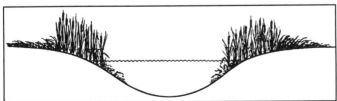

Figure 12–3 Sketch of a water study area

c. On a large sheet of map paper, outline the water study area. Transfer your data to the large map. Show the approximate scale of the map. Indicate which way is north.

d. Make your map as detailed as possible.

Table 12–4 Data on our water study area

Sketch	Location	Water Depth	Temperature Air	Water	Rate of Flow

2. Use a stringed meterstick, a weighted string, and a long pole to measure the depth of water at various places in the water study area. Record your measurements on the map of your water study area.

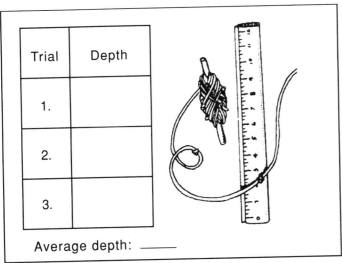

Trial	Depth
1.	
2.	
3.	

Average depth: _____

Figure 12–5 Measuring the depth of water

3. Measure the temperature of the air. Measure the temperature of the water at several depths. Record these data on your map.

4. Measure the rate of water flow, if any. (The rate of flow helps determine the kinds of food in the water and the feeding strategies of organisms. It also plays a large part in the amount of dissolved oxygen in the water.)

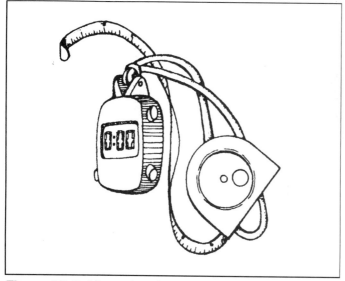

Figure 12–6 Measuring the rate of water flow

    a.   Measure and mark with stakes a distance of 30 meters along the path of the waterway.

    b.   Throw an orange or a ball into the water above the upstream marker. Using a stopwatch, measure the time in seconds it takes to reach the downstream marker.

    c.   Find the rate of flow by dividing the distance by the time the orange took to cover it.

        Distance (m) ÷ Time (sec) = Rate of flow (m/sec)

    d.   Record the rate of flow.

5. Repeat procedure 4 at places where water appears to be moving at different rates. Record your data.

6. Prepare a report on the data your group collected to share with the rest of the class.

TEAM B. DISSOLVED SUBSTANCES

Acid rain is caused by sulfurous acids and nitrous acids in the upper atmosphere. These acids form when sulfur oxide gases or nitrogen oxide gases dissolve in water. The acids fall in rain, snow, or fog. Figure 12–7 shows the major sources of these gases.

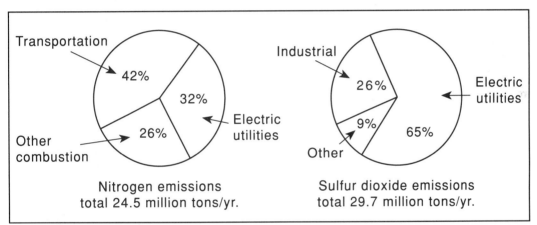

Figure 12–7 Sources of gases in acid rain

Sulfur oxides are produced mainly by coal-burning power plants and industrial boilers. Nitrogen oxides are emitted by automobiles and coal-fired boilers.

Acid rain kills animal life in lakes, affects the growth of plants, harms the respiratory system of humans, and damages buildings and statues.

Acid rain is not new. It used to be just a local problem in areas downwind from power plants and industrial sites. But the tall smokestacks that now send waste gases high into the atmosphere have made acid rain a problem in many places. Rain falling in the eastern United States and Canada, for instance, is 10 to 100 times more acidic than it was 20 or 30 years ago. The map in Figure 12–8 shows areas of the United States now affected by acid rain.

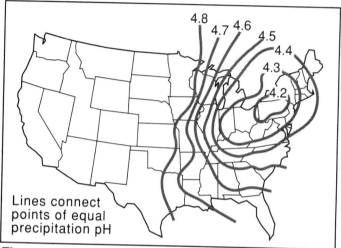

Lines connect points of equal precipitation pH

Figure 12–8 Areas affected by acid rain

Acid is measured on a *pH scale* ranging from 0 to 14. A reading of 0 is extremely acid; 14 is extremely alkaline, or basic; 7 is considered neutral. The smaller the number, the greater the acidity. The larger the number, the greater the alkalinity.

The pH scale is designed so that a change of 1 unit represents a tenfold change in acidity. For example, pH 5 is 10 times as acid as pH 6; pH 4 is 100 times as acid as pH 6. Natural values of pH in freshwater systems are commonly between 5.5 and 8.0. Acid rain and other sources of acid can change the pH of water systems, thereby altering their chemical and biological balances. Figure 12–9 shows the effects of various pH levels.

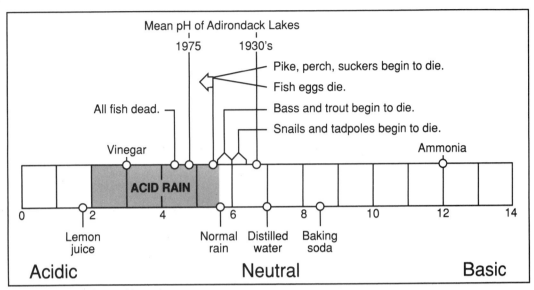

Figure 12–9 The pH scale

Salinity

Salinity is a measure of the amount of salt and dissolved minerals in a water sample. It is an important property because it determines not only which life forms can live in the water but also affects its density. Recall from your studies of buoyancy and density in physical science that clean, fresh water has a density of about 1.0 g/mL, but a saturated Epsom salt solution has a density of about 1.2 g/mL. Recall the effect of density on the buoyancy of water.

Water with dissolved salts and minerals in it is not pure. Freshwater lakes, rivers, and streams all contain some dissolved matter. Water that is a mixture of fresh water and salt water is said to be *brackish.* Water with a very high salt content is called *brine.*

One of the most common methods for determining the salinity of a water sample is measuring its density with a *hydrometer*. Figure 12–10 shows a hydrometer calibrated for a range of densities from 1.00 to 1.06 g/mL.

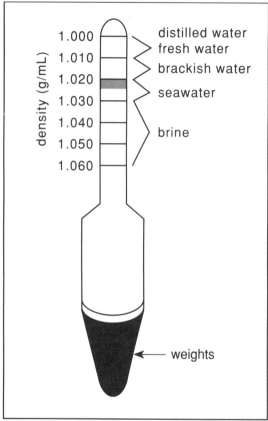

Figure 12–10 An aquarium hydrometer showing the density range of water samples in g/mL

The higher the hydrometer floats in a water sample, the higher the water's salinity. The lower it sinks, the lower its salinity.

Materials
- pH indicator paper, wide-range
- several jars for water samples
- hydrometer
- watch or clock

Directions

1. Collect water samples from several places in the water study area. Label the samples so you know where each came from.

2. Use pH indicator paper to measure the acidity of the water samples. Chemicals in pH paper change color in the presence of acids and bases. A standard color chart supplied with the test paper shows the pH level.

   a. Immerse a piece of pH indicator paper in a sample of water.

   b. Observe the color change within the first 30 seconds.

   c. Compare the color of the pH test paper with the color chart supplied with the paper.

   d. Record the pH value of the sample.

3. Use a hydrometer to measure the relative salinity of the water samples.

   a. Put a water sample in a jar large enough to hold the hydrometer.

   b. Put the hydrometer in the water.

   c. Read the temperature. Record the density from the hydrometer.

d. Compare the hydrometer reading with
the diagram in Figure 12–10. Record the
salinity as

• fresh water	(density 1.00–1.01 g/mL)
• brackish water	(density 1.01–1.02 g/mL)
• seawater	(density 1.02–1.04 g/mL)
• brine	(density 1.04+ g/mL)

4. Add your data to the map of the water study
area prepared by the Environment Team.

5. Prepare a report on the data your group
collected to share with the rest of the class.
Be prepared to explain the following:

a. The formation and effects of acid rain

b. How a hydrometer is used to measure
salinity and how changes in salinity
affect density and buoyancy

c. Why the temperature must be recorded
when using the hydrometer to measure
salinity

d. Your data on pH and the salinity of water
samples

TEAM C. DISSOLVED GASES

Recall from Ecology Investigation 15, Major Gases in the Air, and
Investigation 16, The Trace Components of Air, that air contains about 21%
oxygen and 0.03% carbon dioxide by volume. These and other gases can
be absorbed by water in a process called *aeration.* They can also enter
water from the life processes of organisms in the water.

Dissolved oxygen is probably the most important gas for organisms living in water. Fish and other water organisms need dissolved oxygen for respiration. Most fish need a concentration of about 5 parts per million (5 ppm) of dissolved oxygen. Although some fish, such as trout, need more, and others, such as carp, can get by with less, most fish are sensitive to even slight reductions in dissolved oxygen. Only the most tolerant fishes can survive when the level of dissolved oxygen drops below 3 ppm.

The maximum of dissolved oxygen that water can hold, called the *saturation value*, varies with temperature. Table 12–11 shows the dissolved oxygen saturation values for various water temperatures. Any dramatic temperature increase that reduces the dissolved oxygen to less than about 3 ppm can kill fish.

Table 12–11 Saturation values for dissolved oxygen in fresh water at sea level

Temperature (°C)	Dissolved Oxygen (ppm)	Temperature (°C)	Dissolved Oxygen (ppm)
0	14.6	15	10.2
1	14.2	16	10.0
2	13.8	17	9.8
3	13.4	18	9.6
4	13.2	19	9.4
5	12.8	20	9.2
6	12.4	21	9.0
7	12.2	22	8.8
8	11.8	23	8.6
9	11.6	24	8.5
10	11.4	25	8.4
11	11.0	26	8.2
12	10.8	27	8.0
13	10.6	28	7.9
14	10.4	29	7.9

Dissolved carbon dioxide in water is also important to living things. Animals and plants produce carbon dioxide as a waste product from their life processes. Carbon dioxide also readily dissolves in water from the air and from natural processes. A high level of carbon dioxide in water usually corresponds to a low level of oxygen. Both harm living things. Polluted water is usually high in carbon dioxide.

Materials

- several jars for water samples
- water test kit for dissolved oxygen
- 250-mL beaker
- 2 medicine droppers
- 50 mL phenolphthalein solution
- 50 mL sodium hydroxide solution
- graduated cylinder
- watch or clock
- graph paper
- thermometer
- apron and goggles

Directions

1. Collect water samples from several places in the water study area. Divide each sample in two. Label the samples so you know where each came from.

CAUTION: Wear an apron and goggles.

2. Using a water test kit, measure the relative dissolved oxygen concentration of each sample.

   a. Follow directions in the kit for testing dissolved oxygen. Since oxygen reactions occur continuously, you should test your samples in the field to get accurate, repeatable results.

   b. Measure and record the temperatures of the water samples.

   c. Graph the data on temperature and saturation levels for dissolved oxygen from Table 12–11.

d. Compare the data on dissolved oxygen in your water samples. How do they compare with the saturation levels for dissolved oxygen?

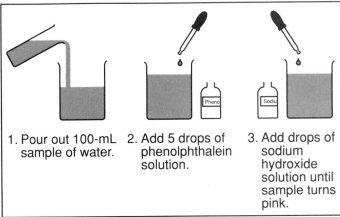

1. Pour out 100-mL sample of water.
2. Add 5 drops of phenolphthalein solution.
3. Add drops of sodium hydroxide solution until sample turns pink.

Figure 12–12 Testing for dissolved carbon dioxide

3. Measure the relative dissolved carbon dioxide in each water sample collected.

a. Pour a 100-mL sample of water into a beaker.

b. Add 5 drops of phenolphthalein solution to the water sample. Mix by swirling.

NOTE: If a light pink color appears in the water and remains after 1 minute, the water sample has no carbon dioxide in it. Record zero in your data table.

c. If no pink color forms, add sodium hydroxide solution to your water sample one drop at a time. Swirl after adding each drop. Count the drops of sodium hydroxide solution needed to turn the water light pink.

NOTE: A light pink color may form, then disappear in a few seconds. Continue adding drops of sodium hydroxide solution until the water stays pink.

    d.   Using the rating scale below, read and record in your data table the number of drops used and the relative dissolved carbon dioxide.

0 drops	No carbon dioxide
1–5 drops	Low carbon dioxide content
6–10 drops	Medium carbon dioxide content
11+ drops	High carbon dioxide content

4. Add your data to the map of the water study area prepared by the Environment Team.

5. Prepare a report on the data your group collected to share with the rest of the class. Be prepared to explain the following:

    a.   The importance and the effects of dissolved gases in water

    b.   How you performed the tests

    c.   Your data on dissolved oxygen and carbon dioxide in the water samples

TEAM D. NUTRIENTS

Plants and animals cannot grow without nutrients in the form of *nitrates* and *phosphates.* These two substances, along with *potassium,* are the major ingredients of commercial fertilizers. Nitrates and phosphates are important in water quality because excess amounts stimulate the growth of *algae.* Large growths of algae, called *blooms,* can clog streams and lakes and reduce oxygen levels at night, making the water unsuitable for many water animals.

Nitrates

Nitrates appear in water systems from the actions of some kinds of bacteria, from animal wastes, from septic tank breakouts, and from fertilizer runoff from farmlands, gardens, and lawns. Nitrates can also form when electrical storms convert nitrogen and oxygen in the air into nitrogen dioxide. This gas combines with rainwater to form nitric acid rain, which reacts with soil minerals to produce nitrates.

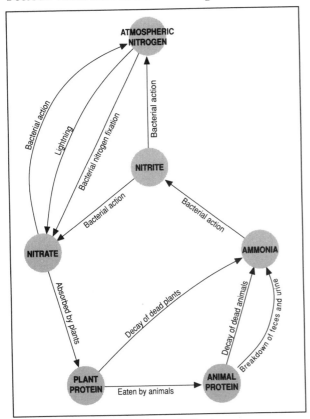

Figure 12–13 Formation of nitrates

High nitrate levels are especially dangerous in drinking water for infants under 6 months. Chemical reactions in the infant's stomach reduce the blood's capacity to carry oxygen. A shortage of oxygen can result in methemoglobinemia, or "blue baby" syndrome, which in extreme cases can kill the baby. Nitrate levels of 10 ppm or higher are dangerous.

Phosphates

Phosphates enter water systems from contact with high-phosphate soils, from phosphate-based detergents, and from runoff from farms, gardens, and lawns. Phosphate concentrations are high in wastewater from homes and industries.

Most natural waters contain .01 to .05 ppm of phosphate. In weak wastewater the average concentration is 5 ppm, in medium wastewater 15 ppm, and in strong wastewater 30 ppm. The phosphate concentration of domestic wastewater can be reduced, but the treatment is so expensive that it is rarely used.

Materials
- several jars for water samples
- nitrate and phosphate test kit
- apron and goggles

Directions
1. Collect water samples from several places in the water study area. Divide each sample in two. Label the samples so you know where each came from.

CAUTION: Wear an apron and goggles.

2. Using a test kit available from chemical suppliers, measure the relative nitrate concentration of each sample. Follow directions in the kit for the test for nitrates.

3. Measure the relative phosphate concentration in each water sample.

4. Add your data to the map of the water study area prepared by the Environment Team.

5. Prepare a report on the data your group
   collected to share with the rest of the class.
   Be prepared to explain the following:

   a. The importance and effects of nitrates
       and phosphates in water

   b. How you performed the tests

   c. Your data on dissolved nitrates and
       phosphates in the water samples

TEAM E. SUSPENDED SOLIDS

A highly productive water system—one with a high capacity for supporting
life—is said to be *eutrophic*. Eutrophic water usually results in choking or
suffocating algae blooms that threaten animal life by depleting the oxygen
in water. An *oligotrophic* system has low productivity and fertility.
Measures of *total suspended solids* (TSS) and *turbidity* determine the
productivity of water.

Suspended solids in water consist primarily of silt, industrial wastes,
human and animal wastes, decaying plant and animal matter, and living
and dead *phytoplankton* and *zooplankton*. The quantity of total suspended
solids is the weight of material suspended (not dissolved) in a volume of
water.

It is difficult to set standards for TSS. Locally established *norms* are
averages of measurements over several years. Wide deviations from local
norms usually signal problems. Values below the norm may signal low
productivity; values above the norm may signal high productivity.

Closely related to TSS is *turbidity*. A turbidity reading tells how much light
passes through water. Because water containing suspended material
absorbs and scatters light rays instead of transmitting light in a straight
line, a turbidity reading can indicate total suspended solids.

Turbidity in groundwater or surface water shows that solids may be
present. Because solids can harm health, turbidity must be kept low.

Materials
- several 1-L jars for water samples
- balance
- funnel
- filter paper
- flashlight

Directions
1. Collect 1-L samples of water from several places in the water study area. Label the samples so you know where each came from.

2. Measure the total suspended solids in each water sample.

    a. Measure the mass of a clean, dry filter paper on a balance. Measure to the nearest .01 g.

    b. Put the filter paper in a funnel. Filter a 1-L sample of water through the filter paper.

    c. Dry the filter paper completely.

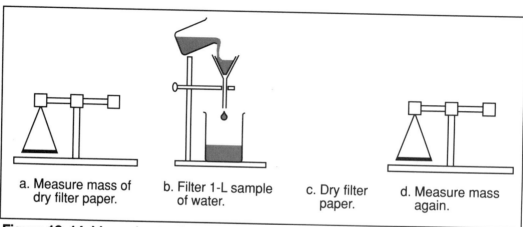

a. Measure mass of dry filter paper.

b. Filter 1-L sample of water.

c. Dry filter paper.

d. Measure mass again.

Figure 12–14 Measuring total suspended solids

d. Measure the mass of the filter paper again. The difference in mass between the first and second measurements is the mass of the total suspended solids in 1 L of water. TSS values are commonly reported in milligrams per liter (mg/L). Record your TSS value.

e. Find out the TSS for the water area you are studying from local officials who monitor water quality.

3. Measure the relative turbidity of each water sample.

a. Swirl the water sample to keep all the solid matter suspended. Shine a light through a jar containing the water sample. Use the same jar for each water sample.

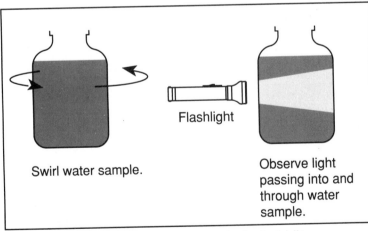

Swirl water sample.

Flashlight

Observe light passing into and through water sample.

Figure 12–15 Testing a water sample for turbidity

b. Observe the scattering of light rays as they pass into and through the water sample.

c. Rate the turbidity using this scale:

0	No turbidity	Light passes through without scattering.
1	Low turbidity	Light passes through with slight scattering.
2	Some turbidity	Obvious absorption and scattering of light rays.
3	High turbidity	Light rays absorbed or highly scattered. Little or no light passes through.

d. Record your data.

4. Add your data to the map of the water study area prepared by the Environment Team.

5. Prepare a report on the data your group collected to share with the rest of the class. Be prepared to explain the following:

a. The importance and the effects of suspended solids in water

b. How you performed the tests

c. Why you used the same equipment in each test

d. Your data on dissolved suspended solids in the water samples

TEAM F. LIVING ORGANISMS

The abundance and variety of organisms living in and around water systems give clues to the quality of the water. Carefully observe the kinds of plants growing around the water in your study area. Are there long grasses? Reeds? Cattails? What kinds of plants are growing in the water? Do they resemble aquarium plants you have seen? Are there water lilies? Do plants grow in shallow water or deep water? What kinds of animals, fish, and insects can you see? Smell the air. What kinds of odors can you detect?

Some forms of life are so tiny that they can be seen only through a microscope. Microscopic living things swimming or drifting in water are generally called *plankton*. Microscopic plants are called *phytoplankton;* microscopic animals are called *zooplankton*. Plankton are important foods for many water animals.

Even smaller than plankton are *bacteria*. Bacteria can be *pathogenic* (harmful) or *nonpathogenic* (not harmful). Any body of water naturally contains some bacteria. It is when the bacteria count is high that we worry. When people swim or surf or water ski, their skin, eyes, ears, and nasal passages are exposed to bacteria. Drinking or accidentally swallowing some impure water also introduces bacteria into the body.

Water can become contaminated with large numbers of harmful bacteria when septic tanks fail, animal wastes are not properly managed, or municipal sewage is not properly treated. The harmful bacteria in these wastes come primarily from human and animal *feces*. Healthy humans and animals all contain some pathogenic and nonpathogenic bacteria.

Pathogenic bacteria in large numbers pose a health risk. The most common illnesses caused by swimming in contaminated water are infections of the eye, ear, skin, and nasal passages. Mild stomach illnesses are also common. More serious waterborne diseases such as typhoid and cholera are rare in the United States because state and federal governments require that almost all discharged wastewater be disinfected by chlorination.

Materials
- several jars for water samples
- plankton tow net
- hand lens or microscope
- water-bacterial pollution kit
- apron and goggles

Directions

1. Observe and describe the plants and animals living in the water and on land in the water study area. Use a data table similar to Table 12–16 to organize and record your observations.

Table 12–16 Observations of living things in the water study area

Location Number	Water or Land	Average Depth	Type of Plants	Number of Different Kinds of Plants	Type of Animals	Number of Different Kinds of Animals

2. Conduct odor tests on samples of water.

   a. Collect water samples from several places in the water study area. Use glass jars, not plastic ones. Label the samples so you know where each came from.

b. Shake the sample. Open the jar and sniff lightly. Disagreeable odors in water often come from decaying plant and animal matter, decomposition of sewage, industrial wastes, or by-products of the life processes of microscopic living things.

c. Record the code letters from Table 12–17 that best describe the odor.

Table 12–17 Qualitative descriptions of water odor

Code	Odor
A	Spicy
B	Cucumber-like
C	Flowery
D	Geranium-like
E	Sweetish
F	Industrial/chemical
G	Chlorine
H	Petroleum
I	Medicinal
J	Rotten eggs
K	Disagreeable
L	Fishy
M	Pigpen
O	Sewage
P	Damp earth
Q	Peaty
R	Grasslike
S	Rotten straw
T	Moldy, damp cellar

3. Get or make a plankton tow net.

a. Refer to the reference booklet "Sampling Methods" for information on making and using a plankton tow net.

b. Collect samples of plankton from the water study area.

c.   Observe the plankton through a hand lens or microscope.

    d.   Describe and record the kinds of organisms you find.

CAUTION: Wear an apron and goggles.

4. Determine the bacterial count of water samples from the water study area.

    a.   Collect several samples of water.

    b.   Obtain a water-bacterial pollution kit. The kit has all the materials. Follow the directions for preparing the test.

    c.   Incubate the bacteria cultures. Count the colonies that result. Record your data.

5. Add your data to the map of the water study area prepared by the Environment Team.

6. Prepare a report on the data your group collected to share with the rest of the class. Be prepared to explain the following:

    a.   The importance and effects of living things, including plankton and bacteria, on the quality of water

    b.   How you performed the tests

    c.   Your data on living things in the water samples

13. PURIFYING WATER

Background

In Investigation 8, The Water Cycle, we learned that water is recycled over and over again. In fact, we still have about the same amount of water on Earth as we have always had. It has been reused many times.

But the water is not always clean. Substances from many sources can contaminate the water, making it unfit for our uses. Table 13–1 summarizes information on major water pollutants.

In wastewater in streams and reservoirs, contaminants are broken down into smaller components by such organisms as bacteria, worms, snails, and one-celled animals. The smaller components are then used as nutrients by algae and water weeds to grow and reproduce.

The process of breaking down matter in wastewater and then using the products to make new living tissue is called *assimilation*. Nearly every stream or reservoir can assimilate some wastewater without harming the living things in the water. However, when there is more waste in the water than living things can assimilate, the water is said to be *polluted*.

The average person in the United States uses about 150 gallons of water a day and produces about 120 gallons of wastewater or sewage. What happens to this water that disappears down the drain?

Table 13–1 Water pollutants and their effects

Pollutant	Source	Detrimental Effect
Plant and animal waste	Wastewater treatment; farm animals; nonpoint source runoff	Can kill aquatic life
Bacteria and viruses	Leakage from septic tanks on porous soils or high water tables; sewage treatment plants; boat discharges; animal feedlots; urban runoff	Contaminates shellfish, causing human diseases when consumed; contaminates groundwater and surface water, causing disease when it is consumed or infection when it is used for swimming or bathing
Nutrients	Agricultural, horticultural, and urban runoff; discharges from industries and boats; sewage treatment plants; septic tanks; animal feedlots	Nutrient enrichment results in algae blooms, causing eutrophication; algae blooms deplete oxygen, killing fish; eutrophication causes some fish diseases
Sediment	Land clearing; dredging; erosion	Clogs waterways; covers habitats and smothers organisms; causes turbidity, shading out plants and altering food chains
Fresh water	Water runoff; land clearing; floods; draining wetlands; channeling streams	Changes salinity patterns, affecting habitats, killing or stunting juvenile organisms; lowers reproduction rates
Temperature	Factories; electric generating plants; urban runoff; sunlight on drought-lowered streams	Alters fish reproduction; reduces dissolved oxygen causing fish kills
Petroleum products	Fuel exhausts; motor oil and grease; power plant emissions; industrial discharges; spills and dumping; leaking underground storage containers; urban runoff	Spills kill aquatic life, damage beaches, destroy wetlands; runoff is toxic to marine organisms, causing death, disease, and reproductive problems
Chlorine	Water treatment plants; swimming pool backwash	Kills aquatic life
Heavy metals (copper, zinc, lead, cadmium, mercury)	Fuel and exhaust from motorboats and automobiles; industrial emissions/effluent; landfill wastes; urban runoff; natural deposits in soils; hazardous waste spills/disposal	Accumulates in fish tissues, causing disease, brain damage, birth defects, miscarriages, and infant deaths when eaten by humans
Toxic waste	Forestry, urban, and agricultural runoff; industrial and municipal effluent; spills or dumping	Causes cancer, birth defects, and chronic illness when consumed in contaminated water or affected seafood

Problem

1. What happens to our wastewater?

2. How can contaminated water be purified so that it can be reused safely?

Materials

- samples of contaminated water
- graph paper
- apron and goggles
- other materials needed for experimental designs

Procedure

1. Divide the class into groups of three or four.

2. Find out what happens to the sewage from your school and your community.

   a. Choose one of the investigations in Table 13–2. The same investigation may be done by more than one group, but all investigations should be completed.

   b. Carry out your investigation.

Table 13–2 Sewage treatment investigations

Group Number	Investigation
1	Find out where wastewater from your school goes. Make a scale drawing of the wastewater system in your school. Look for such evidence of the sewer system as manhole covers, drains, and gutters. Post the drawing.
2	Find out where the wastewater from your community goes, what kind of treatment it gets, and where it is dumped. Report to the class.
3	Find out about primary treatment of sewage, what processes and organisms it uses, and how pure the treated water is. Report to the class.
4	Find out about secondary and tertiary wastewater treatment, what processes and organisms it uses, and how pure the treated water is. Report to the class.
5	Find out how a septic tank works, what processes and organisms it uses, and how pure the resulting water is. Report to the class.

3. Design a way to purify a sample of water.

    a.   Develop a plan in your group. Write out the plan. Include a flow diagram. List the materials you will need.

    b.   Have your plan approved by your teacher for safety. Your teacher will give your group a sample of contaminated water.

CAUTION: Wear an apron and goggles.

    c.   Carry out your plan. Measure the pure water you get. Measure the time the process takes. Record the results. Share your plan and results with other groups.

Summary

¶1. What kinds of treatment is sewage given in your community?

    a. Where is sewage from your school and community treated?

    b. Which level of treatment (primary, secondary, or tertiary) is best for your community? Why?

    c. How does a septic tank work to treat sewage?

    d. What effect would absorption, percolation, and capillarity of water in soil have on the operation of a septic tank?

2. If the average person produces 120 gallons of sewage a day,

    a. How much sewage does a person produce in a year?

    b. How much sewage does your school produce in a day? In a year?

    c. How much sewage does your community produce in a day? In a year?

    d. How does the national average of sewage produced by one person compare with your estimate of your own water use in Investigation 9?

¶3. Prepare a summary report of wastewater treatment in your community. Share your report with students in other schools, states, or countries.

    a. Find out how sewage treatment is alike and different in other communities.

    b. Which wastewater problems or issues in other communities are similar to those in your community? Which are different?

4. Share the results of your water-purifying designs with the class.

   a.   Explain how you purified your contaminated water sample. Tell how much purified water you got and how long it took to get it.

   b.   Make a bar graph of the quantities of purified water obtained by each design.

5. Is your sample really pure? How can you tell?

   a.   What does "pure" mean?

   b.   Would you drink your "pure" sample? Why or why not?

6. Compare natural and technological systems of purifying water.

   a.   How is water purified naturally? List the ways.

   b.   How are wastewater assimilation in a stream or reservoir and wastewater treatment in a sewage treatment plan similar? How are they different?

   c.   What happens to treated sewage water dumped from a sewage treatment plant?

Challenge

   1. In some parts of the world desalination is used to make fresh water.

   a.   Find out how much water costs in your community.

   b.   Find out how much desalinated water costs.

   c.   Why is desalination not widely used to produce fresh water?

   2. Arrange to visit the sewage treatment plant in your community. Identify the parts of the treatment system.

3. Invite a person from the agency responsible for sewage treatment in your community to speak to your class.

   a. Ask the person to explain the operation of the sewer system and the treatment plant.

   b. Be prepared to ask questions about wastewater management in your community.

4. In what ways could you reduce the amount of sewage you produce each day?

   a. Make a plan to reduce your sewage by 10%.

   b. Decide how following your plan would affect your lifestyle.

   c. Try out your plan.

   d. In class discuss other ways to conserve water and reduce sewage.

14. MANAGING WATER RESOURCES

Background
Water is a vital resource. But who owns it? And who is responsible for ensuring its quality?

Several bodies of law determine who has a right to use our nation's water. Federal laws take top priority. But much of the land is controlled by states or cities, so they determine who may use most of the water. The policies of industry and the habits of people also determine how water is used.

Water User Rights
During the 200 years of our history, four important legal principles about the rights to use water have evolved in the United States. The states have built their legal systems of water rights on one or more of these four principles:

> *Riparian or Common Law Rights.* The person who owns the land above a water source has absolute ownership of underlying groundwater and may use it with no limits on the amount.

> *Reasonable Use Rights.* This rule restricts the right to "reasonable" use of water. A landowner's right to use water is limited only when the water supply is not adequate to meet immediate demands.

> *Appropriation Rights.* This rule is "first come, first served." The people who used the water first have the strongest claim to the water supply when it is limited. This rule could stop the drilling of new wells in areas that are considered fully developed.

> *Correlative Rights.* All landowners have the same rights to the groundwater they need to supply their lands on top of the water supply. If too many are trying to use the water supply, the courts decide how to divide it. This rule can lead to lengthy and costly legal battles.

Other rights, known as overriding rights, can take priority over the four legal principles of water rights used by the states.

Overriding Rights include
- federal rights to water for land reclamation and conservation
- Indian reserved rights for Indian reservations
- Pueblo rights to communal water supplies in former Spanish territories
- federal rights to water needed for national security

Government Agency Roles

Governments not only determine who may use water; they also monitor the quality of water. Both federal and state governments pass laws setting up agencies to make and enforce regulations on water quality. County and city governments also pass laws or codes to control water quality in their jurisdictions.

Two kinds of government agencies manage water quality. The first kind is *regulatory agencies,* which enforce laws dealing with water quality, disposal of wastes, and wastewater treatment. Examples of such agencies are the federal Environmental Protection Agency, state departments of health, state departments of environmental management, and county and city agencies that grant permits and inspect water systems.

The second kind, *nonregulatory agencies,* manage, develop, and monitor natural resources. These agencies rarely have authority to enforce water quality laws, but they usually work closely with regulatory agencies to protect and improve water quality. Examples are the Tennessee Valley Authority, the Bureau of Reclamation, and the Soil Conservation Service. At the local level there are sewage and water supply boards. These agencies collect data on water resources, conduct research, build and operate reservoirs, promote conservation of resources, and participate in activities related to water quality management.

Federal and state agencies share responsibility for water quality in several ways. Federal agencies often set standards and write regulations that are enforced by state regulatory agencies. State agencies determine the amount of wastewater treatment required of cities or industries to protect quality in streams and lakes. Cities and industries collect water samples, test them, and submit monthly reports to the state agencies to show whether the level of treatment is consistent and sufficient to prevent pollution.

Federal Legislation

Our national concern for clean, fresh water is reflected in a long history of federal legislation. The first federal law to protect the nation's waters from pollution was the Rivers and Harbors Act of 1899. Stronger legislation was passed in 1948. Under this law, the states retained primary responsibility for water quality standards and management. The federal government supplied money for research. The law provided only weak punishments for offenders.

During the 1960s, amendments provided for federal water quality standards, federally approved state standards, and increased funding for research. However, as water pollution increased in many areas of the country, public concern led to two more important environmental laws.

The National Environmental Policy Act of 1969 set the stage for all environmental protection laws that followed. In response to this act, the states created or strengthened their own water quality or water resource agencies. The act also required environmental impact statements for all major activities that might damage the environment.

The federal Water Pollution Control Act (Clean Water Act), passed in 1972 and amended in 1977 and 1987, is the basis for most current water quality regulations. Other federal laws that deal with water quality are the Safe Drinking Water Act passed in 1974 and amended in 1977 and 1986, the Toxic Substances Control Act passed in 1976 and amended in 1984, and the Surface Mining Reclamation and Control Act passed in 1977.

Shifting Emphases

Major changes of role are unlikely in water management. But as point sources of pollution come under control, attention is shifting to nonpoint sources. The Clean Water Act of 1972 had only weak provisions for nonpoint sources because there were few practical methods of controlling them. Now nonregulatory agencies are working to develop, demonstrate, and promote practical techniques for controlling nonpoint sources.

The Personal Dimension

Water conservation is the practice of using water resources efficiently and protecting them from pollution. Wise use of our water resources has become more and more important as demands from industries and cities mount. The costs of distributing water and treating wastewater are rising steadily. It is becoming more urgent that each of us develop good water-conservation habits. An abundant supply of clean water is essential for public health and economic growth.

Problem

How are water resources managed in my community?

Procedure

1. Divide the class into groups of three or four. Decide which group will take responsibility for fact-finding in procedures 2–6 below.

2. Find out what principles of water rights determine water use in your state. Prepare a report to the class.

3. Find out what groups *manage* the water supply and the sewage treatment facilities in your community. Prepare a report to the class.

4. Find out what groups *regulate* the water supply and sewage treatment facilities in your community. Prepare a report to the class.

5. Find out which citizens' groups in your area work on water resource management.

   a. Contact one or more of these groups. Find out what their concerns are and what they are doing about them.

b. Collect information, brochures, leaflets, posters, and other materials from each organization.

c. Invite a guest speaker from one of the organizations to tell the class about water conservation.

6. Find out what individuals and groups can do to conserve water.

7. Develop a class water-conservation code. Prepare a list of rules to live by to practice water conservation.

8. Discuss the code in class. Then revise your rules as necessary.

a. List reasons for each rule.

b. After the discussion take a vote on adopting the code.

c. Follow the rules in your water-conservation code for a month.

Summary

1. How do federal and state water use rights affect you as a user of water?

2. How do groups managing the community's water supply and sewage treatment affect you as a user of water?

3. How do groups regulating your community's water supply and sewage treatment affect you as a user of water?

4. How do federal and state water pollution laws affect you as a user of water?

5. How can following a conservation code benefit you and others?

6. What are the similarities and differences between rights, laws, and codes?

7. Do you agree or disagree that "having enough quality water ultimately comes down to the decisions of individuals"? Why?

New Vocabulary for Section B

acid rain
aeration
algae blooms
assimilation
bacteria
brackish
brine
density
dissolved gases
eutrophic
hydrometer
nitrates

nonpathogenic
nonpoint source
nonregulatory agencies
norms
oligotrophic
pathogenic
pH
phosphates
phytoplankton
plankton
point source
pollutant

rate of flow
regulatory agencies
salinity
saturation value
sewage
source
total suspended solids
turbidity
wastewater
water conservation
water rights
zooplankton

15. PLANNING FOR THE FUTURE: A SIMULATION

Background

Welcome to Kaiholo, a wonderful place to live. Kaiholo, on our state's windward coast, has a unique environment—steep mountain ridges to the north and the ever-changing ocean to the south.

The dominant feature of the area is Wailana Marsh, covered by grasses, cattails, and other aquatic plants. The marsh is a nursery for hundreds of animals that spend their lives there or move into the ocean as adults. By holding vast amounts of runoff from the mountains during our frequent heavy rainfalls, it controls flooding in our community.

The Kaiholo community has grown rapidly in the last 30 years. Thirty years ago it was largely uninhabited. Only four vacation homes had been built. Wailana Marsh covered much of the area. Figures 15-1 through 15-4 show how the community has changed over the years.

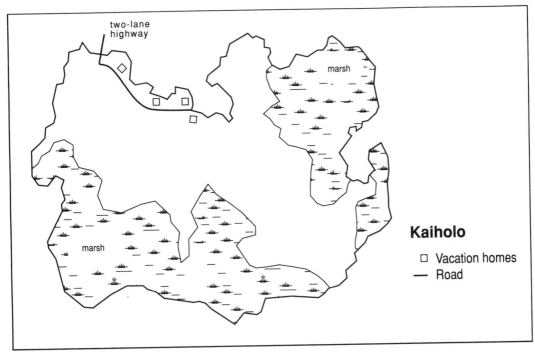

Figure 15–1 Kaiholo 30 years ago

- A winding two-lane road over the mountains connected Kaiholo to other parts of the state.
- Four vacation homes formed a small community.
- The marsh dominated the area.
- The population was 42.

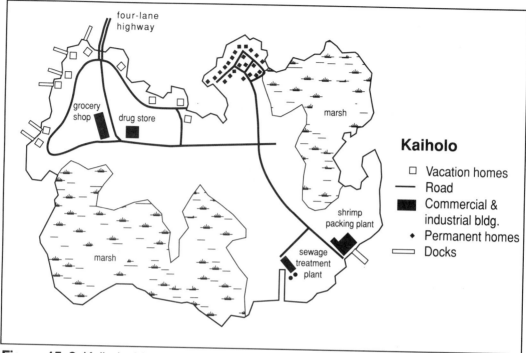

Figure 15–2 Kaiholo 20 years ago

- A four-lane highway tunneled through the mountains, connecting Kaiholo to other parts of the state.
- Travel time to Kaiholo was short.
- A housing development provided homes for workers in the community and commuters who worked outside.
- A shrimp-packing plant employed local workers.
- A sewage treatment plant used primary treatment to process wastewater.
- A supermarket and drug store served the needs of the community.
- The population was 5,523.

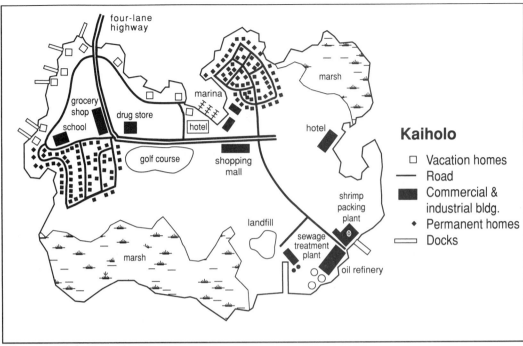

Figure 15–3 Kaiholo 10 years ago

- The shrimp-packing plant expanded, employing more workers.
- More housing was built as the community grew.
- A sanitary landfill handled solid wastes.
- An oil refinery employed workers.
- A shopping mall served the growing community.
- Two hotels, a golf course, and a marina served the needs of tourists and the community.
- A new school provided education for youngsters.
- The population was 22,271.

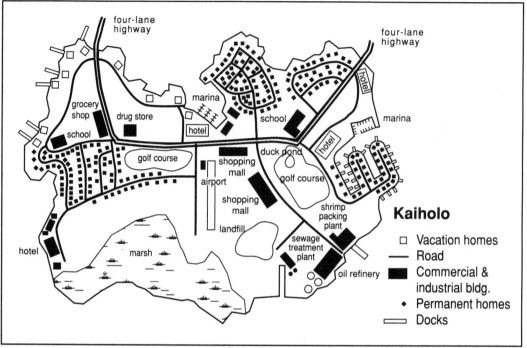

Figure 15–4 Kaiholo today

- A second four-lane highway makes travel to and from Kaiholo even easier.
- A small airport was recently completed.
- Two more hotel complexes, a public marina, and another golf course provide for the needs of an increasing tourist trade.
- The sanitary landfill was recently enlarged.
- A new housing development with boat ramps attracts fishermen and water enthusiasts.
- A second school is needed.
- A pond has been dredged on the golf course to attract migrating birds.
- The population is 57,836.

As you can see, our community has grown remarkably in 30 years. The demands of the population for space, water, and recreational facilities have grown with it. With all the building, Wailana Marsh has been greatly reduced in size. We now face new challenges.

The question now before the community is what to do with what remains of Wailana Marsh. Three proposals have been presented. A town meeting has been called to discuss the issue and to advise the city planning department. People representing many points of view have come to this meeting. They all feel very strongly about their positions.

Proposal 1. Drain the marsh. Create an expanded marina and housing complex. Channel the water into the ocean.

Proposal 2. Drain the marsh. Create a business, industry, and housing complex. Channel the water into the ocean.

Proposal 3. Leave the marsh as it is.

Activity
Help decide the future of Wailana Marsh.

Materials
• chart paper
• colored markers

Procedure
1. Examine the maps of Kaiholo in Figures 15–1 through 15–4.

    a. Look at Figure 15–1. What percentage of Kaiholo was marsh 30 years ago? How much is marsh now?

b. Look carefully at the amount of
    development.

    • How has transportation changed?
    • What industries have been added?
    • What recreational facilities have been
       added?
    • What public services have been
       provided to meet residential and
       industrial needs?
    • What impact do these public services
       have on water resources?
    • In what ways have people used the
       marsh? What have been the effects?
    • Why is the marsh important to
       Kaiholo?

2. Prepare to present a position, discuss the
    problems, and make decisions on the future
    of Kaiholo and its water resources. You may
    need to argue for a position that is not your
    own.

    a. Work with a partner or a small group.

    b. Your teacher will assign a role and
        position to each group. You and your
        partners will present the position.

    c. Read the role you are to play.

    d. Prepare a position statement to be given
        at a town meeting. Use the information
        you have been given and add information
        of your own. Try to convey the strong
        feelings associated with your position.
        Be ready to compromise.

3. Play out the simulation on the future of Wailana Marsh.

    a.   Decide who will chair the meeting.

    b.   Prepare a large map of present-day Kaiholo. Post it in the front of the room.

    c.   Open the meeting by calling for testimony on all positions represented. Have each person tell what should be done with the remaining marsh and why.

    d.   After the testimony, open discussion on the issue. Make lists or drawings of proposed uses of the marsh. At the end of the discussion, vote on the proposals.

Summary

¶1. List the needs identified in the town meeting that you think are important. Rank them from most important to least important.

¶2. What proposed developments, if any, were in the plan adopted? How will these developments affect water resource management in the community?

3. What proposed developments were not included in the adopted plan? Why not?

¶4. Did you have difficulty finding a balance between development and conservation? If so, what were the problems?

¶5. Did you find cases in the planning process where the wishes or needs of a person or a small group became more important than needs of the whole community? Which cases? What compromises were made?

¶6. How does this simulation relate to real-life situations in your community? Do some land and water issues parallel issues in this simulation? Which ones?

New Vocabulary for Section C
simulation

APPENDIX 1. MEASUREMENT

TOOLSHEET 1. INTRODUCTION TO MEASUREMENT

In science we observe and describe the properties of things we see. Some properties—size, weight, duration, and temperature, for example—can be measured.

Measuring is determining the amount or quantity of a property by comparing it with a standard. A *standard* is a defined value of a property. For example, a second is the standard for measuring time.

The Metric System of Measurement

The metric system of measurement, devised by the French in 1791, has been adopted by all major nations. Scientists around the world use it to avoid having to convert measurements between systems.

Table 1 lists basic units of measurement and devices for measuring them. The toolsheets that follow explain the units and tell how to use the devices.

Table 1 The metric system of measurement

Measurement	Basic Unit of Measurement	Measuring Device
Length	Meter (m)	Metric ruler, meterstick
Mass	Gram (g)	Metric balance
Area	Square meter (m^2)	Metric ruler, metric area grid
Volume	Cubic meter (m^3)	Metric ruler, metric area grid, overflow container
Capacity	Liter (L)	Metric graduated cylinder, graduated beaker
Temperature	Celsius degree (°C)	Thermometer
Time	Second (sec)	Timing devices

Units in the metric system are based on multiples of ten, making calculations easy. Prefixes in the words for units tell the multiples and fractions of the basic units. For example, the prefix *milli* refers to one one-thousandth (1/1,000) of the basic unit. Thus in length there is a millimeter; for mass there is a milligram; and for time there is a millisecond. Table 2 lists the prefixes used in the metric system.

Table 2 Prefixes in the metric system of measurement

Prefix of Unit Measurement	Multiple of Unit Measurement	Example of Equivalent Measurements
Myria-	Ten thousand	10,000 m = 1 myriameter
Kilo-	One thousand	1,000 m = 1 kilometer (km)
Hecto-	One hundred	100 m = 1 hectometer (hm)
Deka-	Ten	10 m = 1 dekameter (dkm)
[None]	One	1 m = 1 meter (m)
Deci-	One-tenth	1/10 = .1 m = 1 decimeter (dm)
Centi-	One-hundreth	1/100 = .01 m = 1 centimeter (cm)
Milli-	One-thousandth	1/1,000 = .001 m = 1 millimeter (mm)
Micro-	One-millionth	1/1,000,000 m = .000001 m = 1 micron (μ)

Uncertainty in Measurement

No measurement is completely accurate; every one contains a degree of *uncertainty,* which may be due to *human error,* because each person makes measurements differently, or to *instrument error,* because no instrument is absolutely perfect.

We assume that some measurements are greater and some are smaller than a "true" measurement. By averaging many careful measurements, we come closer to the "true" value than we can with one measurement.

TOOLSHEET 2. METRIC LINEAR MEASUREMENT

Length is a measure of *distance* between two points. The standard unit of length in the metric system is the *meter*. The meter was originally defined as one ten-millionth (1/10,000,000) of the distance between the equator and the north or south pole.

A *metric ruler* is used for measuring length. The commonly used units are the meter (m), the centimeter (cm), the millimeter (mm), and the kilometer (km).

Using a Metric Ruler

1. Measure the distance between two points as shown in Figure 3.

    a. Put the zero mark of a ruler at one of the points.

    b. Note the marking on the ruler at the other point.

2. Read the distance directly from the unit marks on the ruler or count the marked units between the points.

    a. Estimate the remainder of the distance in tenths of the marked unit.

    b. Read the distance in one kind of unit. For example, read "35 mm" or "3.5 cm," **never** "3 cm and 5 mm."

3. Record the distance in the measured unit or its equivalent in another unit.

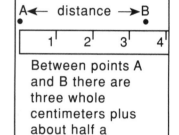

Between points A and B there are three whole centimeters plus about half a centimeter.

The distance between points A and B is about 3.5 cm.

Equivalent lengths: .035 m = 3.5 cm = 35 mm

Figure 3 Using a metric ruler

Equivalents of some units of length:

1 m	= 100 cm	=	1,000 mm
.01 m	=	**1 cm**	=	10 mm
.001 m	=	.1 cm	=	**1 mm**

TOOLSHEET 3. INTRODUCTION TO GRAPHING

A *graph* is a "picture" of numerical data that shows relationships between two or more measured observations. Graphs can be used to average data and make predictions.

Making a Graph

1. Record your measurements in a data table. See Figure 4.

2. Mark and label the axes on a sheet of grid paper. See Figure 5.

   a. Draw the *horizontal axis* along one of the lines running from left to right.

   b. Draw the *vertical axis* along one of the lines running up and down.

   c. The horizontal and vertical axes meet at a point called the *origin*.

   d. Label each axis with the name and unit of measurement.

3. Determine a *scale* or number of units represented by each grid line. For example, grid lines might represent a time of 10 seconds or distances of 2 meters or 5 centimeters. Note that the scale is marked at the lines, not the spaces between the lines. Mark and label each scale. See Figure 6.

Data on the Movement of a Balloon

Time (sec)	Distance (m)
0	0 (start)
1	4
2	11
3	12
4	16

Figure 4 Data on the movement of a balloon

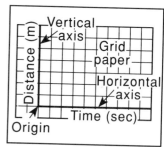

Figure 5 Labeling a graph with units of measurement

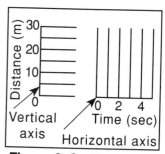

Figure 6 Scaling a graph

a. Choose a scale large enough to include all your measurements.

b. Select simple and convenient units. Note that equal spaces between lines represent equal scaled measurements.

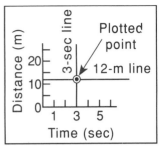

Figure 7 Plotting data

c. Use enough space for the scale on each axis to keep from crowding the data. Begin the scales at the origin. Move upward on the vertical axis, to the right on the horizontal axis.

4. *Plot* a point on the graph for the intersect of each pair of measurements. Circle each point to make it easy to see. See Figure 7.

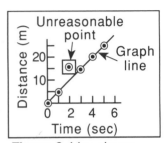

Figure 8 Line drawn through plotted points

5. Put a box (❑) around any plotted points that seem unreasonable. See Figure 8.

6. Draw a line or curve through the points that make a pattern showing relationships between the measured observations. See Figure 8.

Checking a Graph

Figure 9 is a sample graph showing what you should have on your graph. Check your graph to make sure it meets these conditions:

1. It is identified with a title, the date, and your name.

2. Its axes are labeled with the kinds of measurement (distance, time, etc.) and the units of measurement (meters, seconds, etc.).

3. The number of units represented by each line on an axis is marked.

4. The plotted points are circled.

5. The line or curve is smoothly drawn through the pattern of points.

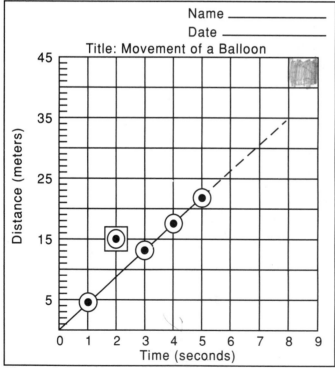

Figure 9 Sample graph of the movement of a balloon

Uses of Graphs

1. Graphs are used to show relationships between measured observations.

   a. If there is a pattern in the plotted points, the observations are probably related. A straight line drawn through points indicates that the ratio between the measurements is about the same for most of the plotted points.

   b. If there is no pattern in the plotted points, the observations are probably not related. See Figure 10.

2. Graphs are powerful tools. They can be used to make predictions about events that were not measured.

   a. Making predictions from data on the graph *within* the range of measurements is called *interpolation.* In Figure 9 it is clear that no one measured the distance the balloon traveled in 4.5 seconds. By interpolating we can see that the balloon probably traveled about 20 meters in 4.5 seconds.

   b. Making predictions from data on the graph *beyond* the range of measurements is called *extrapolation.* For example, in Figure 9 a dashed line extends the pattern of data points beyond the ones measured. By extrapolating we could predict that the balloon would probably travel about 35 meters in 8 seconds.

3. Graphs are often used to average the data from pairs of readings. Identical data points are shown by short lines radiating from a plotted point. The graph line represents average measurements. See Figure 10.

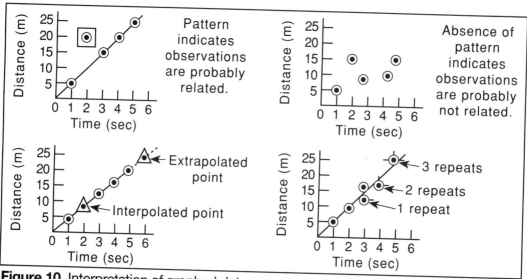

Figure 10 Interpretation of graphed data

TOOLSHEET 4. METRIC MASS MEASUREMENT

Mass is a measure of the amount of "stuff" or matter in a thing. The *gram* is the standard unit of mass in the metric system. It was originally defined as the mass of 1 cubic centimeter of pure water at 4 degrees Celsius.

Weight is a measure of the pull of gravity on an object. Weight is often confused with mass. The weight of an object changes when the pull of gravity changes, but its mass does not change. For example, the force of gravity of the moon is one-sixth that of Earth, so an astronaut on the moon weighs only a sixth as much as he does on Earth. But the mass of the astronaut remains the same because his body is composed of the same amount of "stuff" on the moon as on Earth.

The instrument used to measure mass is called a *balance*. The kilogram (kg), gram (g), and milligram (mg) are common units of mass.

Using a Balance

Figure 11 is a sketch of a typical Dial-O-Gram balance. Each division on the upper beam represents 100 grams. The lower beam is subdivided into 10-gram units. Each division on the dial represents 1 gram. The *vernier scale* measures hundredths of units. Your teacher will show you how to use the vernier scale if your balance has one.

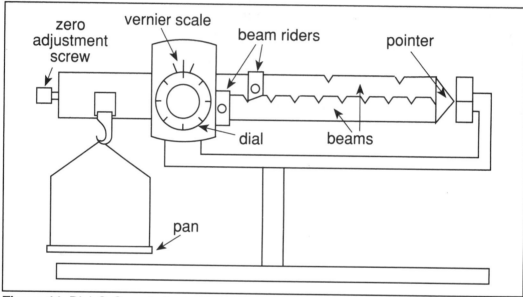

Figure 11 Dial-O-Gram balance

To use a Dial-O-Gram balance or one like it, follow these steps:

1. Clean the balance pan.

2. Put all the *beam riders* in the notches at zero and turn the dial to zero. Check for balance.

   a. The device is balanced when the pointer swings an equal distance above and below the zero point or comes to rest at zero.

b. If the pointer does not come to rest on zero, turn the zero adjustment screw in or out until it does.

3. Measure the mass of an object.

    a. Put the object on the balance pan.

    b. Approximate the mass by moving the riders on the beam. Make sure the riders rest in the notches.

    c. Adjust the riders and the dial until the pointer swings equal amounts above and below the zero on the scale or comes to rest there.

4. Determine the mass by adding the readings on the riders and the dial.

5. Record the mass in grams or equivalent units.

    Equivalents of some units of mass:

1 kg	=	1,000 g	=	100,000 cg	=	1,000,000 mg
.001 kg	=	**1 g**	=	100 cg	=	1,000 mg
.0001 kg	=	.01 g	=	**1 cg**	=	10 mg
.00001 kg	=	.001 g	=	.1 cg	=	**1 mg**

Care of the Balance

1. Return the riders and the dial to their zero positions.

2. Wipe off any spills in the balance pan.

3. Cover the balance.

Using Containers on a Balance

Sometimes you will use a container to hold a substance—liquid, gas, or fine particles—that cannot be put directly on the balance pan. Then you must subtract the mass of the container to determine the mass of the substance. Follow these steps:

1. Use the balance to determine the mass of the empty container. Read and record its mass.

2. Put the substance into the container. Measure and record the total mass of the container and the substance.

3. Subtract the mass of the empty container from the total mass of the container and the substance.

$$\text{Mass of substance} = \text{Mass of container and substance} - \text{Mass of empty container}$$

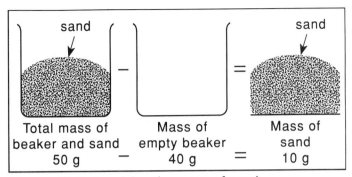

Figure 12 Determining the mass of sand

4. Record the mass of the substance in the measured unit or its equivalent. See point 5 under "Using a Balance" for equivalents of some units of mass.

TOOLSHEET 5. METRIC AREA MEASUREMENT

Area is the amount of surface of an object. Its two dimensions, length and width, are linear measurements. Some commonly used units of metric area measurement are the square meter (m^2), the square centimeter (cm^2), and the square millimeter (mm^2).

You can use a *metric area grid* to find the approximate area of a flat surface regardless of its shape. You can find the area of a regularly shaped surface by calculation.

A grid is a set of crisscrossing horizontal and vertical lines. Because the lines are equal distances apart, they make squares of equal size.

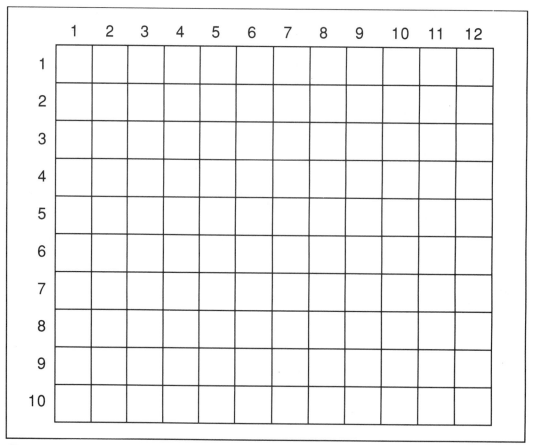

Figure 13 Metric area grid ruled in square centimeters

The squares in the sample metric grid shown in Figure 13 are 1 cm long and 1 cm wide. Each square in the grid has an area of 1 square centimeter (1 cm²).

Using a Metric Area Grid

To use a metric area grid to find the area of a flat surface, follow these steps:

1. Lay the object on a grid paper so that one edge lies on a grid line. Trace the outline of the object on the grid paper. Remove the object.

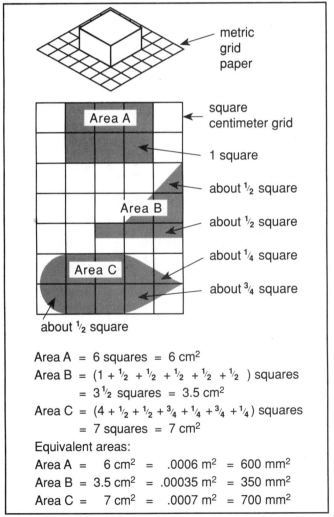

metric grid paper

square centimeter grid

1 square

about ½ square

about ½ square

about ¼ square

about ¾ square

about ½ square

Area A = 6 squares = 6 cm²
Area B = (1 + ½ + ½ + ½ + ½ + ½) squares
       = 3½ squares = 3.5 cm²
Area C = (4 + ½ + ½ + ¾ + ¼ + ¾ + ¼) squares
       = 7 squares = 7 cm²
Equivalent areas:
Area A =   6 cm² =   .0006 m² = 600 mm²
Area B = 3.5 cm² = .00035 m² = 350 mm²
Area C =   7 cm² =   .0007 m² = 700 mm²

Figure 14 Measuring area on a metric area grid

2. Measure the surface area of the object.

   a. Count the whole squares in the outline.

   b. Estimate the fraction of each partial square in the outline.

   c. Add the whole squares and the fractions of squares.

3. Record the area in the measured unit or its equivalent.

   Equivalents of some units of area:

1 m²	=	10,000 cm²	=	1,000,000 mm²
.0001 m²	=	**1 cm²**	=	100 mm²
.000001 m²	=	.01 cm²	=	**1 mm²**

Calculating Area

To calculate the area of a square or rectangular surface, follow these steps:

1. Measure the length and width of the object with a metric ruler.

2. Multiply the length by the width.

   Area = Length × Width

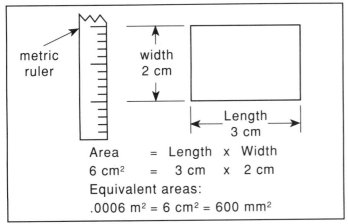

Figure 15 Calculating area

3. Record the area in the calculated units or an equivalent. See point 3 under "Using a Metric Area Grid" for some equivalents of units of area measurement.

TOOLSHEET 6. METRIC VOLUME MEASUREMENT

Volume is the amount of space occupied by an object with three dimensions: length, width, and height. Some units of volume measurement are the cubic meter (m^3), the cubic centimeter (cm^3), and the cubic millimeter (mm^3).

Capacity is the amount of space occupied by a liquid, a gas, or a collection of solid particles. It is the volume that can be filled by a substance. The *liter* (L) is the standard unit for measuring capacity. Another commonly used capacity unit is the *milliliter* (mL). The volume filled by 1 cubic centimeter of a substance is 1 milliliter. Thus 1 mL is equal to 1 cm^3.

You can find the volume of a regularly shaped object by multiplying the linear measurement of its three dimensions. You can find the volume of an irregularly shaped solid by measuring the liquid it displaces. Use a *graduated cylinder* to measure the volume of displaced liquid.

Calculating Volume

The standard unit for measuring and expressing volumes of objects is the cubic centimeter. It is equal to the volume of a cube measuring 1 centimeter on each edge.

To find the volume of a rectangular solid, follow these steps:

1. Find the area of the base of the object. See Toolsheet 5, Metric Area Measurement, for information on measuring area.

2. Use a metric ruler to measure the height of the object.

3. To calculate the volume of the object, multiply the base area by the height. See Figure 16.

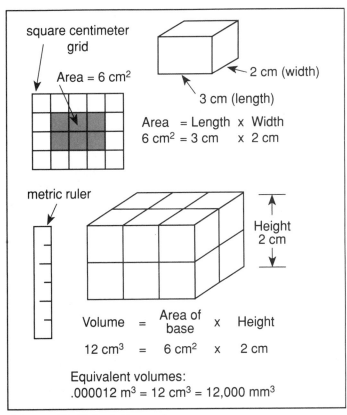

Figure 16 Calculating volume

4. Record the volume in the measured unit or its equivalent.

Equivalents of some units of volume:

$$\begin{array}{rcl}
\mathbf{1\ m^3} & = & 1{,}000{,}000\ cm^3 & = & 1{,}000{,}000{,}000\ mm^3 \\
.000001\ m^3 & = & \mathbf{1\ cm^3} & = & 1{,}000\ mm^3 \\
.000000001\ m^3 & = & .001\ cm^3 & = & \mathbf{1\ mm^3}
\end{array}$$

Using a Graduated Cylinder to Measure Volume

A *graduated cylinder* (also called a *graduate*) used to measure volume is marked in milliliters. A volume of 1 mL is equal to a volume of 1 cm³.

To measure the volume of a liquid, follow these steps:

1. Set the graduate on a flat, level surface and pour the liquid to be measured into it.

2. Bring your eyes directly opposite the bottom of the *meniscus*, the thick curved band marking the surface of the liquid. See Figure 17.

3. Read the volume of the liquid.

   a. Read the mark at the bottom of the meniscus.

   b. Estimate the volume in tenths of the unit marked on the graduate.

4. Record the volume in the measured unit or its equivalent.

   Equivalents of some units of volume:

1 L	=	100 cL	=	1,000 mL
.01 L	=	**1 cL**	=	10 mL
.001 L	=	.1 cL	=	**1 mL**

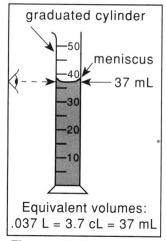

Equivalent volumes:
.037 L = 3.7 cL = 37 mL

Figure 17 Reading a graduated cylinder

Using an Overflow Container to Measure Volume

An object put into an *overflow container* full of liquid pushes some of the liquid out of the container as the object sinks. The liquid that is pushed out is called *displaced liquid*. It flows through the spout of the overflow container into a *catch container*.

The volume of an object that sinks completely is equal to the volume of the displaced liquid. But if the object floats, the volume of the displaced liquid is equal to just the volume of the submerged part of the object.

To measure the volume of a solid object, follow these steps:

1. Fill the overflow container with water. Let the excess water flow through the spout into a catch container. Empty the excess water from the catch container.

2. Put the empty catch container under the spout of the overflow container.

3. Determine the volume of the object.

    a. Put the object into the overflow container.

    b. Let the displaced water flow into the catch container.

    c. Pour the displaced water into a graduated cylinder. See Figure 18.

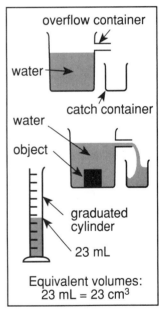

overflow container

water

catch container

water

object

graduated cylinder

23 mL

Equivalent volumes:
23 mL = 23 cm³

Figure 18 Using an overflow container to measure volume

4. Read the volume of displaced water in the graduated cylinder. See points 2 and 3 under "Using a Graduated Cylinder to Measure Volume" for information on reading marks on a graduated cylinder.

5. Record the volume in the measured unit or its equivalent.

Equivalents of some units of volume and capacity:

1 L	=	1,000 mL	=	1,000 cm³	=	1,000,000 mm³
.001 L	=	**1 mL**	=	1 cm³	=	1,000 mm³
.000001 L	=	.001 mL	=	.001 cm³	=	**1 mm³**
1 L	=	.001 m³				
1,000 L	=	1 m³				

TOOLSHEET 7. INTRODUCTION TO DENSITY

Density is the relationship between the mass and volume of an object or a substance. It may be expressed as the number of grams in 1 cubic centimeter (g/cm³) of an object or as the number of grams in 1 milliliter (g/mL) of a substance.

The density of an object or a substance can be determined from a graph of its mass and its volume. Density can also be calculated by dividing the mass of an object by its volume.

Using a Density Graph

A density graph shows the relationship between the mass and volume of an object or a substance. Mass measurements are plotted on the vertical axis, volume measurements on the horizontal axis.

To determine the density of an object made of the same material throughout, follow these steps:

1. Measure and record the mass and volume of several different samples of the same kind of object.

2. Make a density graph. Plot the masses of objects measured in step 1 on the vertical axis. Plot the volumes of objects measured in step 1 on the horizontal axis. Draw a line through the pattern of points for each kind of object. See Toolsheet 3, Introduction to Graphing, for information on constructing a graph.

3. Read the density graph.

   a. On the graph find the *density point*—the point on the density line or curve that intersects the 1 cm³ or 1 mL line.

Data on the Density of an Object	
Mass of Sample (g)	Volume of Sample (cm³)
9.0	3.0
7.0	2.5
6.0	2.0
4.5	1.5

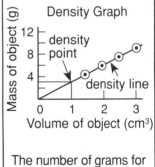

The number of grams for the density point is 3 g.

Density of object = 3 g/cm³

Equivalent densities: 3 g/cm³ = 3 g/mL

Figure 19 Determining density from a graph

445

b. Read the number of grams on the vertical axis corresponding to the density point.

4. Record the density in g/cm³ or g/mL. (1 g/cm³ = 1 g/mL.)

Calculating Density

1. Determine the mass and volume of a substance. See Toolsheet 4, Metric Mass Measurement, and Toolsheet 6, Metric Volume Measurement, for information on measuring mass and volume.

2. To calculate the density of the substance, divide its mass by its volume.

$$\text{Density} = \frac{\text{Mass}}{\text{Volume}}$$

3. Record the density in g/cm³ or g/mL. (1 g/cm³ = 1 g/mL.)

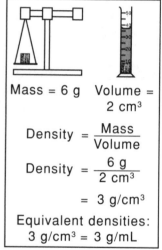

Mass = 6 g   Volume = 2 cm³

$$\text{Density} = \frac{\text{Mass}}{\text{Volume}}$$

$$\text{Density} = \frac{6 \text{ g}}{2 \text{ cm}^3}$$

$$= 3 \text{ g/cm}^3$$

Equivalent densities:
3 g/cm³ = 3 g/mL

Figure 20 Calculating density

TOOLSHEET 8. TEMPERATURE MEASUREMENT

A *thermometer* measures the temperature—the hotness or coldness— of substances. Scientists around the world use the degree Celsius (°C) as the standard unit of temperature.

Using a Thermometer

1. Carefully take a thermometer out of its case.

2. Gently put the bulb of the thermometer in direct contact with the substance whose temperature you want to measure. Hold the thermometer vertically.

3. Bring your eyes directly opposite the level of the liquid column in the thermometer.

4. Read the temperature.

   a. Read the highest mark on the thermometer below the top of the liquid column.

   b. Estimate the height of the liquid column beyond the highest mark in tenths of the units indicated on the thermometer.

5. Record the temperature of the substance in °C.

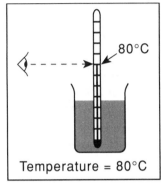

Figure 21 Reading a thermometer

Care of the Thermometer

1. Prevent the thermometer from dropping or rolling.

2. Use the thermometer to measure temperatures only within its range. **Do not** overheat it.

3. **Do not** use the thermometer for stirring.

4. If the liquid in the column splits, put the thermometer in a container of methanol and dry ice to recombine the liquid.

5. After using the thermometer, rinse it with tap water and let it dry.

6. Carefully replace the thermometer in its case.

CAUTION: Use alcohol thermometers. If you have only a mercury thermometer, be extra careful. Mercury can damage your health. If a mercury thermometer breaks, take these precautions:

1. **Do not let the mercury contaminate shoes.**

2. **Do not sweep up the mercury with a broom.**

3. **Use a syringe or a medicine dropper to pick up pools of mercury.**

4. **Sprinkle zinc metal powder on small spills. The powder will form a relatively safe amalgam that can be thrown out with other solid laboratory wastes.**

5. **Because it is almost impossible to pick up all bits of spilled mercury, ventilate the room for a long time after a spill.**

TOOLSHEET 9. TIME MEASUREMENT

Devices used to measure the passage of *time* include clocks, watches, and metronomes. They measure time in seconds (sec), minutes (min), or hours (hr). Long periods are measured in days, months, years, or centuries; very short periods are measured in milliseconds.

Using Timing Devices

1. Measure the time between the start and finish of an event.

   a. At the start of the event, read and record the time registered on the timing device.

   b. At the finish of the event, read and record the time registered on the timing device.

   c. Determine the time of the event by subtracting the final time from the starting time.

   Time of event = Final time – Starting time

2. Record the time of the event in the measured unit or its equivalent.

   Equivalents of some units of time:

1 hr	=	60 min	=	3,600 sec
1/60 hr	=	**1 min**	=	60 sec
1/3,600 hr	=	1/60 min	=	**1 sec**

APPENDIX 2. CERTIFIED *FAST 1* TEACHERS

1970–71

Pago Pago Afualo
Bette S. Carter
Chester L. Christensen
Sr. Joan Cornett
Sadie R. DeVirgilio
Alice Farmer
Ronald M. Flegal
Randall G. Fontes

Caren C. C. Goo
Malcolm Harris
Arlene M. Inamine
Donald M. Inamine
Sr. Jeannette Joaquin
Floyd M. Larson
Kay Hew Len
Frank E. Lutz

Sr. Ellen Joan Malone
Louise Matsushige
Martha D. McDaniel
Sr. Anne Maura
  McGarvey
Janet Ohta
Masao Okasako
Trinidad F. Sebastian

Marie Sugita
Tomasi F. Tukuafu
Peter Walker
Mary M. Weigle
Corrine Wong
Pauline Yanagisawa
Donald B. Young

1971–72

Calvin Abe
Caroline Abe
Thelma Akau
Barbara Baker
Corinne Briten
Claudia Chun
Pauline DeSai
Judith Driscoll
Marilyn Fujikawa
Douglas Fujimoto
Susan Fukunaga
Daniel Hallgrimson
Pamela Hashimoto

Vernon Hee
Ross Hiatt
James Hiramoto
Craig Holland
Donald Hughes
William Husztek
Barbara Jones
Sr. Eva Joseph
Takayoshi Kawahara
Kathleen Kim
Roger Kim
Maryann Kobayashi
Sr. Brenda Lau

Faustina Lazo
June Low
Kingsley Luke
Stanley May
Emma Mimura
Daniel Mito
Robert Miyabuchi
David Miyauchi
Raymond Mow
Ayako Nakata
Linda Nunokawa
Mae Oda
Richard Oyama

Steven Pascua
Robert Pels
Bertha Sakimura
Larry Sayre
Gwendolyn Shigekane
William Shigetani
Seiji Shimabukuru
Leonora Springer
Roy Takayama
Jane Takayesu
Howard Tenma
Jeanette Wong
Ronald Yamada

1972–73

Thomas Abe
Florence Asato
Alama Ayers
Sr. M. Matthew Brazil
Patrick Cockett
Norman Cox
Kay Crumley
Margaret Dierdorff
Claudette Enriques
Sr. M. Nicholina
  Estevez
Cathryn Fay

Michael Gaber
Cary Honda
Dave Hotaling
Mark Hubbard
Richard Ishii
Gretchen Y. Y. Jong
Milton Kanehe
Richard Kimitsuka
Satoe Kunioki
Rex Layne
Edwin Lindsey
Judith Machiguchi

James Matsumoto
Frank Mattos
Betsy Moneymaker
Robert Morimoto
Betty Morioka
Ann Nagamatsu
Sr. M. Raymond
  Orquejo
Daniel Pang
Sr. M. Matthias Pardo
Douglas Pendleton
Sr. Bernadine Perez

John Reising
Lon Renard
Nancy Rocheleau
Peggy Shimabuku
Toshie Shishido
Lorraine Silva
Twylla-Dawn Steer
Linda Suprenant
Velma Tanahara
Albert Uyeno
Marvin Villines
Margaret Wilson

1973–74

William Abbey
Josie Clausen
Sr. M. Tereshita
  Constantino, O.P.
Margaret Cox
Sharon Dillon
Ernest Dela Cruz
Adeline Fleming
JoAnn M. Fu

Mary Guerrero
Jay Ishimoto
Barbara Jamile
Timothy Jerry
Delano Kawahara
Jerry Kawahara
Kathleen Kimura
Stephen Kow
Roy Ledesma

Rick Mayor
David McHugh
Mona Y. Miyamura
Florence K. Miyashiro
Raymond Morikawa
Wayne Nakai
Donald S. Quon
Axeline Rodrigues
Dennis Santiago

Winona Sears
Joan Snook
Mary Streveler
Chris Town
Eugene Uegawa
Kathleen Yamamoto
Steven Yim

1974–75

Richard Akiyama
Sr. Beatrice Alop
James Barry
Donald Chaney
Janet Chin
Frances Chin-Chance
Reynold Choy
Howard Date
Meng Sung Doty
Pamela Finley
Michael Fisher
Pauline Foss
Sandra Fujio

Charles Giuli
Martha Haia
Yolanda Hall
Marlene Hapai
Pauline Higa
Jane Hiraoka
John Hom
Sr. Helen Janssen
Michael Kawaguchi
Michael Kawahara
Margo Lau Kong
Laurie Lindsay
Marie Maddison

Miriam Mita
Witkon Nelson
Eva Nishina
Lorraine Noda
Helen Nowaki
Stella Okita
Karlen Ono
Arlene Oyabu
Ronald Pang
Nelda Quensell
Douglas Rice
Darrel Smith
Theresa Smith

Richard Taira
Ellen Tanaka
Sr. Emerita Tejano
Barbara Thompson
Byron Toma
Emil Wolfgramm
Josephine Wong
Allen Yamada
Tokio Yamaguchi
George Yamamoto
Rudolph Zimbra

1975–76

Aichy Aisok
Aromon Aningi
Edison Anjain
Sr. M. Auxiliadroa, O.P.
Andy Bill
Julia Borges
Charlotte Cambra
Virginia Carollo
Myrna Cooper
Judith DelliColli
Juda Eradrik
Mary Fernau
Cynthia Fujii
Mark Henry

Akinori Imai
Jimmy James
Carl Jeadrick
Morris Jetnil
Ishmael John
Bedinin Joseph
Kaiboke Kabua
Glenn Kadota
Carol Ann Kato
Jackie Katz
Sandra Kinro
Bangrike Komanta
Ebita Kotton
Patrick Lang

Bandrik Langidrisk
Jelton Lanki
Joseph Laszlo
Kasuo Leander
Utaro Lincoln
Frances Lodge
Hester Manigault
Linda Melcher
Nang Nangmine
Poly Navarro
James Rivera
Maria Consuelo Rogers
Harry Sam
Sr. Aurelia Sanchez

Louise Souza
Eleanor Summers
Edith Tamashiro
James Teshima
Andrew Tibon
Hellis Titok
Gene Tsuhako
Lynne Ushida
Minnie Wigfall
Dora Wiley
Sharon Yamagada

1976–77

James Bartz
Mary Bender
George Ching
Pam Coffey

Sandra Decker
Thelma Grant
Lillie Heyword
Maxine Nagamine

Thomas Proctor
Jo Shepard
Maxine Tanner
Br. Kevin Thomas

Jean Watson
Helen Wesley
Joy Whisenant
Darice Young

1978–79

Diane M. Banks
Marilyn Bliss
Dale K. Bordner
Barbara Culliney
April Doi

Jean Hatashima
Judith Kawamata
Kingsley Luke
Blanche McHugh
Mae Mikami

Florence Pasion
Sr. A. Sumagaysay
Edward J. Valente
C. Cecil Wilkinson
Barbara K. Yamamoto

Bert Yamasaki
Caroline Young

1979–80

Billie-Ann Adachi
Thomas Arinaga
Thomas Chun

Molly Corcoran
Clarice Drose
Lorene Hata

Kathryn Lee
Warren Low
Alan Ramos

1980–81

Emma Sue Amos
Michael W. Dabney
Kathleen D'Amico
Astrid Ferony
Charles Gillow

Gary Greeder
Jimmy Hicks
Dorothy Hosoda
Sandra Linsky
Tholman Luey

Sr. Pia Macauba, O.P.
James Schulz
Seiji Shimabukuro
Judi Smith
Daniel Tada

Harold Takahashi
David White
Patricia Young

1981–82

Deborah Boltz-Hinojosa
Carol Brennan
Barbara Dodge

Craig Nakamura
Florentina Ritarita
John Southworth

Cynthia Suehiro
Terri Towata
Lillian Wong

1982–83

Janet Armstrong
Sterling Bell
Robert Bliss
Delores Bolling
Mitchell Braddon
Ronald Briscoe
Remi Cabrera
Richard Caudill

Gines Cornelio
Nellie Falsgraf
Susan Green
Gail Hayashi
Kathryn Inouye
Anne Tuney Layton
Annette Kearns
Barry Kelly

Ann Kennedy
Marsha Kristol
Douglas Logan
Jim Mahar
Frank Mattas
Linda Mattas
Mary McKiinzie
Susan Meyer

Suzanne Michelony
Richard Mills
Mark Muranaka
Maureen Muranaka
Glen Nakamura
Marcus Pottenger
Mark Shanahan
Paul Thorp

1983–84

John Barbano
Jeri Bryden
Jim Buck
Mary Carlson
Arlene Chang
Nancy D'Ameto
Mark Durlacher
M. Kathy Eaton
Rowland Gaal
Peg Geringer
Juanita Gex
Jeff Gingrich

Jean Gize
Charlene Gonzales
Marsha Harbin
Kathlyn Harris
Elizabeth Igra
Dan Judnick
Marlynn Kaake
Barbara Kalama
Bonnie Kleeberg
Wayne Kozuma
Arthur Kurrasch

Mike Laney
Martina Lawlor
Howard Lucas
Justin Mew
Kathy Molina
Reiko Nakazawa
Risa Quon
William Rourke
Thomas Scarlett
Betty Stanley
Jody Timm

Allison Trembley
Bill Vallem
Jane Vartanian
Ann Wall
Sylvia Waters
Carol White
John White
Linda Wight
Frank Yamasaki

1984–85

Mike Bakis
Linda Barror
Jack Bettencourt
Sr. M. Edna Billones, O.P.
Vern Burrows
Dave Carlson
Mike Carroll
Dennis Conklin
Lonnie Cook
Rick Copus
Bob Corbett
Bill Cosby
Dale Cretser
Gary Cross
Joe Deleon
Alva Duke

Lynda Elias
Cathy Fatzer
Jef Fern
Richard Garmire
Cindy Geddes
Maureen Gouveia
Judson Hall
Florence Harker
Nanna Hartsell
Beverly Hays
Marie Hodges
Claudette Holland
Bruce Inlow
Gary Johnson
Kyra Johnson
Ron Johnson

Don Kennedy
Dan Kohl
Gertrude Martin
Manley Midgett
Ed Newburg
Grace O'Leary
Patricia Page
Phyllis Perez
Mike Reid
Burch Robbins
Guy Romero
Marcus Rosario
Frank Sheldon
Jeff Sheline
Beverly Shook
Alan Shratter

Norma Siagan
Juda Sigrah
Austin Jack Smith
Martha Soares
Frank Souza
Georgia Stamp
Richard Stewart
Jim Teixeira
Ted Walsh
Rich Wickersham
Jan Wrede
Eric Wuersten
Marilyn Wyatt
Linda Yarbrough
Charles Yonce
Jon Young

1985

Pasquale Aceto
Jim Adams
Amy Addison
Barbara Alcorn
Wende Allen
Robert Anderson
Laureen Andres
Francis Angellotti
John Archer
Judy Atkins
Janet Bailey

Richard Balouskus
Joel Baum
Carolyn Beaver
Carol Best
Celeste Blankenship
Sharon Bond
William Boyce
Stacy Boyle
Sylvan Braa
Alan Brainard
Patricia Brinson

Ray Brooks
Kevin Brown
Aurelia Burke
Terry Dean Burleson
Bonnie Bush
Stephen Cadley
Dennis Carls
Alfred Casayuran
Frances Cashwell
Ruben Castanon
Mike Caudill

Melissa Champlin
Martha Chaney
Karen Chappel
Clarence Coates
Norm Coates
Steve Colgan
Frances Conte
Beatrice Cotten
Alan Cranston
Frederick Cravatt
Armental Crawford

1985 (continued)

Gue Creedon
Gary Culp
Caroline Daly
Patrick Damelio
Gary Danet
Phyllis Daniel
Bill Davis
Joanne Davis
Lewis Davis
Jodean Dela Cruz
Alfred Derenske, Sr.
Pam DeVaun
Jeannie Donaldson
Robert Drake, Sr.
Millard Duchan
Marrion Dunn
James Durgee
Lois Early
Kimberly Edwards
Terry Edwards
Dale Emig
Wesley Emig
Carolyn Emrich
Rita Estridge
Kay Etscorn
Susan Fahlberg
Richard Falcigno
Jonathan Fern
Charlene Fields
Alan Fiero
Sue Flowers
Stan Ford
Maria Fragnoli-Ryan
Martha Fritz
John Fuiell
Vickie Furlough
Jonette Gallagher
Marylee Gaynes
Dennis Gleason
John Gonzales
Carolyn Goolsby
Carol Gordon

Debbie Graves
Jerald Graves
Peggy Gray
Gene Griffith
Jane Haff
Jimmy Hale
Tim Hall
Rosalyn Hancock
Tonya Hancock
Linda Hanson
Scott Hays
Joe Holleran
Phil Hubbard
Phillip Ikemoto
William Johnson
Ken Jones
Michael Jones
Kim Keado
Barbara Klarsch
Ron Kline
Laura Kolb
Pat Krupa
Julie Lacitignola
Nancy Lam
Frank LaMontange
John Larson
Jeanette Lassiter
Helen Lawing
Betty Lewis
Karen Lind
Teresa Long
Debra Lowry
Theodore Lucas
Joyce Maggio
Kathy Manger
Mike Mannshardt
Billy Martin
Shirley McAuley
Lynn McCartin
Elinda McCray
Dale McDuffie
Ernie Mellas

Susan Michael
Curtis Michols
Edith Miller
Faye Miller
Bennie Mims
Beverly Moore
Susan Moran
Robert Morgan
Michael Morres
Nancy Morris
Marlyn Myers
Elaine Nagle
Steve Nardo
Gerald Nordstrom
Daniel Ochs
Ernest Odell
Meridith Olson
Michelle Pearce
Eric Pearlstein
Doreen Peck
Libby Peeler
Lucille Picagli
Linda Poore
Edla Pope
Tanya Pouls
Gaston Pulley
Jean Quattrocchi
Cathy Redman
Amy Reid
Lawrence Reith
Janet Rhodes
Mark Rose
Julia Rushing
Joyce Sasaki
Jim Scarnati
Sharon Schmidt
Wesley Schraeder
Carolynn Sears
Bob Sensenig
Carol Seros
Diane Sharp
Martha Shaw

David Shearard
Gerry Shearin
Bert Siegel
Kathleen Sikes
Kathy Krebs Siqueland
Bruce Sleeper
Janie Smith
Lili Smith
Sr. M. Peter Somollo
Becky Stetson
Ernest Stewart
Gary Sunich
Shirley Swanson
Sandra Tedder
Cindy Tessier
John Test
John Thunen
Craig Tice
James Timson
Eileen Torrey
Mary Trent
Fred Tresselt
Frances Tucker
Irene Uzgiris
Viola Vaughan
Emma Wall
Ruth Ward
Cornelia Weathers
Charles Weaver
Dale Westcott
Dorothy Whitaker
Kim Whitley
Jim Wiley
Mary Wilson
Regina Wilson
Ralph Wise
Dean Yamato
Raymond Yeaton
Daryl Zarpentine
Vicki Zuber

1986

Cynthia Adams
Joan Adams
Joel Agrimson
Willa Agurs
Barbara Allen
Jose A. Alvarez
Ken Anderson
Paul Anderson
Pamela Andrews
Susie Armocido
Emma M. Armstrong
Debbie Avery
Gloria Ayot
Elaine Bailey
Jane Baker

Margie Barnette
Gary Barringer
Susie Bartosh
Tommy Bates
Dorothy Battle
Marylynne Bauer
Rosa Bazemore
Carol Begert
Eileen Eaton Bemus
Carol Billings
Annette Bingham
Thelma Bingham
Barbara Blackmail
Edward Bludnick
Stephen Bombara

Pamela Bookout
William Boudman
Carmen Brewington
S. Brittain
Nancy Brittenham
Bill Brookes
Gilbert Brown
Juanita Brown
Patricia Browne
Bruce Bruntil
Alice Buchanan
Lisa K. Burd
Linda Burkhart
Louise Burks
Linda Burrows

Catherine Callwood
Dee Cannady
Paul Carroll
Tom Castro
Survilla Cherry
Joan Christian
Marla Christopher
N. Church
Jeffrey Clayton
Maureen Cockerline
Diane Colclough
Jewell Coleman
Kathy Coltrain
Francis Cools-Lartigue
Susie Craw

1986 (continued)

Jane C. Crawford
Deborah Curbow
Jenny Curlee
Barry Curseaden
Janno Daniel
Connie Danner
Tamara S. Davies
Larry Davis
Sharon Davis
Betty Dean
Eran Dedoes
Mavis Deich
Rolanda Desrosiers
Colette Dilworth
Donna Dold
Judy Dorety
Jim Doughty
June Doughty
Janice Drenkhahn
Frances Dwyer
Phyllis Edgerton
Janet Edwards
Rita Moore Elliott
Anna Enriques
Clark Everett, Jr.
Dolores Everhart
Gary Ficken
Larry Finnestad
Ellen Francois
Bob Fraser
Katherine Fujii
Toshiyuki Fukuoka
Laura Gable
Liz Gallagher
Carmen Garana
Beth Gemhus
Steva Gentry
Joyce Germany
Ann Marie Gibbs
Dennis Giuntini
Elaine Goins
Antoinette Gombeda
Cynthia Gonzalez
Erline Goodman
David Goodwyn
Kate Grace
Lorin Grahn
Dick Gran
John Green
Patricia Green
Joy Gregory
Mary Gregory
Maggie Gremli
Sarah Grice
Betty Griffin
Gloria Guerra
Ida L. Guirty
Mary Gullickson
Betty Hair
Karen Hall

Robert Hall
Rosa White Hampson
Johnell Hankins
Terri Hardin
Debra Hardy
Maxie Hardy
Lyra Harrigan
Rita Harris
John Harvin
Ginger Hemrick
Oliver Hendrickson
Linda Hicks
Alice Hollan
Joy Holman
Lisa Homrig
Gail Hooper
Doug Hovde
Laura Hughes
Leigh Hunter
Sandra Jacobson
Susan James
Corliss Jenkins
Larry Jensen
Catherine Jernigan
Nancy John
Mary Bess Johnson
Shannon Johnston
Gerald Jones
Mei Ling Joseph
Joan Keenan
Richard Kei
James Kerr
Joe Kilby
Jessie Kimball
Carolyn Kinder
Frances King
Kathy King
Phyllis King
Kathy Kinsman
Barbara Kmetz
Jean Knight
Marsha Knox
Joretta Koontz
Pat Kurowski
Jean Lanier
Jeff Lasala
Amy Lawson
Robert Lehman
Kay Lewis
Donna Liberatore
Catherine Su Lich
Nelson Lindsay
William Lomax
Cindy Low
Stanley Lucas
Norbert Charles Lux
Joseph Macmillan
Mercedes Manalili
Beth Manring
Nancy Manson

William S. Marcelo
Sally Martin
Ken Martinelli
Rita Mason
Edward Matodobra
Lee Maxey
Peggy Mayle
Linda McCarthy
Danita McDonald
Erma McDonald
Jean McInnis
Jim McKinney
Mary Merrick
Cathy Merritt
Norma Mieras
Ruby Miller
Mary Moffa
Shirley Momiyama
Nigel Moore
Martha Morgan
Jeannette Morris
Edward Morrison
Terry Muffley
Virginia Mullis
Roy Myers
Ron Nauer
Margery Navarro
Mary D. Nevsimal
Debbie Niles
Mary Nordstrom
Mae Oda
Hiro Okawachi
David O'Leary
Anita O'Neill
Jim O'Neill
Laurie Oppenheimer
Luann Oswalt
Annie Owens
Steve Parisian
Faye Parker
Sue Parks
Jan Parsons-Hurlbut
Joyce Parzik
John Pauls
Shirley Pauls
D. K. Pedersen
Cyril Pereira
Josephine Perry
Clifford Phifer
Gina Pinto
Cliff Pitzfer
Roger Pitzschler
Jean Pope
Jean Poythress
Melonie Pratt
Dorothy Ralph
Amy Rathburn
Deborah Readinger
Cynthia L. Reyes
Lois Rhodes

Mary Riddick
Lisa Roberts
Michael Robinson
Veronica Ross
Donald L. Routson
Deborah Ruby
Lenore Rypkema
Debbie Saie
Judy Sainsbury
Kay Sandberg
William Sanders
Steven Saslow
Affie Sawyer
Bob Scheldrup
Paulette Schuler
John Sekara
David Te Selle
Beryl A. Watson Shaw
Rose Shinkawa
Kent Simms
Teresa Sink
Harold Smith
Jo Ann Smith
Mary Smith
Melody Smith
Wycliffe Smith
Frances Snyder
Linda Spiller
Candace Sprauve
Grayce Stacey
Jocelyn Stagger
Bill Stets
John Stewart
Mickey Stoker
Susan Stokke
Donald Stone
David Strait
Richard Strohkirch
Dawn Stroupe
John Sumita
Jim Sutherland
Kevin Svinth
Elizabeth Talacek
Christine W. Taylor
Bonnie Temple
Angela Thomas
Linda Thomas
Gerald Thompson
Rick Towle
Cheryl Treadwell
Melrose Treasure
Louis Tremblay
Norma Trevino
Karen Tripple
Carol Vallejo
Doug Van Etten
Peter A. Van Hagen
Rose Ann Verheyen
Pegge Vines
Ron Waldman

1986 (continued)

James Waldroup
Robin Walker
Robert Wall
Mary E. Walton
Alan Ward
Retha Ward

Carson Watford
Valaria Wheatley
Josephine Wheeler
Joyce Whitfield
Karen Lea Whitley
Jim Wiitala

James Wilcox
Barbara Williams
Christie Williams
Keith Williams
Marie Williams
Regenia Williams

Rosamund Williams
Lora Wilson
Roy D. Wingo
Jean Wuerst
Kevin Young
Valerie Yurkovich

1987

Sebastian Amor
O'Dell Anderson
Sara Arnette
Carol Arnold
Lisa Arzberger
Donald Austin
Brenda Kay Avery
Dan Baker
Onita Baker
Natalie S. Barman
Julie R. Bautista
Gean Lynette Beasley
Martha Bellis
Gary Benner
Diane M. Bernaciak
Gunnar Berquist
Shelley Bielec
Cathy Bierman
Debbie Billings
Arlen Bloodworth
Tudor Bogart
Mark Bond
Jerry Brecher
Linda Brines
Thomas Brown
David Brumfield
Shirley Bryant
Clary Carlson
Mary Carowan
Barbara Casey
Jean Chaplin-Davis
James F. Chase
Darryl Christian
Debbie Cooke
Stephen Coon
Mollie Coor
Carl Cotton
Georgia Covington
Jo Ann Covington
Deborah Craig
Alice S. Crawford
Rita Crawford
Gordon Crocker
Allan Csuka
Camille R. Cubit
Ted Dauer
Joe Davalos
Wayne DeBose
Rhonda Dennard
Katie Devery-Wilcox
Lori Dower

Daniel B. Downs
Jane Driver
Arnold T. Duckett
Patricia L. Dugger
Ann Duncan
Jannie W. Duncan
Joyce Eckert
Barbara A. Elam
Gail Elmore
Barbara Emerson
John S. Faubl
Tony Favatella
Martha Felder
Alan Felker
Beth Fields
Bob Fowler
Delores Frantz
Lynda Freeman
Marlene Fuller
Brenda Garner
John A. Garveuto
Diane Gaskin
Phil Gleb
LuAnn Glenn
Dan Goehring
Nancy Goodrum
Jimmie L. Graves
Joyce L. Greer
Jacquelyn Gregory
Peggy Grice
Shirley Grimsley
Jane C. Gross
Carol Hall
Brad Hamblet
Joyce Hardison
Alan Hargus
Barbara Harrington
Dana Harris
Christine W. Hartman
Judith Hazen
Carol Hefter
Pam Hester
Carolyn B. Hill
Neal Hirasaki
Gerri Hirasawa
Sei Ishikawa
Casandra Jennings
Sharon Jernigan
Bessie R. Johnson
David Johnson
Joni Johnson

Wanda Johnson
Dave Jones
Barb Jurecki
Gail Kasm
Martha Kazaniwsky
Ophelia Keaton
Hazel Kenner
Donna Keough
Rex Kerbs
Iris P. Kilpatrick
Thomas F. Kilpatrick
Willis Kleinsorge
Ken Knappe
Evelyn Komegay
Michael Kuthan
Margaret A. Kuzy
Steven Lach
Sue Laycock
Jay Lederman
Virginia Ledgerwood
Skip Lee
Rebecca Lindley
Darrell Linton
Jack Lochbaum
Donna Loftin
Ethel Lofton
Robert Lovell
Kevin Magner
Linda Mahn
Bonnie C. Marshall
Lu Matsumoto
Richard Matsushima
Carolyn K. Maxwell
Athena McCarthy
D. Scott McCormick
Maria McDaniel
Carol McGill
Sherry J. McIlwain
Annie McLaurin
Sophia McLawhorn
Linda McMillan
Marcella McRae
Diane Medeiros
Donna Miller
Gloria Milne
Judy Mitchell
Geneva N. Moore
Teretha Moore
Betty Moorer
Gayle Morgan
Alvie Moritz

Avis Morton
John Moses
Jane Murphy
L. Bennett Myers
Genzo Nakayama
Kathy Lynn Nawlin
Bill Neal
Quinn Nelson
Verdelle Newby
Karen Newcomb
Karin A. O'Donnell
C. Richard Olander
Richard Ono
Shirley Opstrup
Sally Ormsby
Debra Otterby
Diane Otterby
Robyn Pace-Sherma
Shirley L. Pate
Donna Pender-Bean
Brenda Perkins
Elizabeth Perkins
Billie Jo Peterson
Shirley B. Peterson
Elizabeth Pickup
Mary Platt
Jeanette Pointer
Laura Powell
Lou Prevost
Jackie D. Purcell
Robbie Kirby Quinn
Shirley Quinn
Minnie Rainey
Jack Raneill
Ellen Ratcliffe
Ruby Reaves
Johnnie Reid
Tommy Reins
Dave Rice
JoAnn Riddle
Hal Rogers
Anne Rolfe
Lynda Rosander
Marcus Rosario
Terry Rose
Shari A. Ross
Robert Rutherford
Mary K. Sawyer
Robin Schmidt
Henry Scholz
Yvonne Scott

1987 (continued)

Mark A. Sehna
Bernita Shaw
Rose Shepard
Jan Slater
Heather Slauzis
Jody Smith
Marjorie Snyder
Charles Stark
Shira Stark
Rachel D. Starks
Thelma Staton
Linda B. Stefaniak
James E. Stephens

Kathy Stevens
Peggy Stubbs
Janet Swain
Carolyn Thewlies
Danny Thomas
David Thompson
Helen Thompson
Virginia Thompson
Margaret Trybys
Jane M. Tyndall
Duane Uusitalo
Terry Vandergriff
Carol vanHaagen

Berta Carroll Vann
Louise Wackerle
Anne Waibler
Brenda J. Wall
Karen M. Wall
Sheila Walter
Josephine Washington
Shirley Watford
Anne Watkins
Elizabeth Watts
Catherine West
Tina West
Laurie Wilkie

Jacqueline J. Williams
Lauren Wilson
Mary W. Wise
Bennie J. Woodard
Deborah J. Wooten
David Work
Karen Worthington
Pat Wright
Debbie Wynn-Springer
Ellen Yamada-Regidor
Melinda S. Zemba

1988

David Addison
Kelly Aldridge
Craig Anderson
Hattie Anderson
James Andrade
Laureen Andrews-Vines
Nancy Arey
Susan Armocido
Dianne Armstrong
Rebecca P. Arrington
Barbara Bacmeister
Mary Barham
Dean Barnett
Barry N. Bean
Rose K. Beavers
David Bennett
Mark W. Benton
Brenda W. Berry
Ed Bishop
Lois G. Bivins
Lucinda Z. Black
Ronald Blandon
Beverly Blount
Kay K. Bobbitt
Patty Boccia
Florence M. Boggs
Mike Bowers
Patricia Braker
Olivia Branch
Nancy J. Bray
Theresa Gail Bridgers
Barbara Brodsky
Carol B. Brown
Carolyn A. Brown
Kenneth Brown
Rhetta Brown
Annie Bullock
William Butler
Vicki C. Callahan
Robert Calloway
Rocco Cancellaro
Lucille Caron
Dorinda Cartin
Susan Caton

Cathy Chavis
Dorothy S. Childs
Phyllis H. Clark
Robin Clark
Catherine Cleare
Patty Shea Cone
Priscilla Conner
Sharon Constantine
Helen Cook
Sadie Cooper
Dorthey W. Cox
Glenda Cox
Whitney Cox
Gene Crane
Barbara J. Cruce
Laura Cummings
James Daniel
Dottie D'Arruda
Janie S. Davis
Charles A. Dempsey
Bryan Denning
Everlena Diggs
Sorrel Dod
John Domench
Debbie Donovan
Carol Drum
David Duffy
Bill Dufour
Faye Dunn
Glennis Dunn
Carol Eckert
Garlie T. Edwards
Linda G. Edwards
Alisa B. Eller
Martha Elmore
Loren M. Faaland
Gail K. Floyd
Jane K. Ford
Pamela B. Ford
Cindy Frazier
Richard Frazier
Jenny Frederick
Steve Fritz
Bill Fuller

Antonella Gallo
Jeannie Galluzzo
Betty Giaimo
William Gilbert
Patricia B. Godwin
Peggy Goodman
Lois Grass
Carol A. Grooms
Roger Hale
Ann Hannon
Kay Harbison
Charles B. Harris, Jr.
Patti Harrison
Evelyn Hart
Donna M. Hartley
Cora A. Hawkins
Elaine V. Hayden
Alice C. Hearne
Sabrina Hehl
Kathy Herrington
Tracy Hicks
Ruth E. High
Susan Hindman
Janice Hirsch
Jennifer Hodges
Mary Holleman
William Horn
Judi Hornbeck
Daphne Hudson
Larece Hunt
Nathen H. Hunt
Vernita Jackson
Bettye Jefferies
Jacqueline W. Jenkins
Brad Joens
Amy M. Johnson
Brenda Johnson
Hazel A. Jones
Mack V. Jones, Jr.
Michael G. Jones
Warren Jones
Jack Kern
Kim Kilday
Chris King

Bob Kovach
Donna Kovach
Diane Krane
Maxine A. Kunkel
Merry Larson
Paulette Lawson
Sylvia Ledford
Marian Lepper
John Lewis
Marsha Lindsay
Marianne Lisowski
Vickie Littleton
Geri Lobello
Brent Long
Robert Long
Marilee Loughran
Mara E. Lovejoy
Tracy M. Mackall
Mark Maeda
Becky Marsh
Barbara Marshall
Kathleen Martineau
Antonia Martinez
Amy Lynn Maynard
Barbara A. McAllister
Judy McCurdy
Garen McDowell
Jimmy McGill
Peggie W. McLean
Ozella McMillian
Gerald P. Meccariello
Gail D. Mellette
Linda E. Messina
Ann Meyer
Franklin Delano Mobley
Dottie Montague-
  Sanders
George Moore, Jr.
Pamela P. Morgan
Doug Morris
Deborah Mrykalo
John Murphy
Candace L. Murray
Lois C. Muse

1988 (continued)

Patricia Myers
Joan P. Nelson
Patricia Newton
E. Bernadett Nuss
Debbie Nyvall
Nancy M. Outlaw
Dorie K. Parubrub
Dean Paschall
David Pederson
Angie Peterson
Susan Pfeffer
Bernard Pickens
Luz Ponce
Garry W. Poole
Judy Pratt
Margaret H. Price
Exie G. Pritchard
Fran Pudlewski
Jim Pudlewski
Susan Quilici
Darlene Rabb
Maryann Rhodes
Donna Bruff Rickard
Allan L. Riddle

Guy Riggs
Karen Ritch
Patti Rivera
John Roberts
Connie Jo Robinson
Dean Rollins
Susan Rosamond
Vera J. Ross
Marilyn H. Roten
Bill Rusin
Doug Ryniker
Sue Salisbury-VanCamp
Virginia Satisky
Rob Sauer
Barbara Schmidtzinsky
Kjell Schroder
Carol Schuerman
Gerald Semanko
Bruce Shadduck
Leta Sheeley
Patty Shell
Nancy Shelly
Martha D. Shepherd
Rodney Shorten

Stephen Slovenz
Ellen M. Smith
Loretta M. Smith
Carolyn S. Snipes
Kathy Sobolewski
Mark Sontag
Susan Sparks
Cynthia Stallings
Debra Stowe
Betty Sturdivant
Nick Szumlas
Paul E. Talbert
Bob Tatum
Caesar Tavares
Sandra Taylor
Bryan Terauchi
Dawna E. Thompson
Janet L. Thompson
Donna Thornburg
Kathleen Ann Thorne
Betty A. Tolar
Jim Turner
Lynn Tushaus
Raymond Tuten

Sally Tysinger
Toula Van Hooser
Brenda O. Varnadore
Cheryl Veasey
John Villanova
Amy L. Walker
Carol Walker
Marnie Walsh
Sherry Walsh
Jamie D. Ward
Gary West
Julie West
Susan White
Sharon White
Margaret Wiederhold
Audrey Williams
Jeanne Williams
Bonnie Willis
Carolyn Winfrey
Jan Wood
Pat Worms
Jean Wright
M. Ilene Yates
Mattie S. Zuick

1989

Donna Ackein
Martha Adams
Amy Addison
Catherine S. Alligood
Frank Allison
Billy M. Allison
Frances Ambrose
Diane Anderson
Gary M. Anderson
Elaine Andrews
Jerry Anthony
Joyce Antrainer
Alice A. Archer
Dilcy Bankston
Rosemary Barker
Susan Barnhardt
Mary C. Barth
Mary Lou Basler
Elizabeth Bateman
Stephen Bates
Carole P. Baxter-Tanner
Rosa R. Bazemore
Mike Becker
Julia Belford
Lun Benjamin
David A. Bennett
Karla Bennett
Anne Bird
William Bird
Barbara A. Blackman
Crystal Blackman
Christine Blackmon
Jane Blais

Melanie Blankenship
Margaret W. Boor
Renee Boulis
Elizabeth Bowen
Grace M. Bowers
Jayne M. Bowman
Merle Boxhill
Judith H. Bragg
Melissa B. Brester
Winifred M. Breuner
Joe Brimstin
Doris Brisson
Michele Brooks
Brian Brown
Horace Brown
Margaret Brown
Sue Brown
Freda Bruton
James O. Bunnel
Cathy Burein
Bruce Burkard
Deborah E. Burke
Robin Burn
Dorothy Burnette
Jackie Burney
Lois Burns
Linda G. Butler
Sandy Byrd
Steve Canipe
Beverly Cantrell
Fred Caramiello
Scott A. Cardwell
Aloa T. Carter

Cathy A. Cash
Randy Cavazza
Jane Cave
John Child
Pam Church
Samantha Church
Elizabeth M. Clair
Paula Clarke
Susan A. Clements
Saundralynn C. Cluney
Mary Anne Coco
Marva M. Coffie
Judy Cole
Curt Collins
Grant Connors
Robert Considine
Sandra Cook
Vera Cooper
Bill Cornett
Dan B. Couture
Ruth Cox
Brenda Craig
Jim Crawley
Norma M. Creed
Elaine Cunningham
Jeanne Dahl
Lu Anne Daniels-Glenn
Connie B. Danner
Anne Davis
Jeanne H. Davis
Kathleen Davis
Lavon Davis
Loretta Davis

Marianne Davis
Ralph Davison
Patricia F. Dean
Richard Delano
Ron DeMuro
Maggie Desch
Vera J. Diggs
Sophia S. Diorietes
Warren R. Dobbins
Kelly Dodson
Juli Donaldson
Linda Dorsey
Richard Druse
Wes Eary
Lucy Eaton
Sarah I. Eller
Nancy Elliot
Ken Ely
Kirk Emmons
Alan Engel
Sue Engstrom
Harriett W. Evans
Judy L. Evans
Thurman R. Everitte, Jr.
Liane Fabre
Robert I. Faulk
James Fawcett
Alan Felker
Elaine Ferguson
Beth Fields
Cynthia Fields
Patricia A. Finkbiner
Larry Finnestad

1989 (continued)

Rondi L. Fizer
Thomas C. Fleming
Leonor P. Fonesca
Pat Fowler
Karen Frato-Hildebrant
Kerry D. Frederick
Deborah Fuqua
Gene L. Gallock
Valerie R. Galvin
Joni Garrison
Leigh Garrity
Cleo Gatling
Joe Gellura
Pauline Gentry
Marian R. Gerst
Joanne G. Gibson
Wayne Gibson
Candyce Giesler
Delores Gillespie
Gerald E. Gillespie
Donna Godley
Julia Godwin
Jocona W. Godwin
Aaron S. Goetz
Shelli Goldsweig
Valerie Goodmon
Mark E. Goveia
Jim Granes
Cosette Grant
Leonia Gray
Joyce M. Greene
Karen B. Greene
Melva K. Greene
Jane Cranmer Gross
Audrey W. Gum
Matilda G. Gurley
Betty W. Hadden
Sandy Haigh
Tessa L. Hale
Pam Hall
Joanne W. Hammond
Vera Hammond
Phyllis Hansen
Lorene Harris
Posey Harris, Jr.
Victoria Harris
Bryan P. Hartley
Karla Hartzog
Carol Hefter
Darrell T. Henderson
Lorna Henson
Michael A. Hernandez
Carol Hetu
Angela Hewitt
Daryl Hicks
Ruth Hight
Dorothy Hill
Martha Hill
Mike Hill
Anne R. Holloman

Alice B. Hopson
James A. Horak
Linda E. B. Horton
Tom Hoskins
Dianne C. House
Doug Hovde
Tonya Howell
Judy Huggins
Ann Hughes
Janice B. Hughey
Cheryl Hunt
Norene P. Hunt
Elizabeth Hunter
Karen Hutchens
Pat Huwa
Allison Iwamoto
Grace Izzard
Dennis Jablonski
Jean Jarrell
Garth Jensen
Glenn Jezuit
Dorothie A. Johnson
Rita Johnson
C. Robert Jones
Daniel K. Jones
Henry Jones
LeRoy Jones
Nancy Jones
Paul Jones
Paul Kaiser
Kenneth C. Kallam
Ron Kamaka
Linda Kapler
Donald Kay
Martha Kazaniwsky
J. T. Keever
Sue Keller
Michael J. Kelly
Doris Kennedy
Steve Kilfoyle
Phyllis M. Kimber
Mattie Belle Kinard
Barbara J. King-Scott
Linda P. Kirby
Marty Kiser
Sondra G. Klein
Daniel J. Knight
Laura L. Kolb
Joretta L. Koontz
Suzanne L. Kuahine
Mike Kuthan
Dave Lagasse
Justina Lagmay
Theresa Lamaze
Jim Lancaster
Emily Land
Saundra Landes
Jay Lederman
Maxine L. Ledford
Katie Lee

David Legere
James Leib
Linda Leigh
Jan G. Leiner
Laura Leonard
Shirley C. Lester
Steve Levesque
Marie Lewis
Tom Light
Victoria Littleton
Terri Livingston
Eva Lizzell
Jacklyn S. Long
Melinda Long
Sherrie H. Long
Kim Loomis
Kelly Lovejoy
Andy Lowe
Terre F. Lucas
Patricia Lucido
Shari Lujan
Daly L. MacGrayne
Maureen Malavenda
Sue Markert
Linda Marshall
Bruce Martin
Michael A. Martin
Gloria J. Mathews
Mary N. Matthew
Mary Helen Maxwell
Jim McCammon
Sandra G. McCarter
Nathan McCorkle
Michael W. McCracken
Claire McDaniel
Joyce McGuire
Donna B. McHenry
Sherry J. McIlwain
Susan McInnis
Mary C. McLeod
Lula D. McNeill
Robert A. Meade
Charlotte Meares
Jennia Meggs
David Melrose
William Melton
Jerry Micetich
A. R. Middlefor
Jude A. Mikal
Donald Miller
Judith B. Miller
Patricia Millili
Ian C. Mills
Bennie Mims
Deborah Mitzman
Roberta Moll
Joy Montgomery
Gene Moore
Camille Moore-Carroll
Nancy Mosher

Charles Mostar
Joyce Mullen
Kathleen Murlphy
Linda Murray
Louis M. Muse
Letitia Myles
Freida Nance
David H. Nason
Gary H. Nelson
Connie Newell
Judy F. Newell
Pat Noelke
Edith L. Nowak
Cindy J. Nuckols
Martha A. O'Hara
Joan Okai
Darlene Okehie
Deborah D. O'Neil
Sally Ormsby
Raquell M. Ornelas
Judith Osborn
Margaret V. Parish
David Parker
Johnnie Parker
John G. Parker
Cathy R. Parks
Nancy Patch
Ruth Pauly
Tom Pauly
Brenda Pearce
Christopher Peascoe
Barbara Pedersen
Calbert Lee Perkins
Merrell Perlstein
Andrea Phekus
Charles R. Philipsen
Elizabeth Philipsen
Virginia Pike
S. Glenn Pope
Robert E. Potter
Beth Powell
Mary Jo Pritchard
Kay A. Purser
Maureen Quillin
Kate Quinn
John Raffo
Amelia R. Ragan
Betty Jane Ramsey
Jeff Ranck
Callie Randolph
Harvey L. Rash, Jr.
Frances M. Ray
Larry Read
Mike Reid
Frank H. Remington
Allen Reynolds
Mary Lou Rhodes
Joyce Richard
Maria V. Riddle
Connie Riley

1989 (continued)

Earl Robbins
Ruth Robertson
Alan Jay Robinson
Jane Robinson
Anna L. Rogers
Larry Rogers
Jeff Roland
John Rolfs
Debra Rollins
Walter Rumery
Kathy Sabella
Dan Salsbury
Cynthia E. Sasser
Ann Scarsborough
George H. Schaab
Bob Schabers
Doug Schaill
Sandra Scheetz
Eva Scheib
Margaret Schlaack
Stephen Schmal
Joan M. Schomaker
Tami Schultz
Robert Schumacher
Debra Scott
Glenda Scott
Sandra Scott
Sam Selby

Todd M. Semke
G. Bernard Shaw
Jerome Shaw
Gerry W. Shearin
Mary Shelburne
Grace Sherwin
Pam Siegmund
Kay Sims
Mary Sinclair
Jane M. Smith
Peter J. Smith
Rex Smith
Gloria Snead
G. W. Snodderley
Charlie Snyder
Jose Sohse
Gail H. Sosna
John P. Spencer
Pamela J. Stallings
Dan Stebbins
Marian Steele
James E. Stephens
Wanda Stevens
Thomas H. Stocker
Maxine B. Stokes
Rita B. Storie
Barbara Strange
Louise Strickland

Bob Summers
Pamela Surrat
Carolyn Sutton
Janet Swain
Ed Swierk
Mark Swinnerton
Robert J. Talbert
Barbara J. Tate
Ted J. Teddesco
Bonnie K. Temple
R. Hardy Tew
H. M. Theilen
Carol Thomas
Catherine S. Thompson
Barbara Thompson-
  Moloney
Eileen Tipton
Stephanie Toney
Caesar S. Travares
Karen Tripple
Art Turner
Robert C. Vaughan
Ellean Vickrey
Jane Vincent
Deborah L. Wagner
Betsy J. Walker
Lucy M. Walters
Virginia C. Ward

David Watkins
Carolyn Watlington
Kathy Watlington
James R. Watson
Sandra Watson
Phil Weber
Pamella Welborn
Mary Jane Wells
Cammie West
Al White
Dana P. White
Crystal R. Whitley
Clara Wiggins
Gayle S. Wight
Stacey S. Wiley
Rhonda Williams
Willow Williams
Wendy Winer
Bernese Witherspoon
Doyle Wood
Belinda Woodson
Judy Wright
Jennifer Wullert
Jennifer Wygal
Gail Young
Sandy Zaban
Donna Zachau
Lowell T. Zeigler

1990

Sandy Adams
Rick Aglipay
Deborah Ahlden
Joe Aimone
Brad Anderson
Fred Anderson
Susan Andrews
Beverly Antilley
Michele Antoretti
Mary M. Archer
Mark Arinaga
Rhonda Armstrong
Jim Atencio
Nancy Atkins
Barry Audrich
Lynn Bacon
Michael Baginski
Krestin Bahr
Raymond Balach
Irene Baldwin
Tanya Bare
Mary Barnes
Jim Barnett
Virginia Barnett
Nancy Barriclow
Brian Barrientez
Steve Barry
Derrith Bartley
Darlene Bates

Dorothy Baumgartner
Thomas Beach
Jean Beaman
Richard Beer
Jim Bell
Wayne Bell
Tom Beninger
Roianne Benjamin
Steve Benos
Michael Bettonville
Susan Bill Blackman
Barry Blalock
Beth Blanchard
Joyce C. Block
Pamela Boatwright
Katherine Boggs
Tammy Boggs
Joe Boisse
Janie Borgman
Cinda Boswell-Schlereth
Pat Bowers
Ann Marie Bradshaw
Greg Brazil
David Breault
Dardrae Breig
Stuart Briber
Pat Brick
Harry Brisson
Barbara Brodsky
Charles Brown

Jenny Bruening
Janell Bryan
Rose Marie Buccieri
Dan Bucich
Mary Bukowy
Mary Burchill
Cathy Burcin
Stacey J. Burd
Bruce Burkard
John Burkholder
Peggy Burris
Cynthia Buscemi
Cresenciana Cabalo
Linda Carlson-Walker
Kevin Carney
Ken Carr
Sandal Cate
Marilyn Cauble
Debbie Chamblee
Norman Chang
Walter Chang
Scott Chappelle
Robert Choate
Marian Christians
David Cignotti
Joe Clark
Steve Clark
Dianna Cline
Stella Coaxum
C. Duff Coburn

Dina Cochran
Yvonne Cohen
Roberta Cole
Elaine Cook
Natalie Cook
Sharon Cornthwaite
Margaret Corp
Chuck Correll
Bill Corrett
Pat Corwin
Dick Cory
Dixie Costley
Katherine Courie
Doug Cowan
David Cowie
Deanne Crichton
Brad Cross
Mary Ann Cubbage
Deborah Curbow
Brian Cushing
Irma Cushing
Claudine Cygan
Pam Darby
Debbie Daurity
Brenda Davis
Esther Davis
Linda Davis
William Davis
Donna Dawkins
Carole Day

1990 (continued)

Pamela Day
Alice Dean
Suzanne Deering
Donna DeFrank
Dan Dellapiazza
John Dembosky
Priscilla Dennison
Mike Denniston
Beth Denton
Thomas Deskovich
Barbara Dietz
Don Dillinger
Gary Dillon
Debra Dimas
Robert Dingre
Kathy Dmytryszyn
Dave Dorion
Gene Dorsa
Jeannie Douglas
Don Douglass
David Dow
Daniel Downs
Ramona Duncan
Cathy Dunn
Craig Durmais
Karen Durrett
Stewart Eastman
Susan Eastman
Ina Eaton
Jewell Edmonds
Phyllis Edwards
Rick Eliot
Dorothea Elmore
Deighton Emmons
Glennon Engelbrech
Sarah Esker
Thelma Esslinger
Dianne Exler
Lyman Fancher
Kay Farrar
Richard Faulkner
Aaron Feik
Robert Ferguson
Maribeth Ficek
Lee Fieldman
Laura Fisanick
Dianna Fisel
Bill Fisher
Kim Fisher
Robert Fisher
Greg Foland
Jane Forristall
Robin Foster
Bob Fowler
Diane Fox
Joan Franke
Carolyn Franklin
Keith Fromby
Robin Frost
Constance Fruendt

Judith M. Fuller
Cindy Funfsinn-Pozzi
Carole J. Fussell
Diane Fussell
Ann Galloway
Imogene Gatewood
Myra M. Gattis
Carol Gattolin
Pat George
Samuel Georgiana
Cindy Giampado
Joanne Gibson
Vicki Gibson
Kam Gill
Mary Gill
Angela Glaub
Chris Godwin
Jeannette Goins
Elizabeth Goldberg
Adrienne Golden-Stone
Joseph Gotelli
Naotashi Goto
Jane Gott
Maureen Gouveia
Rosanne Graef
Less Graff
Jimmie Graves
Ann Greene
Nelda Griffith
Karen Griffon
Tom Groff
Carol Grooms
Rebecca Gulickson
Jennifer Haig
Mary M. Hailey
Donna Hall
Jessie S. Hamilton
Jewel Hamlett
Louise Handley
Johnell Hankins
Virginia Hankins
Linda Hansen
Sheryl M. Hardesty
Sheridan Harding
Patricia Hargrove
Mary Harris
Cheryl Hart
Deborah J. Hart
Clair Hartle
Warren Hartwell
Calvin Hastings
Martin Hauptman
Jo Ann Hauser
Jerry H. Havens
Cora A. Hawkins
Mildred Haywood
Pat Hazellief
David Hazlett
Clarence Hedgepeth
David Hedgepeth

Bob Heilsberg
Anne Hemmer
Lisa Henderson-Rowe
Jeff Hendricks
Nella Hope Henninger
Joseph Herman
Karen M. Herron
Lana Herron
Doris Hessee
Lillie Heyward
Carolyn Hicks
Mary Hill
Howard Hince, Jr.
Diane Hink
Carol L. Hinton
Neil Hivala
Diane Hobbs
Pat Hoefler
Wayne Hoff
Linda Hogan
Susan Holtje
Michael Hornack
Dale Hultgren
Richard Hultman
Vicki Hursh
Eleanor Huskins
Martha Hutchison
Louise Irvine
Randall Jackson
Teron Jackson
Vernita Jackson
Angela Jacobs
Jaqueline Jaggers
Jeanette James
Robert L. James
Iris Jarrett
Maria Jeffery
Melanie Jenkins
Bruce Johnson
Dana Johnson
Kent Johnson
Robert Johnson
Pamela Johnston
Bernie Jokiel
Ray Jokipii
Torrey Joy
Jim Judson
Angela Juffey
Barbara Karn
Betty Karp
Jana Katterhorn
Mary Kay Kelly
Linda Kersey
Paul Kilkenny
Jean Ann King
Julian King
Melissa King
Bill Kintzley
Kathy Kirkman
Terry Kish

Clifford Kitts
Rachel Kizer
Ron Klinger
Mary Kolb
Joseph Kraemer
Rebecca Krueger
Tim Kulak
Reid Kunishige
Nancy Kuode
Cindy Kustello
Suzanne Lamb
Tom Langley
Peter Larmour
Ann LaRoue
Kathy Larsen
B. J. Larson
Cheryl M. Larson
Nancy Lasater
Anne Lau
Davis Laughlin
Francis Lawkins
Robin Lawrence
Ruth Lawrence-Berrey
Arnold Lawson
Chuck Layton
David Lee
Sharlene Lee
Dennis Leingang
Malo Lema'i
Ken Leonard
Uila Leota
Agnes Lesniahowski
Anthony Liberatore
Lee Lichtenstein
John Licursi
Charlotte Lindsey
Glenn Lindsley
Gayle Little
Timothy Lloyd
Xanthe Locke
Don Loebach
Dean Lofton
Charles London
Marilyn Lonigro
Frank Lopez
Mary Evelyn Lough
Ken Lucas
Norma Ludwig
Rosanna Lupien
Mark Lutzenhiser
Alan Macgregor
Carole MacIntyre
Lloyd Mackey
Lori Mackey
Jan Mahaffey
Douglas Maker
Mary Jo Mannes
Dana Mansden
Alex Mares
Karen Marks

1990 (continued)

Dolores Martin
Edward Martin
Kari Martin
Kathy Martin
Nancy Martin
Ruth Martin
Sidney Martinez
David Mathis
Nancy Matlack
Ed Matodobra
Nancy Matsukawa
Martha McBride
Sammy Ann McCarley
Athena McCarthy-
   Graham
Cammie McCracken
Charlotte McDonald
Mary Jane McDonald
Daltina McDuffie
Bonnie McEntire
Robert McGregor
Roland McIntosh
Janet McKee
Jim McNaughton
Molly McNeill
Dennis Mehalic
Tom Melia
Joe Memmel
Dave Meyer
Paul Meyers
Kevin Michael
Ron Michaels
Margaret Michaud
Polly Mierke
Christopher Miller
Nellie Mills
Kathy Missel
Marlene Mitchell
Sharon Mitchell
Judity Monnich
Dennis Monroe
Robert Montoya
Greg Moore
Sandra Moore
Dawn Moorehouse
Peggy Morgan
Linda Morris
Mike Morris
Gerald Morrow
Bill Morse
Bruce Mortimer
Judy Mose
Charles Moser
Barbara Moulthrop
Mike Mullan
Virginia Mullan
Linda Ann Musumeci
Kim Nakashima
Mona Nassar
Patricia Naylor

Vernon Nellis
Don Nelson
Eric Nelson
Kathy Nelson
Michael Nelson
Michelle Nelson
Steve Nelson
Wendell Nelson
William Dee Nichols
Deborah Niles
JoAnne Nixon
Erica Nunes
Tammy Nunez
Donald Nush
Mark Okuda
Greg Olson
Sammy Overby
Carol Owens
Paul Ozier
Stacy Ozier
Susan Paddock
Alison Paine
Greta Paith
Wallace Palm
Joy Palmer
Sharon Palmer
Jim Paolini
Minnie Parham
Patricia Parrish
Shirley Patt
Toni Paya'n
Shannon Peddycord
Barbara Pedersen
Sue Peed
Elizabeth A. Pentecost
Amy Petrenko
Rick Philipsen
Judy Pierce
Mike Pierce
Sabra Pierce
Lynne Pike
Charles Piper
Gloria Piroschak
George Pokrajac
Jim Ponti
Charlie Popovich
Sandy Powell
Rick Powers
James Pressley
Sandra Prigel
Diane Procell-Regua
Miranda Proctor
Linda Proetsch
Christie Purdon
Tammi Rachels
Russ Radden
Allyson Ragland-
   Coleman
Jill Rain
Lisa Ramsey

Rebecca Ramsey
Mary Rance
Laura Randall
Renee Randall
Jeff Ranek
Steve Raph
Wandra Raynor
Lisa Regan
Ann Reid
Mary Rice
Mary Richardson
Paulette W. Riley
Fiona Rimstad
Robin Ringland
Homer L. Ritter
Alice J. Roberts
Thomas Roberts
Trine Rodriguez-
   Martinez
Doug Romano
Shelley Ross
Joyce M. Rosser
Juanita Rudolph
Arlene Ruffin
Ronald Ruokonen
Jim Sagray
Susie Salstrom
Angie Samuels
Randa Sanders
Bob Sargent
Linda Savarino
Jim Sawl
Kim Scarlett
Curtis Schlinkmann
Kathleen Schmidt
Lisa Schmidt
Charlotte Schneider
Carol Schramm
George Schuttinger
Marcia Schwartz
Connie Schwingle
Della Scott
Janice Scott
Gerald Self
Nancy Seltmann
Jerry Semanko
Sandra Sermos
Paul Shaver
Peg Sheehan
Charles Shellito
John Sherman
Nancy Sherman
Jenny Shibayama
Larry Shirk
Sara Tyler Shive
William Shoaf
Wesley Shoemaker
Elizabeth Sigman
Patty Silkman
Beverly Simmons

Connie Singleton
Thomas Small
Denise Smith
Gary Smith
LeeAnne Smith
Robert Smith
Sam Smith
Sandy Smith
Sarah F. Smith
Les Snyder
Marilyn Snyder
Marjorie Snyder
Nancy Snyder
Bud Solebello
Patti Soule
Emanuel Sousa
E. Bernell Sparks
Veronica Speck
Jennie P. Stancil
Tony Stanley
Jim Stark
Susan M. Starnes
Virginia Stephenson
John W. Sterling
Linda Stewart
Carolyn D. Stezer
Susan Stinchfield
Jerry Strain
Merrelle Stubbs
J. Tim Sturges
Judy Stutzman
Meg Sutcliffe
Kathleen Sutton
Sylvia Swayze
Peggy Sweat
Russel Tanaka
Opal Tart
Marcia Taylor
Ray Taylor
Hattie Teachey
Carol Tempel
Laurie Thush
Brian Tiland
Larry Tillack
Amelia Tipton
Linda Tobar
Leonard Tom
Kathy Tomsha
James Tone
Barbara Toner
Stephanie Tony
Robert Towle
Steve Treichler
Jo Trombini
Jackie Trump
Rodney Tucker
Ben Tupper
Mark Turnau
Sherrilynn Turner
Lynn Tushaus

1990 (continued)

Rodger Twitchell
Allison Tyler
Rob Tyne
Stewart Tyner
Arthur Valiquette
Terrie Van Belois
Wes Van Vuren
J. P. vanEttinger
Tammie Veinotte
Anna Marie Villalobos
Jan Vogler
Patricia Waddell
Ginger Walbrath
Jane Walker
Sylvia Walker

Terry Walker
Dolly Wallace
Dwayne Wallace
Joanne D. Walsh
Craig Waltman
Gene Wargo
Darline Waring
Mary Frances Warren
Cameron Weaver
Randall Weddle
Phyllis J. Weeks
Melissa Wegmann
Leila Welch
Lisa Welch
Cynthia Weller

Robin Wells
Coral Wert
Michael White
Pat Whiting
Brian Wickens
Jim Wilcox
Kay Wilde
Lyle Willey
Carole Williams
Deborah Williams
Regina Williams
Robin Williams
Emily Wilson
Robert Wilson
Carolyn Winfrey

Pegi Winters
Rose Wlos
Mary T. Wolff
Jimmy Wood
Mike Wootman
Catherine Worden
Charles Worden
Miriam Wright
Theodosia Wright
Graig Wrolstad
Robert Wyatt
Michael Wyckoff
Sandra Young
Ricardo Zapata

1991

Richard Aaron
Kim Abrams
Timothy D. Adkerson
Roy Aho
Christine B. Ajamiseba
Paula Renee Allen
Raymond Alley
Esteban R. Alustiza
Joyce Amato
Wright Anderson
Cathleen M. Antonio
Rhonda Archey
Marie Arnold
Lisa E. Aronow
  Frothingham
Sharon Asher
Bob Ashley
Rae Beth Austin
Anne Averitt
Debra Bahr
Benjamin Bailey
Lisa L. Baker
Jeff Baldwin
Rosalind Banks
Gayle Barbour
Rosa B. Barfield
Mary Barr
Willis Barrett
Steve Barry
Anne Baskin
Robert Bass
Marian Baucom
Michael Belgrave
Debra D. Bennett
James Bennett
John E. Benson
Joseph Blind
Edward Blindt
Heidi Bloemker
Jeanne Bogdanovich
Kathryn H. Bohling
Janet Bone
Nancy Borsuk

Janet W. Bosch
Daniel P. Bourcier
Stormy Brady
Linda Brenner
Leslie J. Brock
Deborah B. Brown
Rosemarie W. Brown
Patti Brzoznowski
James D. Burger
Richard Burke
Pat Butler
Avanace Byrd
John E. Caldwell
Thomas Campo
Dennis Carlyon
Carl W. Carpenter, Jr.
Mary E. Carr
Robert L. Carr, Jr.
Marilyn J. Carrafiello
Jean R. Carroll
Mary Ellen Carroll
Thomas Carver
Mary Cate
Nancy Chamberland
Sharon Chappell
Sylvester D. Chickering
Linda Chororos
Anithea Christian
John J. Cirrincione
Robert Colassacco
Debera Byrd Colleton
Pamela Collinsworth
Gregory T. Colyar
Karen E. Comer
Timothy J. Connell
Alice Cook
Barbara Cooper
Leonides R. Corpuz
Vivian Crawford
John Crivaro
Janice Cross
Deborah D'elena
Madeleine L. Dammann

Deanna Danforth
Sue Darby
Susan E. Darr
Suzanne L. Davidson
Mae Dejesus
Raymond L. Delehant
Edwin L. Demi
Christine Derouin
Mary Dibble
Olga T. Dickens
Catherine M. Dickerson
Timothy Dickson
Thomas W. Dingee
Sophia Diorietes
Mary Beth Dishinger
Pansy E. Dobson
Patricia Dochtermann
Jeffrey Dotson
Amanda R. Douglas
Jeannie Douglas
Mildred B. Douglas
Bruce A. Downing
Judy Dumas
Robert Dwyer
Judene Dyer
Wanda Edgerton
Lois M. Edmond
Alva Edwards
Brenda S. Edwards
Joan Edwards
Ladonna S. Ehler
Deborah Ann Eischen
Condary Ellis
Glennon A. Engelbrecht
Janet L. Enloe
Carole Eschen
April Evans
Tamara May Faircloth
Sharon Farrell
Robert Fegely
Michael Feldstein
Rachel Fields
David M. Fisher

Lori G. Fisher
Ray Fisher
Jesse Flores
Frank Foulkes
Marguerite Fowler
Ruth Ann Fox
Judith Frank
Joann Fraser
Max Frederich
Larla French
Michael Fulton
Carole Fussell
Daniel Gagner
Marian Gallager
Steven D. Garrett
Edward Gauthier
Michael T. Gavin
Jennifer Geib
Ann C. Geisinger
Denise Giacomini
Angela Gibbons
Angela Gilchrist
Lorinda Gingell
Sarah Gobel
Adrienne Golden-Stone
Sergio Gomez
Dennis J. Goretski
James Green
Malcolm T. Greer
Francis D. Grevera
Lauren Groff
Theresa Guevel
Chris Gundersen
Barbara Hagerman
Cynthia Bass Hall
Kristen Hall
Nancy E. Hall
Tom Halstead
Cathy Halterbaum
Barbara Harhison
Ruth Autio Harju
Cliff Harris
David Harris

1991 (continued)

Lezondra Harris
Mary Harris
Sharon M. Hass
Robyn B. Hawley
Michael Hayes
Grace Heath
Janet Henry
Doris Hessee
Linda Hester
Angela Hewitt
Linda Hewitt
Denise Hill
Eileen Hill
Denise Hilyard
Barbara Ho
Judith C. Hoelscher
Norman A. Holbert
Lynda B. Holland
Kristy J. Hollenbeck
Eugene T. Holmgren
Debra Homeier
Debra D. Honeycutt
Joann L. Howard
Calvin D. Huffman
Angie Hughes
Berniece Hunsucker
June Hutchinson
Valerie T. Inouye
Bruce Irving
John Isberg
Tom James
Margaret Jerman
Karen K. Johns
Bob D. Johnson
Patricia Johnson
Barbara Jones
David P. Jones
Donna Jones
Patricia Jordan
Sharon A. Jordan
Janice J. Kammerich
Laura Kane
Jacqueline Katz
Ann M. Kazinski
Joan Kenny
Janice King
Kathleen King
Margaret Kinney
Vicki Kirchner
Gerald J. Klawitter
Terry L. Kluesner
Frederick Kluge
Doris Knittel
Mary Knoch
Mary Ellen Komorowski
Katherine J. Kucewicz
Barbara C. Kuebler
David H. Kulenkamp
Eddie Kyles
David L. Labolle

Brenda Laliberte
Robert Lammert
Cheri Lamont
Cynthia E. Lamoureux
Cindy Langdon
Loretta S. Langdon
Scott R. Lankford
Michael Laughlin
Arnold Lawson
John Leitzinger
Mike Lepisto
Kurt Leslie
Alice K. Lewis
Harold Liner
Robert Stevens Link
Jennifer Lipinski
Debra Litman
Cleveland C. Livingston
Carol Lucas
Judy Lyons
Pauline M. Lyons
Marylou Mackintosh
Marjorie M. Magaoay
Fritzi Manson
William S. Marcelo
Herbert S. Mark
Lynn R. Martens
Roy T. Matsui
Frank E. Maxim
Bernard Maynard
Sharilyn McCracken
Jane Ann McCullough
Debra McCullough
Kimberly McGarth
Holly McGinness
Janice McIntyre
Betty McLaughlin
Vicki McLaughlin
Laurie McMurray
Sharon McNeil
Leanne M. Merila
David J. Mervinsky
Ronnie Miller
Nina Moock
Michael Moore
Tecola Moore
Suzette Moran
Steven Moretto
Stephen Morneault
Thomasina Murphy
August Murray
Larry Murray
Susan A. Murray
Linda Musemeci
Mary M. Nail
Lynda W. Naylor
Debbie Neal
Samuel L. Nelson
James J. Newton
Viorene I. Newton

Barbara Nick
Sarah Janet Odom
Bill Olson
Donna Ouzts
Mary M. Owens
Gail P. Pacheco
Luis Padilla
B. Paris Pallis
Elliott Parivar
Alan Parker
Chris Pascal
Mary A. Patton
Charlotte Payne
Teresa Pelfrey
Enrico Perruzzi
Matt Peters
Lucille Picagli
Michael S. Piekarski
Peggy Plattner
Mary Porter
Carol G. Poteat
George Pratt
Marlene Pratt
Gayle Priest
Lois A. Prosek
Michael Quinn
Debra Radford
Clyde Rainey
Shirley E. Ray
Gail Redberg
Annie Jo Reed
Lori M. Reed
Diane Regua
Charlene Reid
Eric T. Reinhard
Stacey Rich
Ron Richards
Gene Ridenour
Paula L. Riggan
Jean B. Riley
Thomas A. Riley, Jr.
Margaret Ripley
Raymond Robb
Bonnie Roberts
Martin O. Roedel
Marc W. Romine
Sylvia Rose
Susan Ruohomaki
Susan J. Ryck
Ron Sacco
Mario A. Sacramone
Maggie Saffen
Peggy W. Sammons
Jennifer S. Sauls
Carol Schleicher
Jennifer B. Schneider
Peter H. Schrank
Marc P. Schwartz
Sandy Schwartz
Michael Scime

Pauline Seales
Daniel Secula
Michael Sedgwick
Brenda Shackleford
Elizabeth Shane
Suellen Shaw
Michael Sheehan
Sherill Shields
Wesley Shoemaker
Mary Alice Shute
Diana C. Skiles
Ann Slattery
Dana E. Slaughter
Peter Small
Linda Smith
Louise Smith
Patricia Smith
Susann K. Snell
Terry R. Sontag
Emanuel Sousa
Carol Stallard
Brian Stanley
Sue M. Steed
Thomas Steib
Reed A. Stephenson
Mary Stewart
Harvey W. Stick, Jr.
Anne Stillman
Roger C. Stillman
Karen Stitely
Mamie C. Stringfellow
James M. Sundeen
Catherine Swinger
Vincent Szewczyk
Erlyn A. Taira
Iris M. Tart
Joanne Taylor
Minnie S. Taylor
Gary R. Tebo
Jan M. Teruya
Betty C. Tew
Stephanie Thibodeau
Sabri Thomas
Janis O. Threatt
Mable Tillman
Linda M. Tobar
Teresa A. Tolksdorf
Kathryn Tolley
Mark Troutner
Michael Troxel
Dianna Trueblood
Mark Trueblood
Jerry Turner
Felix Turtur
David Twaddle
Gemma Twaddle
Carole A. Vahsholtz
J. P. Vanettinger
David Vasques
Linda C. Veit

1991 (continued)

Ronald Vivio
A. J. Walker
Norma P. Walters
Donald Walton
Maynard Walton, Jr.
Grant Warwick
Terry J. Weakley
Iris Lynn Weiner

Tom Weiss
Nancy J. Wells
James A. Wesley
Cathleen Westall
Joyce W. Whitfield
Wesley Wiggins
Kay L. Wilde
Jane Willett

E. Woody Williams
Madonna A. Williams
Paul Williams
Earl Wilson
Marc C. Wilson
Rachel Wilson
Betty J. Winkler
Melvin R. Wollenburg

Byron S. Woodside
William Wright
Billy R. Yawn
Nancy Yeager
Barbara Yeater
John Edward Young, Jr.
Chris G. Zarka
Bonnie Ziegenfuse

1992

Robin D. Adams
Chris Ajamiseba
Carol R. Alarie
Colleen C. Alba
Mark A. Angotti
Deana R. Armstrong
Peggy C. Bailey
Susan K. Baker
Jackie A. Banks
Cheri A. Barkley
Julius Barnes
Jane Elizabeth Bartlett
Joseph A. Basque
Maren Olsen Behrend
Sheryl K. Beliveau
Karin R. Berger
Lois B. Berwanger
Renwick P. Bibilone
Laura J. Blackwell
Theresa J. Blanks
Georgia Blockmon
Richard O. Blunt
Mary Ann Bommarito
Bernardine Bonczek
Catherine A. Borgmann
Joan Borovatz
Joann O. Bowen
Kate K. Bragado
Mary B. Braning
Misty D. Brannan
Jeffrey M. Breiten
Roy M. Bridgers
Neal D. Bridgnell
Tamara M. Brilhante
Beulah M. Brooks
Mabel L. Brooks
Sherry L. Brown
Lisa Ann Bruns
Rose C. Brunsman
Noreen Bubalo
Elizabeth V. Buchy
Susan E. Butzin
Rita A. Carter
Cynthia A. Cashel
Frances S. Cashwell
Mary E. Cefalo

Vera L. Chandler
Mark Chando
Martin F. Charleville
Candy S. Chauvin
Donald A. Cherry
Frances K. Chow
George A. Chwastyk
Steven E. Clemmons
Sara J. N. Cliffe
Judy F. Coats
Jay J. Collins
Elizabeth D. Cook
Marsha N. Cooke
Deborah A. Corvelle
Fiona K. Cosmann
John N. Cosner
Patricia S. Costello
Martha Courtney Ladd
Sarah J. Cureton
Marcia A. Damiano
Harold E. Daniel
Rebecca E. Daniels
Edward J. Darling
Mary Ann S. Daust
Jane F. Davis
Meredith L. Davis
Kay E. Dawson
Leon A. Debaer
Eric G. Deleissegues
Christopher J. Delorey
Margaret Ann Detwiler
Lisa L. Dickens
James M. Dickson
Brent A. Dillon
Daniel S. Doane
Rebecca B. Dobbins
Brenda L. Dodson
Roberta Doelling
Magdalena Donaldson
Jerome A. Donatell
Joan A. Downs
Richard C. Druse
Mary R. Dudash
Frances Dulude
Rose A. Duncan
Pamela A. Duval

Earle W. Edwards
Johnny B. Edwards
Samuel L. Edwards
Maureen Eldridge
Phyllis A. Eller
Teresa B. Enzor
Jerrie Eubanks
Andrew B. Evans
Arthur N. Ewald
Calvin N. Ewell
Wilbur Fast
Mumtaz S. Fazal
Agnes Feltkamp
William L. Ferguson
Michael Fillipow
Paul D. Fiore
Maria M. S. Fisher
Mary A. Floyd
Margaret M. Fortner
Elaine B. Freeman
William G. Friedel
Darlene K. Fuchs
Gloria J. Gancarz
Doug Gaudet
Georgana Gearhart
Marie Genoni
Tozia A. George
Susan Gherardini
Nancy B. Gibbs
Patricia A. Gibbs
Pamela S. Gilbert
Kathryn M. Giles
Sr. John Gilligan
Kathleen Glenn
Patricia L. Gloriod
Genevieve Goessling
Jayne Gore
Sue C. Goslyn
Richard T. Granger
Patricia J. Grant
Patricia J. Green
Loretta A. Greiner
Dawn H. Grubb
Sr. Laura A. Gruber
Robert A. Grygiel
Phillip D. Hagedorn

Remedios Haley
Rhonda Hampton
Michael G. Hancock
Bridget M. F. Hanson
Lenox D. Harrelson
Marsha Jane Harrelson
Mary A. Hayes
Susan A. Hayes
Patty M. Heitz
Emilia Henion
Jeanette G. Henke
Joann V. Hennings
Lauranne M. Hess
Christine S. Hess-Baker
Genia L. Hester
Marguerite D. Hill
Rosa B. Hill
Rhonda R. Hills
Irene V. Hoey
Lisa A. Hogan
Ronda Hoops
Lynn G. Hoover
Joseph P. Howard
Lana M. Howe
Eugenia Idica Sitts
Annete Irby
Kathryn E. Irwin
Marian D. Jackson
Susan C. Johnson
Tony G. Johnson
Marian L. Johnston
Glenda C. Jones
Sonia Jordanenglish
Denise E. Kachlic
Karen L. Kaiman
Gidget Karlof
Jennifer H. Kaylor
Janet A. Keen
Catherine M. Keleske
Carolyn A. Kelly
Dawn R. Kelly
Linda K. Kertz
Evelyn M. Kornegay
Cynthia Kinlaw
Sarah L. Kissinger
Arlene J. Koly

1992 (continued)

Melanie D. Kozlowski
Rose Ann Kraft
Jon K. Krause
Mary J. Kremer
Cheryl A. Kreuzer
Nancy K. Krull
Annette M. Krzesinski
Robert J. Kuchta
Alfred J. Kuntz
Janet E. Kurz
Margaret L. La Cerra
Judith A. Lachance
  Whitcomb
Jennifer F. Lambdin
Patricia E. Lane
Ann Roth Leach
Carol A. Leach
Michael L. Lefko
Lavine Raeann Leiper
Elizabeth W. Lesto
Jean Q. Lloyd
Jeanette M. Lloyd
Rita M. Loretta
Nancy Loughlin
Deborah G. Love
Julia Luetkenhaus
Linda L. Luger
Michelle M. Lumsden
Greta M. Lynch-Douglas
Carla S. Maasen
Jeffrey J. Mack
Margaret T. Macmillan
Cynthia E. Macon
Lori D. Madden
Daniel J. Maloney
Salvatore W. Mantia
Patricia P. Marino
Eleonora Martelli
Barry L. Mason
Melvia Mason
Eugene M. Matera
Kaui P. Maukele
Thomas M. McKenna
Pamela A. McCarley
Glen A. McDevitt
Erich O. Mees
Helen E. Mester
Karin C. Mettler
Nancy K. Michal
Gary E. Midkiff
Susan E. Miles
Melissa L. Millan
Lee A. Miller
Robin W. Minton
Kathleen A. Mitchell
Linda L. Mitchell

Diane M. Monahan
Elnora Montemayor
Dana L. Montgomery
Larry Moran
Leslie A. Moreno
Carolyn H. Moser
Kathy C. Mueller
Josephine M.
  Mulholland
Fred E. Muller
Don A. Murphy
Mary S. Murray
Glennon G. Naeger
Mari H. Nakamura
Rick A. Neigel
Lynne M. Nelson
Thomas E. Nevins
Marlynne K. Nishimura
Carol A. Novak
Debra T. Nowocin
Marguerite M. Obrien
Thomas J. O'Donnell
Terry L. Oglesby
Amy M. Okino
Deborah D. Onate
Jo Lee Orton
Steven S. Ostrenga
Mary P. Ostrowski
Donna M. Ott
Thomas R. Oves
Lorena Padgett
Kathryn A. Pagano
Mark T. Palmer
Liset Palmitessa
Dennis J. Panicucci
Sally J. Parker-Johnson
Harry S. Parlin
Vivian A. Parlin
Archie J. Pate
Philip M. Patin
Don H. Payne
Barbara R. Pearson
Linda H. Perkins
Matthew E. Phillips
Edith G. Pierce
Beth Pilarski
Victoria C. Plummer
Anita L. Powell
Jean W. Powell
John F. Prendergast, Jr.
Scott G. Presho
Ishmael J. Prioleau
Elizabeth K. Prusaitis
Elise D. Pullium
Bobbie H. Purser
Gail A. Pursley

Frances Ray
Nancy B. Ray
Geraldine J. Rebman
Frank D. Rettinger
Lynnann M. Reuter
Arlene J. Rhein
Scott Robbins
Susan L. Robbins
Dennis A. Robinson
Jane Robinson
Joan C. Robinson
Sharon M. Robinson
Vernon K. Rogan
Wesley C. Rogers
Martha Rohfritch
Nancy C. Rohlfing
Barbara S. Rohrs
Gloria Ronzach
Constance J. Roth
Steve E. Roth
Judith E. Rowe
Julie D. Rowe
Mary E. Ruebusch
Saralynn L. Rusher
Claude E. Russell
Thomas J. Ryan
David A. Salerno
Richard B. Sanborn
William H. Sanders
Natalie J. Schaefer
Ann H. Schick
Michelle L. Schmiemeier
Yvonne M. Schultz
Donna M. Scott
Jeffrey L. Scott
James Sedivec
June B. Seligson
Mary L. Seyer
Anna M. Shewlakow
Joyce C. Shore
Cheryll T. Shuford
Janice M. Sifers
Rosemary Ann Silva
Vaalele L. Simati
Barbara A. Simmons
Donna M. Skidmore
Nancy M. Slewoski
Andrew J. Smith
Frank P. Smith
Cephas C. Spaulding
Michael Walter Stamp
Rebecca A. Stanton
Joyce A. Stephens
Rebecca S. Strong
Dawn D. Stroup
Montye Suggs

Jim D. Sughrue
Jeffrey F. Swedberg
Steven C. Swenson
Melissa Symonds
Gail H. Taira
Billie Ann T. Takahashi
Andrew R. Talbot
Michael Talleur
Soo Boo Tan
Gary A. Tashjian
Rebecca B. Tedder
Kyle A. Theisman
Bernadette Mary
  Thompson
Margaret J. Thompson
Ann M. Thuet
Brigitte L. Thummel
Bernadette A. Tille
Diana S. Timmerman
Eric Tong
Jonathan W. Tong
Rose Margaret Treilibs
Tim B. Trigani
Terrell W. Tucker
Tammy S. Uetrecht
Victoria M. Van Lieshout
Gary G. Vanantwerp
Timothy D. Vaughan
Lehua M. Veincent
Kirk H. Vestal
Susan A. Vinson
Janice A. Volz
Stanley M. Walczak
Lance C. Webb
Deborah L. Weeks
Coleen Heanu Weller
Patricia A. Wernet
Barbara A. White
Gertha H. White
Nancy L. Williams
Charles E. Wilson
Judith W. Wilson
Mary K. Wise
Richard P. Wise
Greg C. Wolf
Wendy J. Wolgan
Stanley Wolkoff
Debra L. Wood
Jeff M. Wood
Carol T. Woodward
Jane E. Wright
Sara Wynn
Denise E. Zacherl
Cheryl A. Zelek
Marie Ziolkowski
Elena Afrina

1993

Evelyn T. Akamine
Nanette Albert Thomas
Carole P. Albrecht
Wendy A. Albright
Nancy G. Allen
Paula Amick
Danny L. Baker
Wayne D. Baldwin
Edith D. Barnes
Katherine G. Barnwell
Lois D. Barron
Francis S. Bartasius
Maxine Bean
Dale Bergerhofer
Julie Bergeson
Patricia S. Berns
Patricia Berry
David A. Blodgett
Jolene S. Bodner
Janet Boren
Dennis D. Bottorff
David E. Boze
Lori Bradley
Carol M. Brady
Isaiah Branch
Mary Ellen Brashler
Robert E. Brennan
Ray J. Bullifin
Katherine L. Bumpus
Mark A. Burbank
Christy L. Burmeister
Patricia H. Burns
Marcia A. Burton
Leon H. Burton, Jr.
Judith Callens
Kathy D. Campoli
Philip J. Carollo
Richard S. Castine
Deana S. Cerroni
Daniel M. Chamberlain
Galina Cherenkova
Lori B. Christopher
Virginia Clay
Carol Y. Clement
Charline Coats
Elizabeth Coghlan
Shirley M. Conradi
Nola M. Cook
Geraldine Cooper
Louise D. Cooper
Roy L. Corpening
Laura L. Covert-Vergara
Walter Cowan
Pamela Cummings
Kathleen M. Curran
Sheila A. Cyboron

Ireen Daigle
Marlene Dailey
Belinda J. Dalke
Eva P. Daniel
Julia A. DeBroux
Sue DeCarolis
Janice M. Delaney
Carolyn Demory
Dana J. Denison
Donna M. DePond
Mary T. Dixon
Robert J. Dod
Katie J. Dougherty
Stephen E. Dougherty
Paul E. Drangeid
Hugh H. Dunn
Thomas J. Dzurison
Marlene F. Egan
Robert A. Eichenberger
Anne H. Elam
Melissa L. Elder
Suzanne G. Elliott
Arthur D. Ellis
Gayle L. Ellison
Carolyn L. Emily
Jane H. Evans
Wilbur J. Fast
Louis Fiorella
Kimberly A. Forgash
Diane W. French
Nancy Fricke
Marilyn S. Gabel
Rick J. Gagliardi
Bruce J. Gardner
Thelma Gardner-Evans
Nancy Garinger
Kent Gillespie
Yulia Goncharova
Rita D. Goodhead
Ann Marie Goss
Alan Graham
Catherine G. Graham
L. Antonine Gratonik
Deette D. Gray
Scott B. Gunderson
Robert G. Guy
Kurt A. Hafley
Laura R. Hage
Rita A. Hagevik
Eva Hamme
Kathleen S. Hammer
Robert Harris
Karen P. Harrison
Jan Hatridge
Sara A. Haugo
Joseph D. Haworth

Keith T. Hayashi
Craig T. Hemond
Errett W. Hicks
Amy L. Hill
Regina A. Hill
Pauleen I. Hirai
Rosemary S. Hiss
Gary L. Hjelm
John C. Hofstrand
Karen F. Hogan
Bradley D. Hohensee
Sandy L. Hood
Russel K. Hopper
Kazimiera Hornberger
Brooke L. Howell
Mark J. Hrabik
D. J. Huddleston
Roy A. Huffman
Gail A. Huizinga
Theresa A. Hussey
Daniel J. Ilagan
Alan Y. Inaba
Sandra Irby
Harry J. Israel
Marilynn I. Jackson
Bland Jean
Candice A. Jenke
Paul A. Jense
Renee Y. Jofferion
Kenneth G. Johnson
Rhonda S. Johnson
Stanley D. Johnson
Teresa Johnson
Frances L. Jones
James I. Jones
Monte C. Jones
Patricia A. Jones
Susan M. Jutz
Kathy G. Kannenberg
Maria D. Kanoy
Karen L. Kanske
Amy L. Kaplan
Sergey Karakozov
Marilynn A. Kauhane
Dayni H. Kawamoto
Francine Kearney-
   Williams
Patsy L. Keenum
Jean E. Kellogg
Laura C. Kennedy
Joseph E. King
Mary Kinney
Jarmila Kirchmayerova
Bruce R. Kivimaki
Mary E. Kohnen
Debra L. Kohuth

Terry L. Kringle
Joseph P. Kristy
Susan K. Kruse
Maria Kubenkova
Mark K. Kurashige
Lilly L. Kwong
Paul D. Lane
Viera Lapitkova
Rhonda R. Larson
Terry A. LeDonne
Suzanne F. Leichtling
Mark D. Leitzinger
Tamara L. Lewis
Dennis C. Lewman
Sharon B. Lineback
Daniel N. Linger
Victoria Lorenz
Robert A. Lovell
Edna L. Luper
Thomas J. Lynn
Bruce S. MacCallum
Terri D. Macdonald
Doris Madison
Susan M. Maeda
Staci Mahagan-McGill
Timothy E. Mahoney
Richard A. Mankus
Julia A. Margraff
Mark E. Marker
Mary Jane Marshall
Bonnie L. Mater
Joan Ann Matusiak
Ann Mayes
Marie Therese Mays
Marilyn McCollum
Michael T. McCormack
Michael J. McCoy
Ellie J. McCully
Gail McDonald
Kathy B. McIver
Ruth L. McLain
Annette L. McLamb
Kirsten McWherter
Vanessa Meads
Oleg Medvedev
Kevin Menaugh
Denise G. Mickel
Gloria B. Mikes
Tonya L. Miller
Michael P. Minahan
John Mitchell
Phyllis M. Moore
Mary C. Morris
Joann F. Morrrell
Wendy S. Moulton
Beverly A. B. Mowrer

1993 (continued)

Sherri Mullen
Thomas Myhre
Frank A. Neal
Robin L. Nelson
James W. Nettles
Barbara I. Neuman
Linda K. Neuner
Sandra G. Nickelson
Deane P. Nielson
Alaina K. Niemeyer
Carole J. Nordhausen
Ellen P. O'Brien
Melinda O'Malley
Richard D. Olson
Jane M. Oteman
Jane V. Owens
Antonio C. Pacilli
Patricia A. Pantano
Phyllis E. Parker
Rosalie C. Parrish
Ron G. Pearson
Kathryn Y. Peck
Kimberly A. Perreault
Stephen M. Perreault
Ruth Pershing
Jon M. Peters
Daniel G. Petnick
Nancy Pieniazek
Lubov Podkorvotova
Terrance W. Pohland
Jo Ann M. Popovsky
Jeremy Potratz
Bradd T. Powell
Rodney R. Powell
Jean M. Prather
Shirley F. Purdy
Dot Quelch
Jennifer L. Ragan
Patrice R. Rallis
Arlene Raterman
Tracy A. Read
Theresa Redington

Patricia A. Reeder
Judith K. Rieke
Fiona A. Rimstad
Richard E. Rivas
Bill W. Robinson
Jean Marie Robinson
Yvonne R. Robinson
Kristine R. Rodgers
Christopher Roos
Roy R. Rubenking
Linda Ruisinger
Lynn C. Rummage
Margaret H. Rusho
Kimberly E. Ryseff
Edward Sacha
Scott A. Salmons
Russell W. Sanders
Jeffrey M. Saslo
Jane H. Sato Tomita
Rich S. Sauers
Ronald P. Savageau
Karen S. Schiemann
P. Gail Schierhoff
Salvatore Schillaci
Wendy S. Schmidle
Timothy M. Schmidt
Linda L. Schmitt
Rebecca D. Scholl
Kim Schuldt
Angela M. Schulte
Robert M. Schulz
Laurie S. Schuster
Maria Schwartz
Betty A. Scott
Susan A. Scribner
Deborah A. Shagena
Cheryl Shattie
Russell K. Shaw
Betty J. Simmons
James L. Simpson
Kathleen K. Singh
Paul F. Sipson

Mark Skiffington
John F. Smeadala
Althea Smith
Debi A. Smith
Joann B. Solari
Kate L. Sorensen
Susan P. Spangenberg
James W. Sparks
John K. Spencer
Joan F. Spezia
Frank A. Stafford, Jr.
Kalyn W. Stanley
Linda C. Staple
Mark P. Steele
Diane M. Steinbruegge
Douglas Stith
Joan M. Stoll
Sandra Stolle
Deborah M. Strope
Kenneth R. Styles
Kay S. Sundquist
Brian J. Swiney
Sharon Tafreshi
Rollinson C. Tait
Lee E. Takagi
Catherine A. Tate
Carol M. Thomas
Corey R. Thomas
Rose M. Thomas
Wendell Thomas
Beth A. Thompson
Mary Louise Thompson
Dolly Thurmond
Eva Trebaticka
Marjorie A. Triller
Thomas N. Tripp
Christine Underwood
Susan B. Uno
Alexander Uvarov
Danial P. Van
  Ravenswaay
Janet E. Van deBerg

Louis P. Velsini
Turkina Vera
Eugene W. Victor
Martha A. Vitek
Steven D. Vogler
Elizabeth Von Der
  Heydt
Pete A. Vraspir
Ben A. Wadsworth
Douglas G. Walker
Marianne Walker
John C. Wallin
Lisa Wannemuehler
Rosalyn E. Washington
Barbara A. Wasik
Vince L. Watanabe
Mike E. Weatherby
Fred G. Werner
Miriam B. White
Pamela L. White
  Fairman
John J. Wicker
Shelley K. Wilhelm
Cynthia C. Williams
Harold Williams
Linda M. Wilson
Mary K. Wineberg
Sandra M. Winter
Gilbert L. Wiser
Janet V. Wolf
Dianne I. Womack
Lynda C. Wood
Gayle H. Wooten
Robin E. Wrenn
Curtis F. Yuma
Judith A. Ziegler
Suzanne Ziegler
Irina Zlognikova
Anna L. Zuccarini

1994

Joe Accardi
Adam Acosta
Jean Adams
Kelly-Jo Adkins
Roy Alden
Chris Almond
Margaret Anderson
Richard Anderson
Leo Applebaum
Christina Baachmann
Natalie Bahr
James Baker

Wayne Baldwin, Jr.
Pamela Barnette
Lisa Baumann
Harriett Beaugard
Vincent Becker
Angela Beerman
Pamela Biggs
Debra Birkemeier-
  Dolan
Steven Bland
Todd Blumenreich
Joyce Boylston

Sheri Braker
Greg Braun
Linda Brennan
Nancy Brice
Dinah Brown
Karen Bruck
Sandra Bryant
William Bunch
Andrea Burns
Nancy Calestini
Lori Cannon
Judith Cernich

Kathleen Chew
Linda Cioffredi
Brenda Clark
Cecile Clements
Paula Cocciante
Cynthia Cole
Melinda Collier
Lois Comrie
Audrey Coppins
Robert Corrick
Thereza Coughran
Tony Coveyou

1994 (continued)

Lori Craig
Sandra Cross
Elizabeth Crowe
Margaret Dacko
Kathleen Davies
Tommy Decker
Phyllis Deem
Denise Descoteaux
Rita Difani
Eileen Doocey
Melissa Dowil
Barbara Drake
Peter Dubas
Debra Dunavant
Christopher Dunlap
Vanice Ellis
Catherine Eppright
Jennifer Fakes
Cheryl Fellner
Judith Fipps
Sandra Fitzwater
Margaret Flink
Janet Foote
Eileen Frese
Christine Garcia
Michele Gibson
Dorothy Glogowski
Jocona Godwin
Debra Good
Gilbert A. Goodall
Marilyn Grant
Karen Greene
Pat Gross
Deborah Hagan
Torrey Hall
Nancy Harris
Cynthia Hasten
Karen Held
David Heyse
Carolyn Hodges
Patricia Hoelscher
Nancy Hogle
Susan Hood
Phyllis Houser
Jerilyn Hunihan
Helen Huskins
Rhonda Hye
Charlene Ishino
Amy Jackson

Ora Jacox
Michael James
Richard Jarvis
Dennis Johnson
Robert Johnson
Elizabeth Johnson-
    Massey
Dorothy Jane Jordal
Jon Jordan
Leila Jordan
Kia Kamp
Coyia Keables
Lisa Kelley
Deborah Kelly
Elizabeth Ann Ketner
Jon Kinoshita
Rebecca Kniebusch
Mary Koga
Kathleen Komos
Rebecca Kuehn
Carol Kuroski
Paul Lane
Scott Lane
Sharon Langston
Suzanne Law
Edith Leary
Theresa Lechert
Thomas Lee
William Leslie
William Lyons
L. Scott Magann
Marie Malo
Ann Malone
Clifford Marin
Jane Marquart
Debra Martello
Angie Maschler
Brad Mashburn
Sharon Maze
Megan McCarthy
Susan McClain
Thomas McLaughlin
Jerry Melton
Sara Mendoza
Nancy Merritt
Linda Michalak
Dianne A. Middleton
Thomas Millay
Victoria Miller

John Minelli
Sarah Mixter
Michele Mohammadi
Nancy Moore
Kathryn Muehlheausler
Jennifer Mueller
Colleen Murphy
Kathleen Murphy
Cindy Nausid
Deanna Nesbitt
Barbara Norem
Michael Norton
Anne Olson
Marie Oughton
Julie Panus
Sheila Pattee
Carmela Pogranicy
Janice Porterfield
Stephen Post
Christine Potter
Issen Powter
Gaynelle Pratt
Donna Quale
Alberto Racho
Ann Ransford
Marsha Ratzel
Marcia Rausch
Frances Ray
Linda Ray
Joe Renzi
Kristin Rieflin
Michael Riordan
Caroline Rivera
Gwen Robbins
Gloria Robinson
Jeanne Robison
David Rudderow
Alan Rutherford
Margaret Salia
Mathilda Salinas
Nancy Saucier
Richard Scanlon
Doug Schaill
Ann Schlaepfer
Donna Schlake
Angela Seigler
Linda Shirk
Barbara Simmons
Leon Smith

Molly Soete
Christopher Stanton
Stacy Stechschulte
Lynn Stillwell
Bob Stobie
Karen Sullivan
Michael Sutton
Rachel Swaters
Sandra Tadych
Susan Taira
Jay Tamaribuchi
Carina Taylor
Marian Taylor
Lloyd Thibodeau
Sandra Thiele
Melissa Thomas
Sharon Thompson
Sandra Toler
Laurann Vanderheyden
Shirley Versemann
Shimo Victoria
Jay Volk
Gail Wallace
Suzanne Ward
Florence Warren
Elizabeth Wateland
Geri Watson
Belinda Webb
Martha Wells
John Wessler
Francenia Whipple
Rhonda Whisnant
Sandra Whitman
Phyllis Williams
Debra Wilson
Barbara Witte
Frederick Woertman
Richard Woodle
Joyce Woods
Karen Woods
John Wright
Alexandra Yen
David Young
Joseph Zahorsky
Garret Zakahi
Susan Zorescu
Carolyn Zukeran

1995

Valda Abdullah
Julia Ague
Joseph Allen
Patricia Allen
Veronica Alston

Wanda Anderson
Sigolwide Aremo
Joan Ashford-Hickson
Massoud Assadi
Beth Baranczuk

Helen Barcaskey
Marion Barta
Mary Lou Basler
Eileen Bechtel
Julia Becker

Frank Beckwith
Diana Belles
Barbara Berghoff
Barbara Blackwell
Marjorie Bowen

1995 (continued)

Vhaness Brinker
Sidney Broadwell
Janet Brooke
Cynthia A. Brown
Natalie Brown
Patrick Brown
Bridget Bryant
Malura Burriss
Kelly Calavano
Ron Cantrell
Thomas Carr
Colleen Carroll
Nicholas Cavlovich
Michelle Checchia
Irene Chung
Lisa Claesson-Gordon
Shifonne Clark
Holly Click
Charles Cole, Jr.
Mary Anne Cook
Michael Cooney
Cyndi Cooper
Michele Corey
Leonidez Corpuz
Cheryl Cousar
Jessica Craig
Patricia Crandall
Sharon Crocker
Timothy Cronin
Dhedra Cross
Ira Cumpton
Gary Cyr
Richard D'Amato
Rebecca Darrough
Pamela Daugherty
William Davis
Maria De Fina
John De Manuele
Barbara Deagle
Christine DeBoer
Susan Denike
Maria Dina DeVera
John DeWitt
Tammy Dowell
Angela Dozier
Trudy Drake
Erika Dresser
Patricia Duncan
Maryann Duvall
Patricia Eaton
Kathryn Ebrahimi
Kimberly Farmer
Diane Farrell
Susan Ferguson-Ellia
Laura Fisanick
Julaine Ford

Leigh Foy
Jean Fridy
Jeanne Gearon
Joanne Gilbert
Jennifer Gill
George Goff
Jacqueline Greene
Sarah T. Gullick
Dianne Gustafson
John Hagan
Elizabeth Hagelberger
David Haggard
Judy Hainline
Carpee Hall
David Hall
Vida Harder
Gary Harris
Peter Hauschka
Mary Heckman
Julie Hendrix
Julie Hercules
Gracie Hightower
Andrea Hines
Karen Hoelscher
Kevin Hogan
Chris Hooker
Elizabeth S. Hunter
Eric Huth
Ellizabeth Anne Hyde
Marianne Iacoboni
Kathy Jansen
Brett Jeross
Wannetta Johnson
Amy Jones
Vanessa Jones
Willette Jones
Stephanie Kamakeeaina
Mary Anne Kauffman
Joanne Keaton
Susan Keiffer-Barons
Carolyn Kelly
Valecia Kelly
Deborah Koch
Geoffrey Korper
Teresa Kozeny
Arthur Kruger
Darlene Kulesza
Cathie Lamacchia
Angelo Lamanti
Daphne Lamonds
Deborah Lander
Patricia Landwehr
Eugene Langan
Mildred Langston
Conrado Laureta
Cecilie Lewis

Karen Lierman
Mark Littorin
Daniel Lopez
George Lower
Amy Lowland
Carol Lucas
Kenneth Lutte
Lucy Lutz
Stacy Mansker
Marlis Martin
Melissa Martin
Jackie Mashore
Charles McCabe
Kenneth McCarthy
Fay McCready
Christine McCullough
Mara McGuire
Lydia McMinn
Judith Metzger
Mark Milanak
Matthew Milanak
David Mischen
Yurinita Mitchell
Paul Mohor
Thomas Molloy
Jan Morgan
Deborah Morrison
Jennifer Morton
Keith Neuhs
Terry Noeth
Jayne Norman
Grace Nwosu
Dawn Ogilvie
Kristi Ogomori
Joycelyn Palmore-Haynes
Deborah Parker
Peter Partch
Maria Passante
Barbara Peach
Robert Pepka
Imogene Pierce
Daniel Pinkham
Mary Plys
David Pope
Beverly Powers
Rena Price
Robyn Proto
Charlotte Rainwater
Mary Redal
Dianne Reed
Patricia Reis
Brian Riggs
Daniel G. Robinson
Kimla Robinson
Mary Rowley
Carvin Rudolph

Debbie Rufkahr
Marva Russell
Lisa Saba
Nancy Sage
Henriette Salvant
Peggy Saunders
Patricia R. Savoy
Michael Scales
Thomas Scanlon
Pamela Schatz
Mary Ann Schnieders
Linda Schnipper
Augustine Schurk
Frank Severino, Jr.
Mary Seward
Thomas Seymour
Theresa Short
Melissa Silva
Deborah Smith
Barbara Snatchko
James Sorteberg
Mary Stell
Carol Stewart
Susan Stewart
Stephanie Summers
David Swenson
Adrienne Talbot
Darren Tanaka
Ellen Terry
Carol Thompson
Janie Thompson
Jacqueline Thuener
Cindy Tollefson
Linda Tonnies
Marilynn Trainor
Nancy Tully
Benjamin Tupper
Ann Wallgren
Lisa Walsh
Robert Wargo
Erin Weaver
Robert Weber
Laurie White
Melanie Wiford
Clark Wilson
Patricia Witson
Doris Wolff
Richard Yee
April Yoder
Connie Yurkovich
Dan Yurkovich
Adam Zucker

INDEX

Boldfaced numbers indicate pages that define entries.

flood plain, **356**
fluids, **83**, 85–93, 101, 102, 122
fog, 120, **217**, 218, 249
fountain, 83–84, 92
freezing, 67–78, 80, 116, 118

gas, 222, 341
  pressure, 114
germination, **150**–173
  germination range, 172
graduated cylinder, 440
grafting, 176
gram, 19, **431**
graphs, 13, 18
  graphing, **426**
greenhouses, **165–167**, 170
ground cover, 306
groundwater, **261**, 353

habitat, **292**
headwaters, **355**
heat, 60–78, 105, 109, 112, 125–143,
  147, 158, 159, 244
horizontal axis, 13, 19, 426
human error, 13, 14, 137, 139, 423
humidity, 119, 120, **211**–215, 245, 247,
  251
hydrologic cycle, **344**–348, 353
hydrometer, 382
hygrometer, 214
hypothesis, **7**, 44, 47, 50, 54, 91, 99,
  101, 106, 110, 116, 117, 123, 137,
  143, 146, 188

ideal conditions, 137, **139**, 143, 144, 147
initial survey, **296–298**
instrument error, 13, 14, 137, 139, 423
interaction, 150, 290, 310
interdependence, 293, 306, 315
interface, **44**
interpolation, 19, **429**
inventory, 302, 304, 306, 328–330
isobars, **233**

life cycle, **291**
life requirements, **292**

loam, 176

manometer, **99**, **111**, 113, 114
marsh, **356**
mass, **16**, **20**, 28–36, 37–45, **431**–435,
  445
matter, 47, 50, 55, 67, 122, 146, 147, 318
melting, 66–78, 80, 116, 118, 125
metric area grid, 23, 24, **436**
metric linear measurement, 10, 12,
  16–17, 19, **424**
metric volume measurement, 24, 29, **440**
micro-environment, **172**
micron, **269**
microscope, 266
mixture, **67**, 75–79, 80, 83, 123–124,
  135, 221
mold, 152, 165

negative axis, 19
niche, **292**
nonpoint source, **371**
nucleation, **251**

oligotrophic system, **391**

paces (distances), 231, 296–297
partial vacuum, **93**, 95
parts per million (ppm), **220**, 224
percentage, 168, 170, 219, 220, 224
percolation, 197–206, 209, 354
pH scale, **380**
phenomenon, **7**, 9, 19, 41, 177, 217,
  225, 226, 248
photosynthesis, 225
physical environment, 150, 225, 305–309
physical properties, **80**–82
plankton, **395**
plant propagation, **174**–176
point source, **371**
pollution *See* air pollution.
population, **307**–312
  density, 309
  frequency, 309
pores, **197**, 206
potometer, **271**–288